TRANSFORM
CALCULUS

with an Introduction
to Complex Variables

HARPER'S MATHEMATICS SERIES

Charles A. Hutchinson, Editor

TRANSFORM CALCULUS

with an Introduction to Complex Variables

by

E. J. SCOTT

Assistant Professor of Mathematics,
University of Illinois

HARPER & BROTHERS, PUBLISHERS

New York

TRANSFORM CALCULUS
WITH AN INTRODUCTION TO COMPLEX VARIABLES

Library of Congress Catalog Card Number : 55 – 6409

CONTENTS

Chapter VII.   Linear Partial Differential Equations

Chapter VIII.   Gamma, Error, and Bessel Functions. Asymptotic Series.   Non-Elementary Integrals.   Integral Equations.

Chapter IX.   Further Problems in Partial Differential Equations

Contents

Chapter X. The Finite Fourier Sine, Cosine, and Hankel Transforms

PREFACE

This textbook is an outgrowth of lectures on certain integral transforms, namely, Laplace, sine, cosine, Hankel, etc., given for the past few years at the University of Illinois to advanced undergraduate and graduate students, the majority of whom were from the fields of physics, chemistry, and engineering. Because it is perhaps the most useful of the transforms developed so far, the bulk of the book is devoted to the Laplace transform. Various approaches from different points of view were presented to students for several years, but it became apparent before long that the most satisfactory approach to the understanding of the Laplace transform, although not necessarily the easiest, was from the point of view of the complex variable. Thus, an introduction to that subject through the residue theory and stressing contour integration was written.

Because the book is intended mainly for engineers and those interested in the application of mathematics, emphasis has been placed on the uses of transforms to the solution of physical problems. These problems have been selected from the fields of chemical, mechanical, civil, and electrical engineering and consider such topics as diffusion, vibrations of rods, beam deflection, transmission lines, etc.

Suitable acknowledgments have been made to sources throughout the book, but the publications of H. S. Carslaw, J. C. Jaeger, R. V. Churchill, and especially those of N. W. McLachlan have been of primary influence.

The author is indebted to Professor Myril B. Reed for a number of valuable suggestions.

Urbana, Illinois
October, 1954

E. J. Scott

TRANSFORM
CALCULUS

with an Introduction
to Complex Variables

CHAPTER I

Functions of a Complex Variable

1.1 Complex Numbers

In order to solve equations such as $x^2 + 1 = 0$ and $x^2 + x + 1 = 0$ it is necessary to introduce numbers of the form $x + iy$, where x and y are real numbers and $i = \sqrt{-1}$, the so-called *imaginary* unit, satisfies the relation $i^2 = -1$. The number $z = x + iy$ is called a *complex* number and the components x and y are said to be, respectively, the *real* and *imaginary* parts of z. We shall denote them by

(1.1.1) $$\operatorname{Re}(z) = x, \quad \operatorname{Im}(z) = y.$$

Complex numbers lend themselves to a geometrical representation if·we agree to call x the abscissa and y the ordinate of a point with respect to a rectangular coordinate system which is known as the complex plane (Fig. 1.1.1). Thus, to the number $z = x + iy$ there corresponds a point (x,y) and conversely. At times it is convenient to think of a complex number as a vector emanating from the origin O and terminating at the point (x,y). In this way we establish a one-to-one correspondence between the totality of vectors in the complex plane and the complex numbers. The length of this vector is said to be the *modulus* of z, or the *absolute value* of z and is denoted by $|z|$. Thus

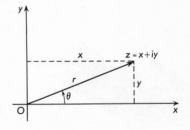

FIG. 1.1.1

(1.1.2) $$|z| = |x + iy| = \sqrt{x^2 + y^2}.$$

From Fig. 1.1.1 it is clear that

$$x = r \cos \theta, \quad y = r \sin \theta,$$

and hence

(1.1.3) $$z = x + iy = r (\cos \theta + i \sin \theta),$$

1

which is known as the *polar* form of the complex number z. In this representation r is the modulus and θ is the so-called *argument* or *amplitude* of z. The abbreviations arg $z = \theta$, amp $z = \theta$ are often used. It should be observed that the argument of a complex number is not unique, since the various values of θ can differ by integral multiples of 2π.

Two complex numbers z_1 and z_2 are equal if and only if their corresponding real and imaginary parts are equal, i.e.,

$$x_1 + iy_1 = x_2 + iy_2$$

implies that $x_1 = x_2$ and $y_1 = y_2$. As a particular case, $x + iy = 0$ implies that $x = 0$, $y = 0$.

The *conjugate* of $z = x + iy$ is defined to be the number $x - iy$ and is denoted by $\bar{z}$, thus

$$\bar{z} = x - iy.$$

The rules for adding, subtracting, multiplying, and dividing complex numbers are the same as those for real numbers. For example,

$$\begin{aligned}
z_1 \pm z_2 &= (x_1 + iy_1) \pm (x_2 + iy_2) \\
&= (x_1 \pm x_2) + i(y_1 \pm y_2), \\
z_1 \cdot z_2 &= (x_1 + iy_1)(x_2 + iy_2) \\
&= (x_1 x_2 - y_1 y_2) + i(x_1 y_2 + x_2 y_1), \\
\frac{z_1}{z_2} &= \frac{x_1 + iy_1}{x_2 + iy_2} = \frac{(x_1 + iy_1)(x_2 - iy_2)}{(x_2 + iy_2)(x_2 - iy_2)} \\
&= \frac{x_1 x_2 + y_1 y_2}{x_2^2 + y_2^2} + i\frac{x_2 y_1 - x_1 y_2}{x_2^2 + y_2^2},
\end{aligned}$$

provided $|z_2| \neq 0$.

We shall make frequent use of the following important inequalities:

$$(1.1.4) \qquad \big||z_1| - |z_2|\big| \leqslant |z_1 \pm z_2| \leqslant |z_1| + |z_2|,$$

which can be proved by simple algebraic or geometric considerations.

1.2 Sets of Points in the Complex Plane

Before considering functions of a complex variable we shall need to define a number of important terms.

By the phrase *set of points* in the complex plane we mean any collection of points. This collection may consist of a finite or infinite number of points. Thus, the points $(1,2)$, $(-3,4)$, $(5,4)$ form a finite set, whereas the points (x,y) satisfying the inequality $x^2 + y^2/3 < 1$ form an infinite set.

A set E is said to be *bounded* if a positive real number M can be found such that $|z| < M$ for all points z of E.

By an *ε-neighborhood* of a point z_0 is meant the set of points inside a circle with center z_0 and radius $\epsilon > 0$, i.e., it is the set of points z satisfying the inequality $|z - z_0| < \epsilon$.

If every point z of a set E has a neighborhood lying entirely within the set, then E is said to be an *open* set. Examples of open sets are the sets of points satisfying the following inequalities

$$\text{Im}(z) < \tfrac{1}{2}, \quad \text{Re}(z) > 0, \quad x^4 + y^4 < 4.$$

If the set of points *not* in E is an open set, then E is called a *closed* set. Thus the set of points satisfying the following conditions

$$\text{Re}(z) \leqslant 4, \quad x^2/4 + y^2/5 \geqslant 1, \quad x^2 + y^2 = 9,$$

are examples of closed sets.

A set E is termed a *connected* set if it is possible to join any two points A,B of the set by a polygonal arc lying entirely within the set. We shall call an *open connected* set a *region*.

1.3 Elementary Functions of a Complex Variable

If the complex variables z and w are so related that to each value of z in a given region of the complex plane there corresponds one value of w, then w is said to be a single-valued function of z and we write $w = f(z)$. An example is $w = z^2 - 1$.

On the other hand, if more than one value of w corresponds to each value of z, then $w = f(z)$ is multiple valued. For example, $w = \sqrt{z}$ is a double-valued function of z.

In defining the elementary functions $\cos z$, $\ln z$, $\sin^{-1} z$, etc., we are motivated by the desire so to arrange matters that these functions reduce to the corresponding functions of a real variable when z becomes x.

A *polynomial* is defined as a function of the form

$$P(z) = a_0 z^n + a_1 z^{n-1} + \cdots + a_{n-1}z + a_n,$$

where $a_0, a_1, \cdots, a_n$ may be complex and n is a positive integer.

A *rational* function of z is defined as the quotient of two polynomials.

In order to define e^z we resort to power series. The convergence of a power series of the form $\sum\limits_{n=0}^{\infty} a_n(z - z_0)^n$ can be investigated by tests analogous to those developed in elementary calculus for series involving real variables. In the real case the interval of convergence of a power series is the entire x-axis, a portion of it, or a single point on it; whereas in the complex case the region of convergence is the interior of a circle with, perhaps, some of the points on the circle. For example, $\sum\limits_{n=0}^{\infty} x^n$ has for its interval of convergence $-1 < x < 1$, whereas $\sum\limits_{n=0}^{\infty} z^n$ has for its region of convergence the interior of the circle $|z| = 1$.

It can be shown that convergent power series enjoy the following properties inside their circles of convergence: (a) they represent continuous functions, (b) the series obtained from them by differentiating or integrating term by term represent the derivative and integral, respectively, of the represented function and, furthermore, that the radii of convergence are the same as those of the original series, and (c) the term by term multiplication of the series is a valid operation.

Since

$$(1.3.1) \qquad e^x = 1 + x + \frac{x^2}{2!} + \cdots + \frac{x^n}{n!} + \cdots,$$

it is natural to define the *exponential* function e^z by the power series

$$(1.3.2) \qquad e^z = 1 + z + \frac{z^2}{2!} + \cdots + \frac{z^n}{n!} + \cdots.$$

It is apparent that (1.3.2) reduces to (1.3.1) when $z = x$. By the Cauchy ratio test it can be shown that this series converges for *all complex* values of z. The reader can readily show that

$$e^{z_1} \cdot e^{z_2} = e^{z_1 + z_2}$$

by multiplying the series expansions of the factors term by term.

The *trigonometric* functions $\sin z$ and $\cos z$ are defined as follows:

$$(1.3.3) \qquad \sin z = z - \frac{z^3}{3!} + \frac{z^5}{5!} - \cdots = \sum_{n=0}^{\infty} (-1)^n \frac{z^{2n+1}}{(2n+1)!},$$

$$(1.3.4) \qquad \cos z = 1 - \frac{z^2}{2!} + \frac{z^4}{4!} - \cdots = \sum_{n=0}^{\infty} (-1)^n \frac{z^{2n}}{(2n)!}.$$

By expanding e^{iz} in a power series and separating the real and imaginary parts, it is easily shown that

$$(1.3.5) \qquad e^{iz} = \cos z + i \sin z.$$

Formula (1.3.5) is known as *Euler's formula*. In a similar manner one can derive the formula

$$(1.3.6) \qquad e^{-iz} = \cos z - i \sin z.$$

Solving (1.3.5) and (1.3.6) for $\cos z$ and $\sin z$, we obtain

$$(1.3.7) \qquad \sin z = \frac{e^{iz} - e^{-iz}}{2i}, \qquad \cos z = \frac{e^{iz} + e^{-iz}}{2}$$

The functions $\tan z$, $\cot z$, $\sec z$ and $\csc z$ are defined as in trigonometry. Thus

$$\tan z = \frac{\sin z}{\cos z}, \quad \cot z = \frac{\cos z}{\sin z}, \quad \sec z = \frac{1}{\cos z}, \quad \csc z = \frac{1}{\sin z}.$$

Euler's formula permits one to write a complex number z in the following form:

$$z = x + iy = r(\cos\theta + i\sin\theta) = re^{i\theta},$$

which is a very useful and convenient representation.

The hyperbolic functions are defined in the following manner:

$$\sinh z = \frac{e^z - e^{-z}}{2}, \qquad \cosh z = \frac{e^z + e^{-z}}{2},$$

$$\tanh z = \frac{\sinh z}{\cosh z}, \qquad \coth z = \frac{\cosh z}{\sinh z},$$

$$\operatorname{sech} z = \frac{1}{\cosh z}, \qquad \operatorname{csch} z = \frac{1}{\sinh z}.$$

We define the logarithm of z as the inverse of the exponential function. Therefore, if

$$(1.3.8) \qquad\qquad w = \ln z,$$

then

$$(1.3.9) \qquad\qquad z = e^w.$$

It is convenient to have an expression for the logarithm of z in terms of its real and imaginary parts. To that end let us set $w = u + iv$. From (1.3.9) it follows that

$$z = x + iy = e^u \cdot e^{iv} = e^u(\cos v + i\sin v).$$

Equating the real and imaginary parts, we get

$$x = e^u \cos v, \quad y = e^u \sin v,$$

which when solved for u and v give

$$(1.3.10) \qquad e^{2u} = x^2 + y^2 = r^2 = |z|^2, \quad \tan v = y/x.$$

From (1.3.10) it follows that

$$u = \ln|z|, \quad v = \arctan(y/x) = \theta \pm 2k\pi, \quad (k = 0, 1, 2, \cdots),$$

where $\ln|z| = \ln r$ is the ordinary real logarithm, and θ is defined to lie in the interval $-\pi < \theta \leqslant \pi$. Hence

$$(1.3.11) \qquad \ln z = \ln|z| + i(\theta \pm 2k\pi), \quad (k=0, 1, 2, \cdots).$$

When $k = 0$ one obtains the so-called *principal value* of the logarithm. It is to be observed that the function $\ln z$ is an *infinitely many-valued* function and is defined for all values of z except $z = 0$, where it is undefined.

It is now possible to define the *generalized power function* $f(z) = z^b$, where b may be real or complex, by means of the relation

(1.3.12) $$z^b = e^{b \ln z}.$$

Because $\ln z$ is, in general, infinitely many valued, z^b also has infinitely many values (except when b is an integer).

As in trigonometry, the inverse of

(1.3.13) $$z = \sin w = \frac{e^{iw} - e^{-iw}}{2i}$$

is defined to be the function

(1.3.14) $$w = \sin^{-1} z.$$

From (1.3.13) we obtain

$$e^{2iw} - 2ize^{iw} - 1 = 0,$$

which is a quadratic in e^{iw} and has for its solution

$$e^{iw} = iz \pm \sqrt{1 - z^2}.$$

Solving this for w, we get

$$\sin^{-1} z = \frac{1}{i} \ln (iz \pm \sqrt{1 - z^2}).$$

It is clear that this function is, in general, infinitely many valued.

In a similar way the reader can verify the following formulas:

$$\cos^{-1} z = \frac{1}{i} \ln (z \pm \sqrt{z^2 - 1}),$$

$$\tan^{-1} z = \frac{i}{2} \ln \frac{1 - iz}{1 + iz},$$

$$\sinh^{-1} z = \ln (z \pm \sqrt{z^2 + 1}),$$

$$\cosh^{-1} z = \ln (z \pm \sqrt{z^2 - 1}),$$

$$\tanh^{-1} z = \frac{1}{2} \ln \frac{1 + z}{1 - z}.$$

The functions just discussed and finite combinations of these obtained by the fundamental operations of addition, subtraction, multiplication, and division are called *elementary* functions.

1.4 Limit, Continuity, and Analyticity of Functions of a Complex Variable

The function $w = f(z)$, defined in some region R, is said to have the limit w_0 as $z \to z_0$, and we write $\lim_{z \to z_0} f(z) = w_0$, if corresponding to every positive number ϵ there exists a positive number δ such that if $|f(z) - w_0| < \epsilon$ whenever $0 < |z - z_0| < \delta$.

If the complex number $z = x + iy$ represents a point in the z-plane with coordinates x and y, then the corresponding value of $w = f(z) = u + iv$ can be represented by a point in the so-called w-plane with coordinates u and v. Thus the function $w = f(z)$ sets up a correspondence between points in the z- and w-planes. If z traces out a curve in the z-plane, then w traces out a corresponding curve in the w-plane.

The preceding definition of a limit can now be interpreted geometrically as follows. Corresponding to $\epsilon > 0$ there exists a $\delta > 0$ such that for all points $z \neq z_0$ lying within the circle of radius δ and center z_0 in the z-plane, the corresponding points w lie within the circle of radius ϵ and center w_0 in the w-plane.

If $f(z_0)$ exists and for each $\epsilon > 0$ there exists a $\delta > 0$ such that $|f(z) - f(z_0)| < \epsilon$ whenever $|z - z_0| < \delta$, then $f(z)$ is said to be *continuous* at the point z_0. This is equivalent to the statements that (a) $f(z_0)$ exists, (b) $\lim_{z \to z_0} f(z)$ exists, and (c) $\lim_{z \to z_0} f(z) = f(z_0)$. If $f(z)$ is continuous at every point of the region R, then it is said to be *continuous in the region R*.

The derivative of $w = f(z)$ at z_0 is defined as in the real variable case. Thus

$$\frac{dw}{dz} = f'(z_0) = \lim_{z \to z_0} \frac{f(z) - f(z_0)}{z - z_0} = \lim_{\Delta z \to 0} \frac{f(z_0 + \Delta z) - f(z_0)}{\Delta z},$$

where we require that the limit exist and be the same regardless of the direction in which z tends to z_0, or $\Delta z \to 0$.

This requirement is a rather severe one and restricts the class of functions which possess a derivative. For example, the function $f(z) = x + 2iy$ does not possess a derivative. This may be seen by examining the ratio

(1.4.1)
$$\frac{\Delta w}{\Delta z} = \frac{\Delta x + 2i\Delta y}{\Delta x + i\Delta y}.$$

If $\Delta y = 0$, that is, $\Delta z \to 0$ along a line parallel to the x-axis, then the limit of (1.4.1) is $+1$. On the other hand, if $\Delta x = 0$, that is, $\Delta z \to 0$ along a line parallel to the y-axis, then the limit of (1.4.1) is $+2$, and obviously the two limits are not the same. One might be led to believe that this requirement is so severe that the class of functions having derivatives is too narrow and therefore of little importance. Fortunately, this is not true, and it is this class that we shall study exclusively.

A function $f(z)$ which is *single valued* in a region R and possesses a *unique derivative* at each point of R is said to be *analytic in R*. It is *analytic at a point* z_0 if z_0 lies inside some region where $f(z)$ is analytic.

Suppose that $w = f(z)$ is analytic in a region R. Substituting $x + iy$ for z, we can write w thus

$$w = f(x + iy) = u(x,y) + iv(x,y).$$

By definition

$$\frac{dw}{dz} = \lim_{\Delta z \to 0} \frac{u(x + \Delta x, y + \Delta y) - u(x,y)}{\Delta z}$$

$$+ i \lim_{\Delta z \to 0} \frac{v(x + \Delta x, y + \Delta y) - v(x,y)}{\Delta z}.$$

Since the derivative is to exist and be unique for all modes of approach of Δz to zero, it is possible to select some special paths. Let us first allow $\Delta z \to 0$ along a line parallel to the y-axis. Then $\Delta x = 0$ and $\Delta z = i\Delta y$. Hence

$$\frac{dw}{dz} = \lim_{\Delta y \to 0} \frac{u(x, y + \Delta y) - u(x,y)}{i\Delta y} + i \lim_{\Delta y \to 0} \frac{v(x, y + \Delta y) - v(x,y)}{i\Delta y}$$

and passing to the limit

$$\frac{dw}{dz} = -i\frac{\partial u}{\partial y} + \frac{\partial v}{\partial y}.$$

Next, let $\Delta z \to 0$ along a line parallel to the x-axis. Then $\Delta y = 0$ and $\Delta z = \Delta x$. Therefore

$$\frac{dw}{dz} = \lim_{\Delta x \to 0} \frac{u(x + \Delta x, y) - u(x,y)}{\Delta x} + i \lim_{\Delta x \to 0} \frac{v(x + \Delta x, y) - v(x,y)}{\Delta x}$$

and consequently

$$\frac{dw}{dz} = \frac{\partial u}{\partial x} + i\frac{\partial v}{\partial x}.$$

If follows that

$$\frac{dw}{dz} = \frac{\partial v}{\partial y} - i\frac{\partial u}{\partial y} = \frac{\partial u}{\partial x} + i\frac{\partial v}{\partial x}.$$

Since two complex quantities are equal if and only if their real and imaginary parts are equal,

(1.4.2) $$\frac{\partial u}{\partial x} = \frac{\partial v}{\partial y}, \qquad \frac{\partial v}{\partial x} = -\frac{\partial u}{\partial y}.$$

These equations are known as the *Cauchy-Riemann equations*.

We have therefore demonstrated (on the assumption that u_x, u_y, v_x, v_y exist) that in order for $w = u(x,y) + iv(x,y)$ to be analytic in the region R it is *necessary* that the Cauchy-Riemann equations be satisfied for all the points in R. That these conditions are at the same time *sufficient* to insure that dw/dz exists uniquely is not at all evident, since we have selected only two of the infinite number of modes of approach to zero. However, by imposing further conditions on the functions u and v we can show that these conditions are also sufficient. For let u and v satisfy the Cauchy-Riemann equations *and* furthermore let the four partial derivatives exist and be *continuous* in R, then $w = u(x,y) + iv(x,y)$ is analytic in R.

Proof: We have

$$f(z + \Delta z) - f(z) = u(x + \Delta x, y + \Delta y) - u(x,y) + iv(x + \Delta x, y + \Delta y) - iv(x,y).$$

Using the law of the mean, we obtain

$$f(z+\Delta z) - f(z) = u_x(x + \theta_1 \Delta x, y)\Delta x + u_y(x + \Delta x, y + \theta_2 \Delta y)\Delta y \\ + i\{v_x(x + \theta_3 \Delta x, y)\Delta x + v_y(x+\Delta x, y + \theta_4 \Delta y)\Delta y\},$$

where θ_1, θ_2, θ_3, θ_4 are numbers between 0 and 1.

Let

$$u_x(x + \theta_1 \Delta x, y) - u_x(x,y) = A_1(x,y,\Delta x),$$
$$u_y(x + \Delta x, y + \theta_2 \Delta y) - u_y(x,y) = A_2(x,y,\Delta x,\Delta y),$$
$$v_x(x + \theta_3 \Delta x, y) - v_x(x,y) = A_3(x,y,\Delta x),$$
$$v_y(x + \Delta x, y + \theta_4 \Delta y) - v_y(x,y) = A_4(x,y,\Delta x,\Delta y).$$

Then

$$f(z + \Delta z) - f(z) = u_x(x,y)\Delta x + u_y(x,y)\Delta y + iv_x(x,y)\Delta x \\ + iv_y(x,y)\Delta y + A_1\Delta x + A_2\Delta y + iA_3\Delta x + iA_4\Delta y.$$

Making use of the Cauchy-Riemann equations, we can write the preceding equation as

$$f(z + \Delta z) - f(z) = u_x(x,y)\Delta x + iu_x(x,y)\Delta y + i\{v_x(x,y)\Delta x + iv_x(x,y)\Delta y\} \\ + A_1\Delta x + A_2\Delta y + iA_3\Delta x + iA_4\Delta y.$$

Combining terms, transposing and taking the absolute value of both sides, we get

$$|\{f(z + \Delta z) - f(z)\} - \{u_x + iv_x\}\Delta z| \leqslant |A_1|\,|\Delta x| + |A_2|\,|\Delta y| \\ + |A_3|\,|\Delta x| + |A_4|\,|\Delta y|.$$

Dividing both sides by $|\Delta z|$, we obtain

$$\left|\frac{f(z + \Delta z) - f(z)}{\Delta z} - (u_x + iv_x)\right| \leqslant |A_1|\left|\frac{\Delta x}{\Delta z}\right| + |A_2|\left|\frac{\Delta y}{\Delta z}\right| \\ + |A_3|\left|\frac{\Delta x}{\Delta z}\right| + |A_4|\left|\frac{\Delta y}{\Delta z}\right|.$$

Now $|\Delta x/\Delta z| \leqslant 1$ and $|\Delta y/\Delta z| \leqslant 1$, hence

$$(1.4.3) \qquad \left|\frac{f(z + \Delta z) - f(z)}{\Delta z} - (u_x + iv_x)\right| \leqslant |A_1| + |A_2| + |A_3| + |A_4|.$$

Since u_x, u_y, v_x, v_y were assumed to be continuous, A_1, A_2, A_3, A_4 all tend to zero as $\Delta z \to 0$. Taking the limit of both sides of (1.4.3), we get

$$\frac{dw}{dz} = \lim_{\Delta z \to 0} \frac{f(z + \Delta z) - f(z)}{\Delta z} = u_x + iv_x.$$

We have thus established the existence of dw/dz for any mode of approach of Δz toward zero.

Therefore, if the real and imaginary parts of a complex function, together with their partial derivatives of the first order, are continuous and satisfy the Cauchy-Riemann equations throughout a region R, then $f(z)$ is analytic throughout R.

Example 1.   For the function $w = \bar{z} = x - iy$, we have the continuous functions $u(x, y) = x$, $v(x, y) = -y$ whose partial derivatives are

$$u_x = 1, \quad v_y = -1, \quad u_y = 0, \quad v_x = 0,$$

which are continuous everywhere. However, the Cauchy-Riemann equations are not satisfied anywhere. Therefore the function $w = \bar{z}$ is analytic nowhere.

Example 2.   The function $f(z) = z^2 = x^2 - y^2 + 2xyi$ has the partial derivatives

$$u_x = 2x, \quad v_y = 2x, \quad u_y = -2y, \quad v_x = 2y,$$

which, together with the real and imaginary parts, are continuous everywhere. In addition, the Cauchy-Riemann equations are satisfied everywhere. Hence $f(z) = z^2$ is analytic everywhere.

Suppose that the partial derivatives of second order exist. Then

$$\frac{\partial^2 u}{\partial x^2} = \frac{\partial^2 v}{\partial x \, \partial y}, \qquad \frac{\partial^2 u}{\partial y^2} = \frac{\partial^2 v}{\partial y \, \partial x}.$$

Now if, in addition, the second order partial derivatives are assumed to be continuous, then the order of differentiation is immaterial and

$$\frac{\partial^2 u}{\partial x^2} + \frac{\partial^2 u}{\partial y^2} = 0.$$

Similarly

$$\frac{\partial^2 v}{\partial x^2} + \frac{\partial^2 v}{\partial y^2} = 0.$$

Hence the real and imaginary parts of an analytic function cannot be chosen arbitrarily, but must satisfy *Laplace's equation*

(1.4.4)
$$\frac{\partial^2 \phi}{\partial x^2} + \frac{\partial^2 \phi}{\partial y^2} = 0.$$

The functions $u(x,y)$ and $v(x,y)$ that satisfy (1.4.4) are known as *conjugate* functions.

Since Laplace's equation occurs frequently in two dimensional problems in hydrodynamics, elasticity, electrostatics, etc., the connection between analytic functions and Laplace's equation makes the study of functions of a complex variable of paramount importance in applied mathematics.

1.5 Line Integrals of Complex Functions

Let C (Fig. 1.5.1) be any continuous curve of finite length joining the two points $A \equiv z_0$ and $B \equiv z_n$, and let $f(z) = u(x,y) + iv(x,y)$ be a continuous function defined at all points of C. Let $z_1, z_2, \cdots, z_{n-1}$ be points of division of the curve C and $\zeta_1, \zeta_2, \cdots, \zeta_n$ arbitrary points of the segments $(z_0, z_1), (z_1, z_2), \cdots, (z_{n-1}, z_n)$. Form the sum

$$S_n = \sum_{k=1}^{n} f(\zeta_k)\,(z_k - z_{k-1}). \tag{1.5.1}$$

The limit of this sum as $n \to \infty$ in such a way that the largest of the segments tends to zero is defined as the *line integral* of $f(z)$ along C. Symbolically,

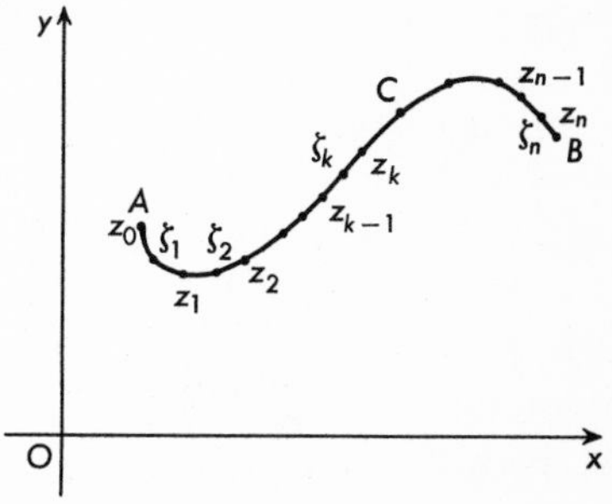

FIG. 1.5.1

$$\int_C f(z)\,dz \equiv \lim_{n\to\infty} \sum_{k=1}^{n} f(\zeta_k)(z_k - z_{k-1}).$$

Let $\quad \zeta_k = \xi_k + i\eta_k, \quad z_k = x_k + iy_k, \quad z_{k-1} = x_{k-1} + iy_{k-1}.$

Separating the sum in (1.5.1) into its real and imaginary parts, we get

$$\begin{aligned} S_n = &\sum_{k=1}^{n} [u(\xi_k,\eta_k)(x_k - x_{k-1}) - v(\xi_k,\eta_k)(y_k - y_{k-1})] \\ &+ i \sum_{k-1}^{n} [v(\xi_k,\eta_k)(x_k - x_{k-1}) + u(\xi_k,\eta_k)(y_k - y_{k-1})]. \end{aligned} \tag{1.5.2}$$

Since $f(z)$ was assumed continuous, the limit of S_n in (1.5.2) exists and is equal to

$$\begin{aligned} \int_C f(z)\,dz &= \int_C (u\,dx - v\,dy) + i\int_C (v\,dx + u\,dy) \\ &= \int_C (u + iv)(dx + i\,dy). \end{aligned} \tag{1.5.3}$$

Hence a line integral of a function of a complex variable can be evaluated by finding the values of two real line integrals. It should be observed that the value of this integral depends, in general, on the function $f(z)$ and the path C.

Example. Evaluate $\int_C (z+1)dz$, where C is the parabola $y = x^2$ joining the points (0,0) and (1,1).

Since $z + 1 = (x+1) + iy$, $u = x+1$ and $v = y$. Therefore from (1.5.3) we obtain

$$\int_C (z+1)dz = \int_C \{(x+1)dx - y\,dy\} + i\int_C \{y\,dx + (x+1)dy\}.$$

Substituting $y = x^2$ on the right side and simplifying, we have

$$\int_C (z+1)dz = \int_0^1 (1 + x - 2x^3)dx + i\int_0^1 (3x^2 + 2x)dx$$

$$= (x + x^2/2 - x^4/2)\Big]_0^1 + i(x^3 + x^2)\Big]_0^1$$

$$= 1 + 2i.$$

Making use of the fact that the absolute value of a sum is less than or equal to the sum of the absolute values, we get

$$\Big|\sum_{k=1}^n f(\zeta_k)(z_k - z_{k-1})\Big| \leqslant \sum_{k=1}^n |f(\zeta_k)|\,|z_k - z_{k-1}|,$$

and therefore after passing to the limit, we obtain

$$\Big|\int_C f(z)\,dz\Big| \leqslant \int_C |f(z)|\,|dz|.$$

Now $|dz| = ds$, so that if $f(z)$ is bounded on C, i.e., $|f(z)| < M$, where M is a constant, then

(1.5.4) $$\Big|\int_C f(z)\,dz\Big| \leqslant M\int_C ds = ML,$$

where L is the length of the curve C. This inequality is of great importance and we shall use it often later on.

1.6 Cauchy's Integral Theorem

Before we give a proof of this fundamental theorem, let us define certain terms which will be of frequent occurrence in what follows.

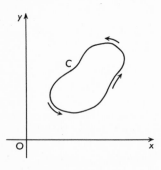

A continuous closed curve C which does not cross itself, and is such that parallels to the x- and y-axes cut it in at most two points is called a *simple closed curve* (Fig. 1.6.1).

If in the process of describing the curve C an observer proceeds so that the region enclosed is to his left, then we say that the curve has been traversed in the *positive direction*.

Regions more complicated than those enclosed by simple curves can,

Fig. 1.6.1

in general, be decomposed into regions bounded by simple closed curves by introducing suitable cross-cuts. Thus in Fig. 1.6.2 the region enclosed by C' has been divided by the cross-cuts AD and BC into the regions R_1, R_2, R_3, each of which is bounded by a simple closed curve.

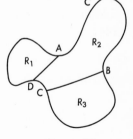

If a region R has the property that *any* closed curve lying in R can be shrunk continuously to a point without crossing the boundary of R, then the region is said to be *simply connected*.

The region within C_2 and without C_1 (Fig. 1.6.3) is not a simply connected region, since a closed curve surrounding C_1 when shrunk to a point would cross the boundary of the region. Regions such as those in Figs. 1.6.3 and

FIG. 1.6.2

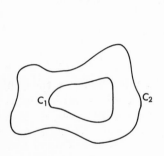

FIG. 1.6.3

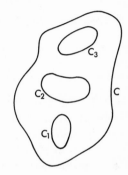

FIG. 1.6.4

1.6.4 are called *multiply connected*. One should observe that these regions can be made simply connected by introducing cross-cuts. For example, Fig. 1.6.5 is a simply connected region, where the cross-cuts are AB, CD, and EF.

In order to prove Cauchy's theorem we shall make use of:

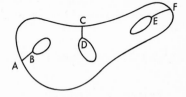

Green's Theorem. If $P(x,y)$, $Q(x,y)$, $\dfrac{\partial P}{\partial y}$, and $\dfrac{\partial Q}{\partial x}$ are continuous single-valued

FIG. 1.6.5

functions in a simply connected region R bounded by a closed curve C, where C is included in R, then

$$\int_C (P\,dx + Q\,dy) = \int\int_R \left(\frac{\partial Q}{\partial x} - \frac{\partial P}{\partial y}\right) dx\,dy.$$

Suppose that R is a simply connected region, C a closed contour lying entirely within R and $f(z) = u + iv$ an analytic function in R. Furthermore, let $f'(z)$ be *continuous* throughout R. Then u, v and their first order partial derivatives are continuous in R and by Green's theorem

$$(1.6.1) \qquad \int_C f(z)\, dz = \int_C (u\, dx - v\, dy) + i \int_C (v\, dx + u\, dy)$$

$$= \int\!\!\int_R \left(-\frac{dv}{dx} - \frac{du}{dy} \right) dx\, dy$$

$$+ i \int\!\!\int_R \left(-\frac{\partial v}{\partial y} + \frac{\partial u}{\partial x} \right) dx\, dy.$$

Since $f(z)$ was assumed analytic, $\dfrac{\partial u}{\partial x} = \dfrac{\partial v}{\partial y}, \dfrac{\partial u}{\partial y} = -\dfrac{\partial v}{\partial x}$, and hence the double integrals in (1.6.1) vanish identically. Therefore

$$(1.6.2) \qquad\qquad \int_C f(z)\, dz = 0.$$

The preceding result is known as *Cauchy's integral theorem.*

Remark. It will have been observed that Cauchy's theorem was proved on the assumption that $f'(z)$ existed *and* was continuous as well. The validity of the theorem can be established, however, by assuming only the existence of $f'(z)$ and not its continuity. This was first done by the French mathematician Goursat.

Example 1. Evaluate $\displaystyle\int_C \frac{dz}{z + 2i}$, where C is the circle $|z| = 1$.

Since $f(z) = \dfrac{1}{z + 2i}$ is analytic within and on the circle $|z| = 1$, by Cauchy's theorem $\displaystyle\int_C \frac{dz}{z + 2i} = 0$.

Example 2. Evaluate the integral of Example 1, where C is the circle $|z| = 2$.

Since $f(z) = \dfrac{1}{z + 2i}$ is not continuous at $z = -2i$, which is on the circle $|z| = 2$, the line integral does not exist.

Example 3. Evaluate the integral of Example 1, where C is the circle $|z| = 3$.

Let $z + 2i = \rho e^{i\theta}$. Then $dz = \rho i e^{i\theta}\, d\theta + e^{i\theta}\, d\rho$ and

$$\int_C \frac{dz}{z + 2i} = i \int_0^{2\pi} d\theta + \int_\rho^\rho \frac{d\rho}{\rho} = 2\pi i.$$

Here $f(z) = \dfrac{1}{z + 2i}$ is not analytic at $z = -2i$, which is within the circle $|z| = 3$.

Suppose that two distinct curves C_1 and C_2 join the points z_0 and z_1 as in Fig. 1.6.6. Then by Cauchy's theorem (on the assumption that $f(z)$ is analytic within the region enclosed by C_1, C_2 and on the curves themselves)

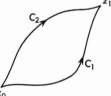

$$\int_{C_1} f(z)\, dz = \int_{C_2} f(z)\, dz.$$

The last equality simply states that *the value of the integral* $\displaystyle\int_{z_0}^{z_1} f(\zeta)\, d\zeta$ *is independent of the*

Fig. 1.6.6

path joining z_0 to z_1.

Consider now a simple closed curve C' lying entirely within the region bounded by a similar curve C (Fig. 1.6.7). By introducing the cross-cut $A_1 A_2$ the multiply connected region becomes a simply connected region to which Cauchy's theorem applies. We have

$$\int_{A_1 A_4 A_1} f(z)\, dz + \int_{A_1 A_2} f(z)\, dz + \int_{A_2 A_3 A_2} f(z)\, dz$$
$$+ \int_{A_2 A_1} f(z)\, dz = 0,$$

and since the sum of the second and fourth integrals vanishes because the integrals are evaluated in opposite directions over the same path, it follows that

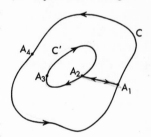

Fig. 1.6.7

$$(1.6.3) \qquad \int_C f(z)\, dz + \int_{C'} f(z)\, dz = 0,$$

where C is taken in the counterclockwise direction and C' is traversed in the clockwise direction. However, if the second integral in (1.6.3) is transposed and *the direction of C' reversed*, then

$$(1.6.4) \qquad \int_C f(z)\, dz = \int_{C'} f(z)\, dz.$$

In a similar manner the reader can show that if there is a finite number of simple closed curves: $C_1, C_2, C_3, \cdots$ lying within the region bounded by C (Fig. 1.6.8), then

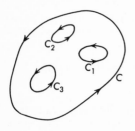

$$(1.6.5) \qquad \int_C f(z)\,dz = \int_{C_1} f(z)\,dz$$
$$+ \int_{C_2} f(z)\,dz + \int_{C_3} f(z)\,dz + \cdots,$$

where $C, C_1, C_2, C_3, \cdots$ are all described in a counterclockwise direction.

We shall now prove the following important theorem:

Fig. 1.6.8

If $f(z)$ is analytic in a simply connected region R, then $F(z) = \int_{z_0}^{z} f(\zeta)\,d\zeta$ is also analytic in R (for any path joining z_0 to z and lying in R), and $\dfrac{dF(z)}{dz} = f(z)$.

Since $f(z)$ is analytic in R, $F(z)$ will be independent of the path joining z_0 to z and hence in forming the difference we can take a straight line joining z to $z + \Delta z$ (Fig. 1.6.9). We have

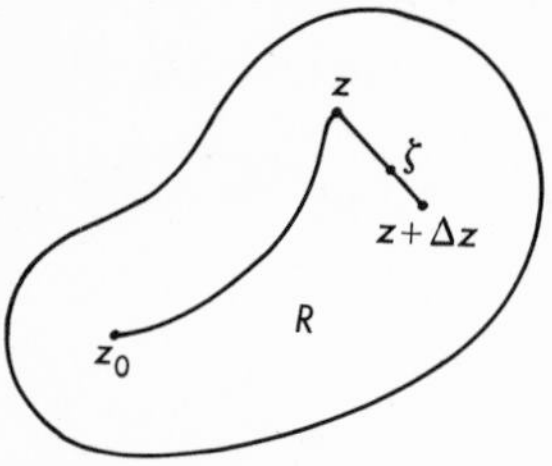

$$F(z + \Delta z) - F(z)$$
$$= \int_{z_0}^{z+\Delta z} f(\zeta)\,d\zeta - \int_{z_0}^{z} f(\zeta)\,d\zeta$$
$$= \int_{z}^{z+\Delta z} f(\zeta)\,d\zeta$$
$$= \int_{z}^{z+\Delta z} f(z)\,d\zeta + \int_{z}^{z+\Delta z} [f(\zeta) - f(z)]d\zeta$$
$$= f(z)\Delta z + \int_{z}^{z+\Delta z} [f(\zeta) - f(z)]d\zeta.$$

Fig. 1.6.9

Transposing $f(z)\Delta z$ to the left and dividing by Δz, we get

$$(1.6.6) \qquad \frac{F(z + \Delta z) - F(z)}{\Delta z} - f(z) = \frac{1}{\Delta z}\int_{z}^{z+\Delta z} [f(\zeta) - f(z)]d\zeta.$$

By hypothesis $f(z)$ is analytic, therefore $f(z)$ is continuous. Hence, corresponding to $\epsilon > 0$, there exists a $\delta > 0$ such that $|f(\zeta) - f(z)| < \epsilon$ whenever $|\zeta - z| < \delta$. Consequently if we take $|\Delta z| < \delta$, (1.6.6) becomes (after taking the absolute value of both sides)

$$\left| \frac{F(z + \Delta z) - F(z)}{\Delta z} - f(z) \right| < \epsilon, \quad |\Delta z| < \delta$$

which is equivalent to saying that

$$\lim_{\Delta z \to 0} \frac{F(z + \Delta z) - F(z)}{\Delta z} \equiv \frac{dF(z)}{dz} \equiv F'(z) = f(z).$$

Any function $\Phi(z)$ such that $\dfrac{d\Phi(z)}{dz} = f(z)$ is called an *indefinite*
integral of $f(z)$.

Suppose, now, that $F(z)$ and $G(z)$ are analytic in a region R and such
that $F'(z) = G'(z) = f(z)$. Then

(1.6.7) $$F'(z) - G'(z) = \frac{d}{dz}[F(z) - G(z)] = 0.$$

If we set $F(z) - G(z) = u + iv$, (1.6.7) implies that $\dfrac{\partial u}{\partial x} + i\dfrac{\partial v}{\partial x}$
$= \dfrac{\partial v}{\partial y} - i\dfrac{\partial u}{\partial y} = 0$, and hence that $\dfrac{\partial u}{\partial x} = \dfrac{\partial v}{\partial x} = \dfrac{\partial v}{\partial y} = \dfrac{\partial u}{\partial y} = 0$. Consequently u and v are both constants and $F(z) - G(z) = \text{const.}$ Thus
we have shown that any two indefinite integrals of $f(z)$ can differ only
by a constant. It follows that

$$\int_{z_0}^{z} f(z)\, dz = F(z) + C.$$

Setting $z = z_0$, we obtain $0 = F(z_0) + C$. Hence

$$\int_{z_0}^{z} f(z)\, dz = F(z) - F(z_0).$$

As in the case of real variables, the preceding result is called *the*
fundamental theorem of the integral calculus.

1.7 Cauchy's Integral Formula

Let $f(z)$ be an analytic function in the region R bounded by a closed
curve C, and let z_0 be any point inside R. With z_0 as center draw a
circle C_ρ with radius ρ entirely within R
(Fig. 1.7.1). It is clear that $\dfrac{f(z)}{z - z_0}$ is
analytic in the region bounded by C_ρ and
C. Hence by (1.6.4) it follows that

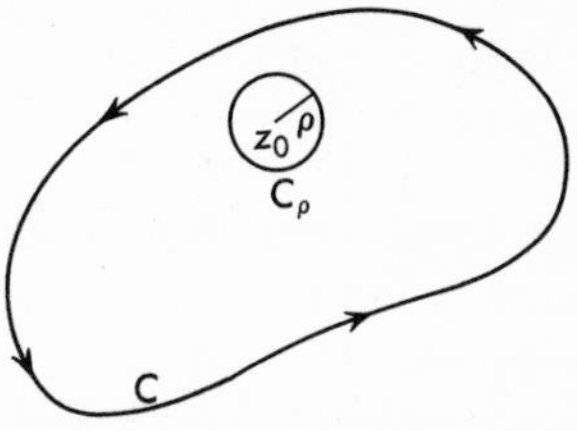

(1.7.1) $$\int_C \frac{f(z)}{z - z_0}\, dz = \int_{C_\rho} \frac{f(z)}{z - z_0}\, dz.$$

Fig. 1.7.1

Now

$$\int_{C_\rho} \frac{f(z)}{z - z_0}\, dz = \int_{C_\rho} \frac{f(z_0)}{z - z_0}\, dz + \int_{C_\rho} \frac{f(z) - f(z_0)}{z - z_0}\, dz.$$

On the circle C_ρ we have $z = z_0 + \rho e^{i\theta}$ and $dz = \rho i e^{i\theta} \, d\theta$. Consequently

$$\int_{C_\rho} \frac{f(z_0)}{z - z_0} \, dz = f(z_0) \int_0^{2\pi} \frac{\rho i e^{i\theta} \, d\theta}{\rho e^{i\theta}} = 2\pi i \, f(z_0).$$

Furthermore, since $f(z)$ is continuous, corresponding to any $\epsilon > 0$ we can take ρ so small that for any z on C_ρ

$$|f(z) - f(z_0)| < \epsilon.$$

Therefore by (1.5.4),

$$\left| \int_{C_\rho} \frac{f(z) - f(z_0)}{z - z_0} \, dz \right| \leqslant \frac{\epsilon}{\rho} \cdot 2\pi\rho = 2\pi\epsilon,$$

i.e.,

$$\int_{C_\rho} \frac{f(z) - f(z_0)}{z - z_0} \, dz = 0,$$

and hence from (1.7.1) we obtain

$$(1.7.2) \qquad \qquad \int_C \frac{f(z)}{z - z_0} \, dz = 2\pi i \, f(z_0).$$

This is *Cauchy's integral formula*. It is remarkable in that the values of $f(z_0)$ at any point z_0 within C can be obtained from the given boundary values of $f(z)$ on C. For instance, if the values of some physical quantity have been measured only along C, then the values of $f(z_0)$ inside C can be computed by Cauchy's formula.

Example 1. Evaluate $\displaystyle\int_C \frac{z^2 - 2z - 1}{z + i} \, dz$, where C is the circle $|z| = 2$.

By Cauchy's integral formula

$$\int_C \frac{z^2 - 2z - 1}{z + i} \, dz = 2\pi i(-1 + 2i - 1) = -4\pi(1 + i).$$

Example 2. Evaluate $\displaystyle\int_C \frac{z + 1}{z(z - 1)} \, dz$, where C is the circle $|z| = 3$.

Again by Cauchy's formula

$$\int_C \frac{z + 1}{z(z - 1)} \, dz = \int_C \frac{2}{z - 1} \, dz - \int_C \frac{dz}{z} = 4\pi i - 2\pi i = 2\pi i.$$

For many purposes it is desirable to express formula (1.7.2) in a more convenient form. To that end, let z replace z_0 as any point interior to C, and let ζ be the variable of integration. Then

(1.7.3)
$$f(z) = \frac{1}{2\pi i} \int_C \frac{f(\zeta)}{\zeta - z}\, d\zeta.$$

By differentiating both sides of (1.7.3) and assuming that differentiation under the integral sign is permissible, we obtain

(1.7.4)
$$f'(z) = \frac{1}{2\pi i} \int_C \frac{f(\zeta)}{(\zeta - z)^2}\, d\zeta.$$

Proceeding in a similar manner it can be shown that

(1.7.5)
$$f^{(n)}(z) = \frac{n!}{2\pi i} \int_C \frac{f(\zeta)\, d\zeta}{(\zeta - z)^{n+1}}.$$

The reader desiring to know how the validity of these steps is established can consult reference 19 in Appendix A.

It should be observed that the results obtained have no counterpart in functions of a real variable. There, the possession of a first derivative by a function does not guarantee the existence of higher order derivatives. Here, we have seen that an analytic function possesses derivatives of all orders.

1.8 Taylor's Series

We shall now make use of Cauchy's integral theorem to expand an analytic function $f(z)$ in a series of powers of $(z - z_0)$. Let $f(z)$ be analytic in a region R, and let z_0 be the center of a circle C of radius r lying entirely within R. Now

(1.8.1)
$$f(z) = \frac{1}{2\pi i} \int_C \frac{f(\zeta)}{\zeta - z}\, d\zeta = \frac{1}{2\pi i} \int_C \frac{f(\zeta)\, d\zeta}{(\zeta - z_0) - (z - z_0)}$$

$$= \frac{1}{2\pi i} \int_C \frac{f(\zeta)}{\zeta - z_0} \left(\frac{1}{1 - \dfrac{z - z_0}{\zeta - z_0}} \right) d\zeta.$$

Also

$$\frac{1}{1 - \dfrac{z - z_0}{\zeta - z_0}} = 1 + \frac{z - z_0}{\zeta - z_0} + \cdots + \left(\frac{z - z_0}{\zeta - z_0} \right)^{n-1} + \frac{(z - z_0)^n}{(\zeta - z)(\zeta - z_0)^{n-1}}.$$

Substituting this result in (1.7.4), we obtain

(1.8.2) $f(z) =$

$$\frac{1}{2\pi i}\int_C \frac{f(\zeta)}{\zeta - z_0}\left\{1 + \frac{z - z_0}{\zeta - z_0} + \cdots + \frac{(z - z_0)^n}{(\zeta - z)(\zeta - z_0)^{n-1}}\right\} d\zeta$$

$$= f(z_0) + (z - z_0) f'(z_0) + \frac{(z - z_0)^2}{2!} f''(z_0) + \cdots$$

$$+ \frac{(z - z_0)^{n-1}}{(n - 1)!} f^{(n-1)}(z_0) + R_n,$$

where $R_n = \dfrac{(z - z_0)^n}{2\pi i}\displaystyle\int_C \frac{f(\zeta)\, d\zeta}{(\zeta - z_0)^n(\zeta - z)}.$

Let us investigate the remainder R_n to see what happens as n increases beyond all bounds. Suppose that M is the maximum value of $|f(\zeta)|$ on C. If ζ is any point on C and z any point inside C, then $|z - z_0| = r_1 < r$ and $|\zeta - z| > r - r_1$ (Fig. 1.8.1). Therefore

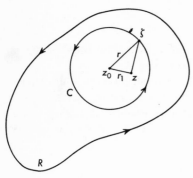

Fig. 1.8.1

$$|R_n| = \left|\frac{(z - z_0)^n}{2\pi i}\int_C \frac{f(\zeta)\, d\zeta}{(\zeta - z_0)^n(\zeta - z)}\right|$$

$$< \frac{r_1{}^n}{2\pi} \cdot \frac{2\pi r M}{r^n(r - r_1)} = \frac{M}{1 - r_1/r}\left(\frac{r_1}{r}\right)^n.$$

Since $r_1 < r$, it follows that for all z within the circle C, $\lim\limits_{n\to\infty} R_n = 0$.

Thus, we have established that the series

(1.8.3) $f(z_0) + (z - z_0)f'(z_0) + \dfrac{(z - z_0)^2}{2!} f''(z_0) + \cdots$

$$+ \frac{(z - z_0)^n}{n!} f^{(n)}(z_0) + \cdots$$

converges to $f(z)$ for every z inside any circle C lying wholly within the region R in which $f(z)$ is analytic. Expression (1.8.3), which is of great importance in the theory of functions of a complex variable, is called a *Taylor's series*.

1.9 Laurent Series

Let $f(z)$ be analytic in the annular region bounded by the concentric circles C_1, C_2 whose common center is z_0 and whose radii are r_1, r_2, respectively. By introducing a cross-cut connecting C_1 and C_2 and using Cauchy's integral formula, we get

$$(1.9.1) \qquad f(z) = \frac{1}{2\pi i} \int_{C_2} \frac{f(\zeta)\, d\zeta}{\zeta - z} - \frac{1}{2\pi i} \int_{C_1} \frac{f(\zeta)\, d\zeta}{\zeta - z},$$

where z is any point within the annular region, while C_1 and C_2 are oriented as shown in Fig. 1.9.1.

Proceeding as in connection with Taylor's series,

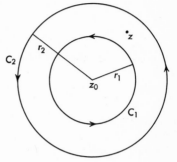

$$(1.9.2)$$

$$\frac{1}{2\pi i} \int_{C_2} \frac{f(\zeta)\, d\zeta}{\zeta - z} = \sum_{n=0}^{\infty} a_n (z - z_0)^n,$$

where

$$(1.9.3) \qquad a_n = \frac{1}{2\pi i} \int_{C_2} \frac{f(\zeta)\, d\zeta}{(\zeta - z_0)^{n+1}},$$

$$n = 0, 1, 2, \cdots$$

Fig. 1.9.1

Now

$$-\frac{1}{2\pi i} \int_{C_1} \frac{f(\zeta)\, d\zeta}{\zeta - z}$$

$$= \frac{1}{2\pi i} \int_{C_1} \frac{f(\zeta)\, d\zeta}{(z - z_0) - (\zeta - z_0)}$$

$$= \frac{1}{2\pi i} \int_{C_1} \frac{f(\zeta)}{z - z_0} \left\{ \frac{1}{1 - \dfrac{\zeta - z_0}{z - z_0}} \right\} d\zeta$$

$$= \frac{1}{2\pi i} \int_{C_1} \frac{f(\zeta)}{z - z_0} \left\{ 1 + \frac{\zeta - z_0}{z - z_0} + \left(\frac{\zeta - z_0}{z - z_0} \right)^2 + \cdots \right.$$

$$\left. + \left(\frac{\zeta - z_0}{z - z_0} \right)^{n-1} + \frac{(\zeta - z_0)^n}{(z - z_0)^{n-1}(z - \zeta)} \right\} d\zeta.$$

Let M' be the maximum value of $|f(z)|$ on C_1. Then, since $|z - z_0| = r_3 > r_1$, $|z_0 - \zeta| = r_1$ and $|z - \zeta| \geqslant r_3 - r_1$ for any point ζ on C_1,

$$\left| \frac{1}{2\pi i (z - z_0)^n} \int_{C_1} \frac{f(\zeta)(\zeta - z_0)^n}{z - \zeta}\, d\zeta \right| < \frac{r_1^n}{2\pi} \frac{M' 2\pi r_1}{r_3^n (r_3 - r_1)} = \frac{M'}{r_3/r_1 - 1} \left(\frac{r_1}{r_3} \right)^n.$$

The preceding quantity tends to zero as n approaches infinity. Therefore

$$(1.9.4) \qquad -\frac{1}{2\pi i} \int_{C_1} \frac{f(\zeta)\, d\zeta}{\zeta - z_0} = \sum_{n=1}^{\infty} \frac{1}{2\pi i} \int_{C_1} \frac{f(\zeta)(\zeta - z_0)^{n-1}}{(z - z_0)^n}\, d\zeta.$$

If we set

$$(1.9.5) \qquad a_{-n} = \frac{1}{2\pi i} \int_{C_1} \frac{f(\zeta)\, d\zeta}{(\zeta - z_0)^{-n+1}}, \qquad n = 1, 2, 3, \cdots$$

then by combining (1.9.4) with (1.9.2) we can write (1.9.1) in the form

$$(1.9.6) \qquad f(z) = \sum_{n=0}^{\infty} a_n(z - z_0)^n + \sum_{n=1}^{\infty} a_{-n}(z - z_0)^{-n},$$

or, briefly as

$$(1.9.7) \qquad f(z) = \sum_{n=-\infty}^{+\infty} a_n(z - z_0)^n, \quad r_1 < |z - z_0| < r_2.$$

The series just obtained is called the *Laurent series expansion* of $f(z)$. It should be observed that if each a_{-n} is zero, then (1.9.6) is a Taylor's series. Furthermore, series (1.9.2) converges everywhere inside C_2, series (1.9.4) everywhere outside C_1, and the sum of the two series converges in the annular region between C_1 and C_2. The general problem of expanding a function in a Laurent series is a rather involved one. When the functions are simple, it may be possible to proceed as in the following example:

Find the Laurent expansion of $f(z) = \dfrac{1}{z(z-2)}$ valid for (a) $0 < |z| < 2$ and (b) $2 < |z| < \infty$.

For (a) we have

$$\frac{1}{z(z-2)} = -\frac{1}{2}\frac{1}{z}\left(\frac{1}{1 - z/2}\right)$$

$$= -\frac{1}{2z} - \frac{1}{2^2} - \frac{z}{2^3} - \frac{z^2}{2^4} - \frac{z^3}{2^5} - \cdots, \quad (0 < |z| < 2).$$

For (b) we obtain by division

$$\frac{1}{z(z-2)} = \frac{1}{z^2} + \frac{2}{z^3} + \frac{4}{z^4} + \cdots + \frac{2^{n-1}}{z^{n+2}} + \cdots, \quad (2 < |z| < \infty).$$

Exercise. Calculate the coefficients in the two preceding series by making use of formulas (1.9.3) and (1.9.5).

1.10 Singularities

Points at which $f(z)$ ceases to be analytic are called *singular points*. Recalling the definition of an analytic function (section 1.4), it is seen that a point z can be singular if: (i) *the derivative fails to exist at* z, (ii) z *is such that it cannot be made the interior point of a region where* $f(z)$ *is single valued*. For example, $z = 1$ and $z = -i$ are singular points of the function $f(z) = \dfrac{1}{(z-1)(z+i)}$ because $f'(1)$ as well as $f'(i)$ fail to exist, whereas $z = i$ is a singular point of $f(z) = (z-i)^{3/2}$ because it cannot be made the interior point of a region where $(z-i)^{3/2}$ is single valued.

The singularities belonging to the first category are of two types: (a) *poles* or *non-essential* singularities and (b) *essential* singularities.

To the second category belong the so-called *branch points*. At these points the derivative may or may not exist. It can be shown, however, that a derivative of some order will fail to exist.

We shall now proceed to a further characterization of these three types of singularities. The distinction between poles and essential singularities can be explained by referring to Laurent's expansion.

Suppose that z_0 is an *isolated singularity* of $f(z)$. By this we mean that there exists a neighborhood of z_0 throughout which $f(z)$ is analytic, except at z_0. Then, by taking the inner circle C_1 (see Fig. 1.9.1) arbitrarily small, we obtain the following Laurent expansion

$$(1.10.1) \quad f(z) = \sum_{n=1}^{\infty} a_{-n}(z - z_0)^{-n} + \sum_{n=0}^{\infty} a_n(z - z_0)^n, \quad (0 < |z - z_0| < r).$$

If in the preceding expansion the number of terms involving $(z - z_0)$ to a negative exponent is finite, then z_0 is said to be a *pole*. Moreover, if a_{-m} $(m \geqslant 1)$ is the last *non-zero* coefficient in (1.10.1), then

$$(1.10.2) \qquad f(z) = \sum_{n=1}^{m} a_{-n}(z - z_0)^{-n} + \sum_{n=0}^{\infty} a_n(z - z_0)^n,$$

and $z = z_0$ is said to be a pole of *order m*.

The finite sum

$$(1.10.3) \quad \frac{a_{-m}}{(z - z_0)^m} + \frac{a_{-m+1}}{(z - z_0)^{m-1}} + \cdots + \frac{a_{-2}}{(z - z_0)^2} + \frac{a_{-1}}{(z - z_0)}$$

is called the *principal part* of the function at $z = z_0$.

Suppose that $f(z)$ has a pole order m, then $f(z)$ has the Laurent expansion (1.10.2). Multiplying this expansion by $(z - z_0)^m$, $z \neq z_0$, it follows that

$$(1.10.4) \qquad (z - z_0)^m f(z) = a_{-m} + a_{-m+1}(z - z_0) + \cdots$$
$$+ a_{-1}(z - z_0)^{m-1} + a_0(z - z_0)^m + \cdots$$

is *analytic* at $z = z_0$, and taking the limit of both sides as z tends to z_0, we obtain

(1.10.5) $$\lim_{z \to z_0} (z - z_0)^m f(z) = a_{-m} \neq 0.$$

Conversely, suppose that $(z - z_0)^m f(z) = \phi(z)$ is analytic at $z = z_0$ and $\lim_{z \to z_0} (z - z_0)^m f(z) = a_{-m} \neq 0$, then $\phi(z) = (z - z_0)^m f(z)$ can be expanded in a Taylor's series about z_0, namely,

$$(z - z_0)^m f(z) = a_{-m} + a_{-m+1}(z - z_0) + \cdots + a_0(z - z_0)^m + \cdots$$

and hence

$$f(z) = \frac{a_{-m}}{(z - z_0)^m} + \frac{a_{-m+1}}{(z - z_0)^{m-1}} + \cdots + a_0 + a_1(z - z_0) + \cdots,$$

which implies that $f(z)$ has a pole of order m at $z = z_0$.

Thus, if m is a positive integer such that

(a) $(z - z_0)^m f(z) = \phi(z)$ is analytic at $z = z_0$,

(b) $\lim_{z \to z_0} (z - z_0)^m f(z) = a_{-m} \neq 0$,

then $f(z)$ has a pole of order m at $z = z_0$, and conversely.

Example 1.   The function

$$f(z) = \frac{z + 2}{(z + 1)(z - 2i)^2}$$

has a pole of order 1 or a *simple* pole at $z = -1$, and a pole of order 2 or a *double* pole at $z = 2i$.   For the functions $(z + 1) \cdot f(z)$

$$= \frac{z + 2}{(z - 2i)^2} \text{ and } (z - 2i)^2 \cdot f(z) = \frac{z + 2}{z + 1}$$ are analytic at $z = -1$ and $z = 2i$, respectively, since their derivatives exist there.   Furthermore,

$$\lim_{z \to -1} (z + 1) \cdot f(z) = \frac{1}{(1 + 2i)^2} \neq 0 \text{ and } \lim_{z \to 2i} (z - 2i) \cdot f(z) = \frac{2(1 + i)}{1 + 2i} \neq 0.$$

Example 2.   The function

$$f(z) = \frac{\sin z}{(z - i)^5}$$

has a pole of order 5 at $z = i$, since $(z - i)^5 \cdot f(z) = \sin z$ is analytic at $z = i$ and $\lim_{z \to i} (z - i)^5 \cdot f(z) = \sin i \neq 0$.

Example 3.   For the function

$$f(z) = \frac{\sin z}{z}$$

at $z = 0$ we have $z \cdot f(z) = \sin z$ which is analytic, but $\lim_{z \to 0} z \cdot f(z) = 0$.

In this case, however, $f(z) = \dfrac{\sin z}{z} = \dfrac{1}{z}\left(z - \dfrac{z^3}{3!} + \dfrac{z^5}{5!} - \cdots\right)$ and

$\lim\limits_{z \to 0} \dfrac{\sin z}{z} = 1$. Hence if $f(z)$ is defined so that $f(0) = 1$, then $f(z)$

$= \dfrac{\sin z}{z} = 1 - \dfrac{z^2}{3!} + \dfrac{z^4}{5!} \cdots$ is analytic at $z = 0$.

In cases such as this, in which a singularity has been removed by properly defining a function, the singularity is called *removable*.

If the number of negative powers of $(z - z_0)$ in a Laurent expansion is infinite, then z_0 is said to be an essential *singularity*. The expansion of $f(z)$ about $z = z_0$ will then be of the form

(1.10.6) $$f(z) = \sum_{n=-\infty}^{+\infty} (z - z_0)^n, \quad 0 < |z - z_0| < r.$$

It is clear that in this case no finite m exists such that $\lim\limits_{z \to z_0} (z - z_0)^m f(z) = \text{const.} \neq 0.$

Example. The function

$$\cos\frac{1}{z} = 1 - \frac{1}{2!z^2} + \frac{1}{4!z^4} - \frac{1}{6!z^6} + \cdots$$

has an essential singularity at $z = 0$.

Branch points are characteristic of *multiple-valued* functions. By definition, a branch point is one such that if a point traces out a small closed path (e.g., a circle) surrounding it, but not enclosing any other singular points, then the value of the function after a complete circuit is no longer the same as it was initially. A few examples will make this clear.

Example 1. Consider the function

$$f(z) = \sqrt{z - z_0}.$$

If $z - z_0 = re^{i\theta}$, then $f(z)$ is a double-valued function whose values are given by

$$f_1(z) = r^{1/2}e^{i\theta/2}$$

and

$$f_2(z) = r^{1/2}e^{i(\theta/2+\pi)} = -r^{1/2}e^{i\theta/2} = -f_1(z).$$

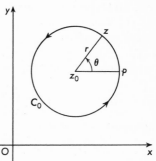

FIG. 1.10.1

These functions are called the *branches* of the double-valued function $f(z)$. Suppose that C_0 (Fig. 1.10.1) is a circle with center at z_0 and radius r. Let z start at the point P on the circle for which $\theta = 0$ so that initially $f_1(z) = r^{1/2}$. Then if z describes the circle once, then arg $(z - z_0)$, i.e., θ, will increase by 2π and arg $f(z)$ will increase by

π. Hence during the process of completing the first circuit, the values of $f(z)$ are those of the branch $f_1(z)$. After one revolution, however, the value of $f(z)$ is not its initial value $r^{1/2}$ but $-r^{1/2}$. Now, during the second revolution the values of $f(z)$ will be those of the second branch $f_2(z)$, and after completing the second circuit the arg $(z - z_0)$ will increase by 2π again, and the argument of $f(z)$ by π, so that the initial value is again obtained. Consequently $z = z_0$ is a branch point, since the initial value of the function was not obtained after one circuit.

We also notice that after a single circuit about z_0 the branch $f_1(z)$ changes into $f_2(z)$, and $f_2(z)$ into $f_1(z)$. Hence a branch point is some-times also defined as a point such that the description of a circuit about it causes an interchange or alteration of the branches of a function.

Suppose now that the curve C_1 is any closed curve exterior to z_0 (Fig. 1.10.2). If z starts at P and traverses C_1, as shown, then in

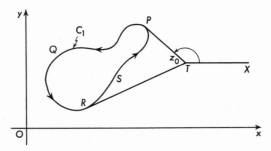

Fig. 1.10.2

describing the arc PQR the arg $(z - z_0)$ increases from $\angle XTP$ to $\angle XTR$. When z traces out the arc RSP the arg $(z - z_0)$ decreases by the same amount, and the total change after one circuit is zero. Therefore, whatever values $f_1(z)$ and $f_2(z)$ had initially will evidently be regained by these branches after a description of the curve $PQRSP$.

Example 2. Find the branch points of

$$f(z) = \sqrt{(z - 1)(z + 1)}.$$

Let $z - 1 = r_1 e^{i\theta_1}$ and $z + 1 = r_2 e^{i\theta_2}$. Then the two branches of $f(z)$ are

$$f_1(z) = (r_1 r_2)^{1/2} e^{i(\theta_1 + \theta_2)/2} \quad \text{and} \quad f_2(z) = -(r_1 r_2)^{1/2} e^{i(\theta_1 + \theta_2)/2}.$$

If z traces a circuit about $z = 1$ (Fig. 1.10.3) which does not enclose $z = -1$, then arg $(z - 1)$ increases by 2π, while the total change in arg $(z + 1)$ is zero, and hence $f(z)$ undergoes an alteration of branches. A similar transition takes place in the branches of $f(z)$ if z describes a circuit about $z = -1$ (Fig. 1.10.4). Therefore $z = -1$ and $z = 1$ are the branch points of $f(z)$.

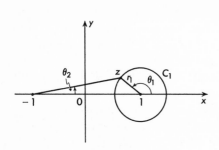

Fig. 1.10.3

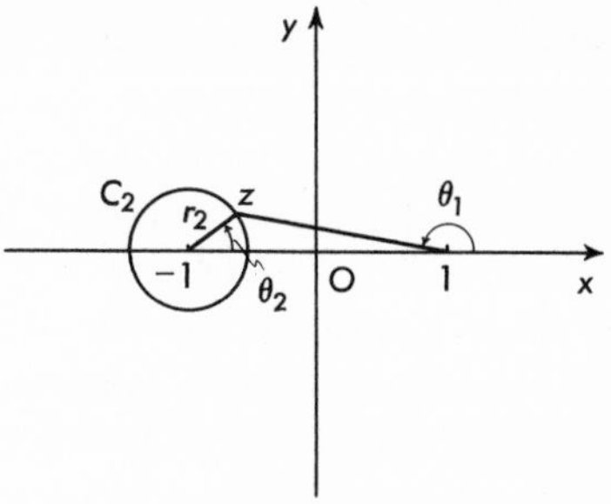

Fig. 1.10.4

If z describes any closed curve C_3 enclosing $z = -1$ and $z = 1$
(Fig. 1.10.5), then θ_1 and θ_2 will both increase by 2π so that

$$f_1(z) = (r_1 r_2)^{1/2} e^{i(\theta_1 + \theta_2 + 4\pi)/2}$$
$$= (r_1 r_2)^{1/2} e^{i(\theta_1 + \theta_2)/2},$$
$$f_2(z) = -(r_1 r_2)^{1/2} e^{i(\theta_1 + \theta_2 + 4\pi)/2}$$
$$= -(r_1 r_2)^{1/2} e^{i(\theta_1 + \theta_2)/2},$$

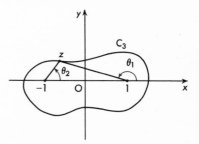

so that the initial value of the function $f(z)$ remains the same. In this
case, therefore, the branches are
unaltered.

Example 3. $f(z) = \ln(z - i)$.
Let $z - i = r e^{i\theta}$. Then

Fig. 1.10.5

$$\ln(z - i) = \ln r + i(\theta + 2k\pi), \quad k = 0, \pm 1, \pm 2, \cdots$$

where $-\pi < \theta \leqslant \pi$. It is seen that $\ln(z - i)$ has an *infinite number*
of branches corresponding to the infinitely many values of k. Suppose
that we choose the particular branch corresponding to $k = 0$, the so-
called *principal branch*. Then

$$\ln(z - i) = \ln r + i\theta.$$

If z describes a| circuit about $z = i$, clearly, θ will increase by 2π and
$\ln(z - i)$ will enter upon a new branch corresponding to $k = 1$.
Therefore the point $z = i$ is a branch point of $\ln(z - i)$. It is evident
that for a traversal of a closed path exterior to $z = i$ the $\arg(z - i)$ has
a total change of zero and no alteration of branches takes place.

In many instances the location of branch points requires a detailed
and careful study of the function. However, in the case of the elementary functions, sufficient information has already been accumulated to
enable one to detect branch points at a glance, or after a brief inspection.
An examination of these functions reveals that branch points can occur
only for those values of z which make the quantity raised to a non-

integral power vanish, or those values which make the quantity whose logarithm is taken vanish.

For example, the branch points of $z^{5/2}$, $\sqrt{1 - z^2}$, $\tan^{-1} z = -\dfrac{i}{2}[\ln (1 - iz) - \ln (1 + iz)]$, $1/\sqrt{z + 1}$, are 0, ± 1, $\pm i$ and -1, respectively.

The theorems studied so far were obtained by assuming the functions to be *analytic*. For these theorems to apply, when multiple-valued functions arise, it is necessary to render them single valued. This is

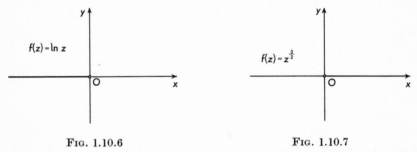

FIG. 1.10.6   FIG. 1.10.7

done by selecting *one* branch of the function and introducing *cuts* or *barriers* so that it is impossible to draw closed curves around the branch points. What branch to select may at times be immaterial, at other times the choice may be dictated by the problem itself. For instance, the choice of one branch may lead to results which are at variance with the way a physical system can behave. Hence, another branch must be selected so that the results are in conformity with the possible behaviour of the system. The cuts or barriers may be introduced in a variety of ways, and the mode of procedure usually depends on the problem under consideration.

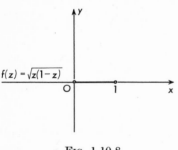

FIG. 1.10.8

Figures 1.10.6, 1.10.7, and 1.10.8 illustrate the manner in which cuts can be made to make the functions $\ln z$, $z^{3/2}$, and $\sqrt{z(1 - z)}$ single valued. In Figs. 1.10.6 and 1.10.7 the cuts extend from the branch points to infinity, whereas in Fig. 1.10.8 we have a finite cut joining the two branch points.

Other possibilities are illustrated in Figs. 1.10.9, 1.10.10, and 1.10.11, where all the cuts emanate from the branch points to infinity.

In the planes from which the branch points and the cuts have been

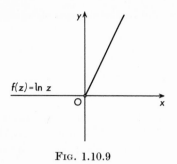

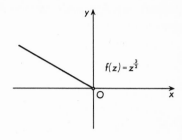

FIG. 1.10.9   FIG. 1.10.10

deleted the functions are single valued and the theorems concerning analytic functions can now be applied.

We shall consider one more example to illustrate the care that must be exercised in dealing with multiple-valued functions.

Example 4. Find the singularities of the function

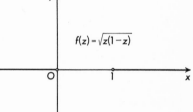

$$f(z) = \frac{1}{2\sqrt{z} + \sqrt{z-1}}.$$

It is clear from what has preceded that $z = 0$ and $z = 1$ are branch points. However, because

FIG. 1.10.11

the denominator of $f(z)$ may vanish for certain values of z, there may be poles in addition. Let us examine this possibility in detail.

Since $\sqrt{z}$ and $\sqrt{z-1}$ are double-valued functions, the function $f(z)$ has four branches, namely,

$$f_1(z) = \frac{1}{2\sqrt{z} + \sqrt{z-1}}, \qquad f_2(z) = \frac{1}{-2\sqrt{z} + \sqrt{z-1}},$$

$$f_3(z) = \frac{1}{2\sqrt{z} - \sqrt{z-1}}, \qquad f_4(z) = \frac{1}{-2\sqrt{z} - \sqrt{z-1}},$$

which correspond to the combinations that can be formed by selecting the different branches of $\sqrt{z}$ and $\sqrt{z-1}$. For instance, $f_1(z)$ is formed by selecting the *first* branch of the $\sqrt{z}$ with the *first* branch of $\sqrt{z-1}, f_2(z)$, by selecting the *second* branch of $\sqrt{z}$ with the *first* branch of $\sqrt{z-1}$, etc.

By introducing suitable cuts, the preceding functions are rendered single valued in the regions from which the cuts have been deleted.

To see whether $f_1(z)$ has a pole we find it convenient to rewrite it by rationalizing the denominator. We obtain

$$f_1(z) = \frac{1}{2\sqrt{z} + \sqrt{z-1}} = \frac{2\sqrt{z} - \sqrt{z-1}}{3z+1}.$$

Now $(3z+1) f_1(z) = 2\sqrt{z} - \sqrt{z-1}$ is analytic at $z = -\frac{1}{3}$ because $\frac{d}{dz}[2\sqrt{z} - \sqrt{z-1}]$ exists, having the value $-\frac{3}{4}i\sqrt{3}$ there. However, $\lim\limits_{z\to-\frac{1}{3}} (3z+1) f_1(z) = \lim\limits_{z\to-\frac{1}{3}} (2\sqrt{z} - \sqrt{z-1}) = 2\sqrt{-\frac{1}{3}} - 2\sqrt{-\frac{1}{3}}$ $= 0$. Therefore $z = -\frac{1}{3}$ is *not* a pole of the branch $f_1(z)$.

For $f_2(z)$ we have similarly

$$f_2(z) = \frac{1}{-2\sqrt{z} + \sqrt{z-1}} = \frac{-2\sqrt{z} - \sqrt{z-1}}{3z+1}.$$

Here $(3z+1) f_2(z) = -2\sqrt{z} - \sqrt{z-1}$ is analytic at $z = -\frac{1}{3}$ since $\frac{d}{dz}[-2\sqrt{z} - \sqrt{z-1}]_{z=-\frac{1}{3}} = \frac{5}{4}i\sqrt{3}$. Also $\lim\limits_{z\to-\frac{1}{3}} (3z+1) f_2(z)$ $= \lim\limits_{z\to-\frac{1}{3}} (-2\sqrt{-\frac{1}{3}} - 2\sqrt{-\frac{1}{3}}) \neq 0$. Consequently $z = -\frac{1}{3}$ *is* a pole of the branch $f_2(z)$.

In like manner it can be shown that $f_3(z)$ *has* a pole at $z = -\frac{1}{3}$ and $f_4(z)$ has *no* pole at $z = -\frac{1}{3}$.

The results may be summarized in Table 1.10.1.

Table I.10.I

Branch	Branch Points	Poles
$f_1(z) = 1/(2\sqrt{z} + \sqrt{z-1})$	$z = 0, z = 1$	None
$f_2(z) = 1/(-2\sqrt{z} + \sqrt{z-1})$	$z = 0, z = 1$	$z = -\frac{1}{3}$
$f_3(z) = 1/(2\sqrt{z} - \sqrt{z-1})$	$z = 0, z = 1$	$z = -\frac{1}{3}$
$f_4(z) = 1/(-2\sqrt{z} - \sqrt{z-1})$	$z = 0, z = 1$	None

Thus, if a function such as $f(z) = 1/(2\sqrt{z} + \sqrt{z-1})$ arises in the solution of a differential equation by the Laplace transform method, different results will be obtained, depending on the branch selected. Therefore, that branch must be selected which leads to results not at variance with the behavior of the physical system being examined. Experience in dealing with such problems is a valuable guide in the selection of the appropriate branch.

1.11 Residues and Cauchy's Residue Theorem

Suppose that the function $f(z)$ is expanded in a Laurent series about the isolated singularity $z = z_0$. Then

$$(1.11.1) \qquad f(z) = \sum_{n=1}^{\infty} a_{-n}(z - z_0)^{-n} + \sum_{n=0}^{\infty} a_n(z - z_0)^n.$$

The coefficient

$$(1.11.2) \qquad a_{-1} = \frac{1}{2\pi i} \int_C f(z)\, dz$$

of (1.11.1), where C is a curve enclosing $z = z_0$, but no other singularities of $f(z)$, is called the *residue* of $f(z)$ at $z = z_0$, and we shall denote it by

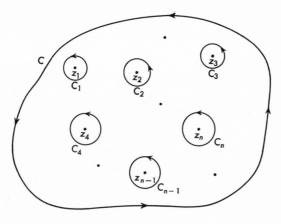

FIG. 1.11.1

$\mathrm{Res}_{z_0} f(z)$, $\mathrm{Res}\,[f(z)]_{z=z_0}$, or $\mathrm{Res}\,(z_0)$ whenever it is clear what function is being referred to.

Suppose now that C is a closed curve enclosing a finite number of singularities $z_1, z_2, \cdots, z_n$ and let $C_1, C_2, \cdots, C_n$ be circles lying within C and having centers at $z_1, z_2, \cdots, z_n$ (Fig. 1.11.1). Then by formula (1.6.5),

$$\int_C f(z)\, dz = \int_{C_1} f(z)\, dz + \int_{C_2} f(z)\, dz + \cdots + \int_{C_n} f(z)\, dz.$$

But $\int_{C_k} f(z)\, dz = 2\pi i\, \mathrm{Res}_{z_k} f(z)$. Therefore

$$(1.11.3) \qquad \int_C f(z)\, dz = 2\pi i \sum_{k=1}^{n} \mathrm{Res}_{z_k} f(z).$$

Formula (1.11.3) is known as *Cauchy's residue theorem*.

Although formula (1.11.2) can be used at all times to compute the residue of a function at a given point, it may be that the Laurent expansion is easier to obtain. In that case the residue is found by inspection. For example, the residue of

$$f(z) = \frac{3z}{(z+2)^2} = \frac{3(z+2) - 6}{(z+2)^2} = \frac{3}{z+2} - \frac{6}{(z+2)^2}$$

at $z = -2$ is 3.

For the function

$$f(z) = \frac{\sin z}{z^4} = \frac{z - \dfrac{z^3}{3!} + \dfrac{z^5}{5!} - \cdots}{z^4} = \frac{1}{z^3} - \frac{1}{3!z} + \frac{z}{5!} - \cdots$$

the Res $(0) = -\dfrac{1}{3!}$.

In other cases we may proceed as follows. If $f(z)$ has a *pole of order* k at $z = z_0$, then its Laurent expansion is

$$(1.11.4) \qquad f(z) = \frac{a_{-k}}{(z - z_0)^k} + \frac{a_{-k+1}}{(z - z_0)^{k-1}} + \cdots$$

$$+ \frac{a_{-1}}{(z - z_0)} + a_0 + a_1(z - z_0) + a_2(z - z_0)^2 + \cdots.$$

In order to obtain a_{-1} let us multiply (1.11.4) by $(z - z_0)^k$, $z \neq z_0$. We get

$$(1.11.5) \qquad (z - z_0)^k f(z) = a_{-k} + a_{-k+1}(z - z_0) + \cdots$$
$$+ a_{-1}(z - z_0)^{k-1} + a_0(z - z_0)^k + \cdots.$$

Differentiating (1.11.5) $k - 1$ times with respect to z and taking the limit as $z \to z_0$, we obtain

$$(1.11.6) \qquad \lim_{z \to z_0} \frac{d^{k-1}}{dz^{k-1}}[(z - z_0)^k f(z)] = (k - 1)! \, a_{-1}.$$

Therefore

$$(1.11.7) \qquad \text{Res}\,(z_0) = \frac{1}{(k - 1)!} \lim_{z \to z_0} \frac{d^{k-1}}{dz^{k-1}}[(z - z_0)^k f(z)].$$

In particular, if $z = z_0$ is a *simple pole* ($k = 1$), then

$$(1.11.8) \qquad \text{Res}\,(z_0) = \lim_{z \to z_0} (z - z_0) f(z).$$

A convenient formula can be derived in this case by writing $f(z)$ in the form $F_1(z)/F_2(z)$, where $F_1(z_0)$ is finite. Using l'Hospital's rule, we have

$$\lim_{z \to z_0} (z - z_0)\frac{F_1(z)}{F_2(z)} = \lim_{z \to z_0} \frac{(z - z_0)\,F_1{}'(z) + F_1(z)}{F_2{}'(z)} = \frac{F_1(z_0)}{F_2{}'(z_0)}.$$

Therefore

$$(1.11.9) \qquad \text{Res}\,(z_0) = \frac{F_1(z_0)}{F_2{}'(z_0)}, \text{ with } F_1(z_0) \neq \infty.$$

Example 1. Find the sum of the residues of

$$f(z) = \frac{e^{-z}}{z^2 - a^2}$$

at its poles.

The preceding function has simple poles at $z = \pm a$. For the residues we have

$$\text{Res}\,(a) = \lim_{z \to a}\,(z - a)\,f(z) = \lim_{z \to a}\frac{e^{-z}}{z + a} = \frac{e^{-a}}{2a}$$

$$\text{Res}\,(-a) = \lim_{z \to -a}\,(z + a)\,f(z) = \lim_{z \to -a}\frac{e^{-z}}{z + a} = -\frac{e^{a}}{2a}.$$

Hence the sum of residues is

$$\frac{e^{-a}}{2a} - \frac{e^{a}}{2a} = -\frac{\sinh a}{a}.$$

Using formula (1.11.9) as an alternative procedure, we also obtain

$$\text{Res}\,(a) + \text{Res}\,(-a) = \frac{e^{-z}}{2z}\bigg]_{z=a} + \frac{e^{-z}}{2z}\bigg]_{z=-a} = \frac{e^{-a} - e^{a}}{2a} = -\frac{\sinh a}{a}$$

Example 2. For the function

$$f(z) = \frac{1}{z(z - i)^2}$$

there is a simple pole at $z = 0$ and a double pole at $z = i$. We have

$$\text{Res}\,(0) = \lim_{z \to 0} z\,f(z) = \lim_{z \to 0}\frac{1}{(z - i)^2} = -1,$$

$$\text{Res}\,(i) = \lim_{z \to i}\frac{d}{dz}\!\left(\frac{1}{z}\right) = \lim_{z \to i}\left(-\frac{1}{z^2}\right) = 1.$$

Hence the sum of the residues is zero.

Example 3. $\qquad\qquad f(z) = \dfrac{\sin z}{z^3}.$

In this instance $\lim\limits_{z \to 0} z^3\,f(z) = 0$, and hence $z = 0$ is *not* a triple pole. If we define

$$g(z) = \frac{\sin z}{z}, \quad z \neq 0$$

$$= 1, \quad z = 0,$$

then $f(z) = \dfrac{g(z)}{z^2}$ and since $z^2 f(z) = g(z)$ is analytic at $z = 0$ and $\lim\limits_{z \to 0} z^2 f(z) = \lim\limits_{z \to 0} g(z) = 1$, we see that $f(z)$ has a *double* pole at $z = 0$.

Therefore

$$\text{Res } (0) = \lim_{z \to 0} \frac{d}{dz} [z^2 f(z)] = \lim_{z \to 0} \frac{d}{dz} [g(z)] = \lim_{z \to 0} \frac{z \cos z - \sin z}{z}$$

$$= \lim_{z \to 0} \frac{- z \sin z}{z} = \lim_{z \to 0} (- \sin z) = 0.$$

L'Hospital's rule was used to find the $\lim\limits_{z \to 0} \dfrac{z \cos z - \sin z}{z}$.

Here and in similar cases it is easier to proceed by finding the Laurent expansion. Thus

$$f(z) = \frac{\sin z}{z^3} = \frac{z - \dfrac{z^3}{3!} + \dfrac{z^5}{5!} - \cdots}{z^3} = \frac{1}{z^2} - \frac{1}{3!} + \frac{z^2}{5!} - \cdots,$$

and hence Res $(0) = 0$.

1.12 Contour Integration

This section will be devoted to the evaluation of a number of real definite integrals by means of the residue theory. The technique and skill acquired in their evaluation will be extremely useful when we take up the problem of finding the inverse Laplace transform. The following examples will indicate the *modus operandi*.

Example 1. We shall first consider an integral of the form

$$I = \int_0^{2\pi} F(\cos \theta, \sin \theta) \, d\theta,$$

where $F(\cos \theta, \sin \theta)$ is a rational function of $\cos \theta$ and $\sin \theta$ which is finite for all real values of θ. Any such integral can be evaluated by residues with the aid of the substitution $z = e^{i\theta}$, for the integral is transformed into one of the form

$$\int_C f(z) \, dz,$$

where $f(z)$ is a rational function of z and C is the circle $|z| = 1$ on which $f(z)$ is finite.

Let us evaluate

$$I = \int_0^{2\pi} \frac{\cos \theta \, d\theta}{a + b \cos \theta}, \quad a > |b|.$$

Making the substitutions $z = e^{i\theta}$, $dz = iz \, d\theta$, $\sin \theta = \dfrac{z^2 - 1}{2iz}$ and $\cos \theta = \dfrac{z^2 + 1}{2z}$, we find that

$$I = \int_C \frac{(z^2 + 1) \, dz}{biz[z^2 + (2a/b) z + 1]}.$$

The poles of the integrand of I occur at

$z = 0, \quad z = z_1 = (-a + \sqrt{a^2 - b^2})/b, \quad z = z_2 = (-a - \sqrt{a^2 - b^2})/b.$

Since z_1 is inside the circle C (Fig. 1.12.1), then z_2 is outside this circle because $z_1 z_2 = 1.$ Therefore

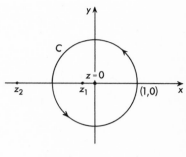

$$I = 2\pi i[\text{Res } (0) + \text{Res } (z_1)].$$

Now

$$\text{Res } (0) = \lim_{z \to 0} \frac{z^2 + 1}{bi(z - z_1)(z - z_2)}$$

$$= \frac{1}{biz_1 z_2} = \frac{1}{bi}$$

FIG. 1.12.1

and

$$\text{Res } (z_1) = \lim_{z \to z_1} \frac{z^2 + 1}{bi(z - z_2)z} = \frac{z_1{}^2 + 1}{biz_1(z_1 - z_2)} = \frac{z_1 + z_2}{bi(z_1 - z_2)} = \frac{-a}{bi\sqrt{a^2 - b^2}}.$$

Therefore

$$I = 2\pi i\left[\frac{1}{bi} - \frac{a}{bi\sqrt{a^2 - b^2}}\right] = \frac{2\pi}{b}\left(1 - \frac{a}{\sqrt{a^2 - b^2}}\right).$$

Example 2. Another type of integral that can be evaluated by residues under certain conditions is

$$(1.12.1) \qquad \int_{-\infty}^{\infty} f(x) \, dx.$$

If $f(z)$ has a finite number of poles, none of which lies on the real axis, and $|f(z)| \leqslant M/|z|^k$ for large values of $|z|$, where M is a constant and $k > 1$, then (1.12.1) can be evaluated by integrating over a contour consisting of a semicircle of radius R in the upper half of the z-plane and the real axis from $-R$ to R (Fig. 1.12.2).

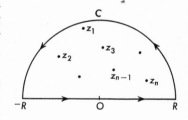

For suppose that $f(z)$ has the poles $z_1, z_2, \cdots, z_n$ in the upper half-plane, and $|f(z)| \leqslant M/|z|^k$, where $k > 1$. Draw a semicircle C large enough to enclose all the poles. Then

FIG. 1.12.2

$$(1.12.2) \qquad \int_C f(z) \, dz + \int_{-R}^{R} f(x) \, dx = 2\pi i \sum_{r=1}^{n} \text{Res } (z_r).$$

Now

$$\left|\int_C f(z) \, dz\right| \leqslant \int_C |f(z)| \, |dz| \leqslant \frac{M}{R^k} \int_C |dz| = \frac{\pi M}{R^{k-1}}.$$

Therefore $\int_C f(z)\, dz \to 0$ as $R \to \infty$. Consequently the limit of equation (1.12.2) as $R \to \infty$ is

$$(1.12.3) \qquad \int_{-\infty}^{\infty} f(x)\, dx = 2\pi i \sum_{r=1}^{n} \text{Res}\,(z_r).$$

An important class of functions satisfying the above conditions is the class of rational functions $f(z) = P(z)/Q(z)$, where $P(z)$, $Q(z)$ are polynomials, $Q(z)$ has no real zeros, and the degree of $Q(z)$ is *at least two greater* than the degree of $P(z)$.

For suppose that

$$(1.12.4) \qquad f(z)$$

$$= \frac{z^m + a_1 z^{m-1} + \cdots + a_{m-1} z + a_m}{z^n + b_1 z^{n-1} + \cdots + b_{n-1} z + b_n} = \frac{1}{z^{n-m}} \frac{1 + a_1 z^{-1} + \cdots + a_m z^{-m}}{1 + b_1 z^{-1} + \cdots + b_n z^{-n}}.$$

Now

$$(1.12.5) \qquad |1 + a_1 z^{-1} + \cdots + a_m z^{-m}| \leqslant 1 + |a_1 z^{-1} + \cdots + a_m z^{-m}|$$

and

$$(1.12.6) \qquad |1 + b_1 z^{-1} + \cdots + b_n z^{-n}| \geqslant 1 - |b_1 z^{-1} + \cdots + b_n z^{-n}|.$$

By taking $|z|$ large enough, we can make

$$|a_1 z^{-1} + \cdots + a_m z^{-m}| < \tfrac{1}{10} \quad \text{and} \quad |b_1 z^{-1} + \cdots + b_n z^{-n}| < \tfrac{1}{10}.$$

Therefore from (1.12.4), (1.12.5) and (1.12.6), we get

$$(1.12.7) \qquad |f(z)| \leqslant \frac{1 + 1/10}{1 - 1/10} \cdot \frac{1}{|z|^{n-m}} = \frac{11}{9} \cdot \frac{1}{|z|^{n-m}}.$$

Hence if $n - m \geqslant 2$, $f(z)$ will satisfy the condition $|f(z)| \leqslant M/|z|^k$, $k > 1$, for large values of $|z|$ and the result (1.12.3) obtains.

As an illustration, let us evaluate the integral

$$\int_{-\infty}^{\infty} \frac{x^2}{(x^2+1)^2}\, dx.$$

The poles of $f(z) = z^2/(z^2+1)^2$ occur at $z = \pm i$, and $|f(z)| \leqslant |z|^2/(|z|^2 - 1)^2 \leqslant 4/|z|^2$ for $|z| \geqslant \sqrt{2}$, since $|z|^2 - 1 \geqslant |z|^2/2$ for $|z| \geqslant \sqrt{2}$. Furthermore, by (1.11.4), the Res $(i) = 1/4i$. Consequently

$$\int_{-\infty}^{\infty} \frac{x^2}{(x^2+1)^2}\, dx = 2\pi i \left(\frac{1}{4i}\right) = \frac{\pi}{2}.$$

If $f(x)$ is an *even* function, then

$$\int_0^\infty f(x)\ dx = \tfrac{1}{2}\int_{-\infty}^\infty f(x)\ dx.$$

Thus in our example $\int_0^\infty x^2/(x^2 + 1)^2\ dx = \pi/4$.

Before we consider further examples, let us prove a very useful lemma which will facilitate the evaluation of certain integrals to be met later on.

Lemma I. If $|F(z)| \leqslant M/|z|^k$ when $|z| > R_0$, where M, k are constants and $k > 0$, then

$$\lim_{R\to\infty} \int_{C'} e^{itz}\, F(z)\ dz = 0, \quad (t > 0)$$

where C' denotes the upper half of the circle $|z| = R > R_0$.

For all points on C' (Fig. 1.12.3), we have

$$z = Re^{i\theta}, \quad |z| = R.$$

Furthermore,

$$|e^{itz}| = |e^{itR(\cos\theta + i\sin\theta)}| = e^{-tR\sin\theta}.$$

Therefore,

$$\left|\int_{C'} e^{itz}\, F(z)\ dz\right| \leqslant \frac{1}{R^{k-1}}\int_0^\pi e^{-tR\sin\theta}\ d\theta$$

$$= \frac{2}{R^{k-1}}\int_0^{\pi/2} e^{-tR\sin\theta}\ d\theta.$$

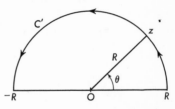

Fɪɢ. 1.12.3

By drawing the graphs of $y = 2\theta/\pi$ and $y = \sin\theta$, it is easy to see that

$$\sin\theta \geqslant 2\theta/\pi, \text{ when } 0 \leqslant \theta \leqslant \pi/2.$$

Consequently

$$\left|\int_{C'} e^{itz}\, F(z)\ dz\right| \leqslant \frac{2}{R^{k-1}}\int_0^{\pi/2} e^{-\theta(2tR)/\pi}d\theta = -\frac{\pi}{tR^k}e^{-\theta(2tR)/\pi}\Bigg]_0^{\pi/2}$$

$$= \frac{\pi}{tR^k}(1 - e^{-tR}).$$

Hence, if $t > 0$ and $k > 0$,

$$\lim_{R\to\infty} \int_{C'} e^{itz}\, F(z)\ dz = 0.$$

Occasionally we shall use the following notation

$$F(z) = O(1/|z|^k),$$

(read $F(z)$ is of order $1/|z|^k$), to mean that there exist constants M, $k > 0$, such that

$$|F(z)| \leqslant M/|z|^k, \text{ when } |z| > |z_0|.$$

If $F(z) = O(|z|^{-k})$, $k > 0$, and $F(z)$ has no real poles, then we can evaluate integrals of the form

$$\int_{-\infty}^{\infty} e^{itx} F(x)\, dx, \quad (t > 0)$$

and consequently, by separating into real and imaginary parts, those of the form

$$\int_{-\infty}^{\infty} F(x) \cos tx\, dx, \qquad \int_{-\infty}^{\infty} F(x) \sin tx\, dx.$$

Should $F(z)$ be a rational function in which the degree of the denominator is at least *one* degree higher than that of the numerator, then we clearly have $F(z) = O(|z|^{-k})$, $k \geqslant 1$. If, in addition, $F(z)$ has no real poles, then

$$(1.12.8) \qquad \int_{-\infty}^{\infty} e^{itx} F(x)\, dx = 2\pi i \sum_{r=1}^{n} \text{Res}\,(z_r),$$

where Res (z_r) is the residue of $e^{itz} F(z)$ at the rth pole in the upper half-plane.

For, using the contour of Fig. 1.12.4, we obtain

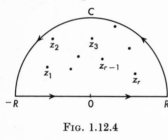

FIG. 1.12.4

$$\int_C F(z)\, e^{itz}\, dz + \int_{-R}^{R} F(x)\, e^{itx}\, dx$$
$$= 2\pi i \sum_{r=1}^{n} \text{Res}\,(z_r),$$

where the poles z_r are inside the contour. Since $F(z)$ satisfies the conditions of Lemma I $\int_C F(z)\, e^{itz}\, dz \to 0$ as $R \to \infty$ and relation (1.12.8) follows.

Example 3. Evaluate

$$\int_0^{\infty} \frac{\cos tx}{x^2 + a^2}\, dx, \quad a > 0,\, t > 0.$$

The function $F(z) = 1/(z^2 + a^2)$ is clearly of $O(1/|z|^2)$ and has no real poles. Therefore from (1.12.8)

$$\int_{-\infty}^{\infty} \frac{e^{itx}}{x^2 + a^2}\, dx = 2\pi i\, \text{Res}\,(ai),$$

since $z = ai$ is the only pole in the upper half-plane. Now the Res $(ai) = e^{-ta}/(2ai)$, hence

$$\int_{-\infty}^{\infty} \frac{e^{itx}}{x^2 + a^2}\, dx = 2\pi i\left(\frac{e^{-ta}}{2ai}\right) = \frac{\pi e^{-ta}}{a}.$$

Separating the preceding integral into its real and imaginary parts, we get

$$\int_{-\infty}^{\infty} \frac{\cos tx}{x^2 + a^2}\, dx + i \int_{-\infty}^{\infty} \frac{\sin tx}{x^2 + a^2}\, dx = \frac{\pi}{a}\, e^{-ta}.$$

Consequently

(1.12.9) $$\int_{-\infty}^{\infty} \frac{\cos tx}{x^2 + a^2}\, dx = \frac{\pi}{a}\, e^{-ta}, \qquad \int_{-\infty}^{\infty} \frac{\sin tx}{x^2 + a^2}\, dx = 0.$$

Since the first integrand of (1.12.9) is even

$$\int_{0}^{\infty} \frac{\cos tx}{x^2 + a^2}\, dx = \frac{1}{2}\int_{-\infty}^{\infty} \frac{\cos tx}{x^2 + a^2}\, dx = \frac{\pi}{2a}\, e^{-ta}.$$

We shall now illustrate how the contour of Fig. 1.12.4 must be modified in order to evaluate integrals of the type

$$\int_{-\infty}^{\infty} e^{itx}\, F(x)\, dx$$

if $F(z)$ satisfies the conditions of Lemma I, but has real poles.

Example 4.   Evaluate $$\int_{0}^{\infty} \frac{\sin tx}{x}\, dx, \quad t > 0.$$

To evaluate this integral we consider $\displaystyle \int_{C} \frac{e^{itz}}{z}\, dz$, where C is the

contour shown in Fig. 1.12.5.   This contour was *indented* at the origin in order to avoid the singularity of the integrand $F(z) = e^{itz}/z$ at $z = 0$.   Within this contour there are no singularities.   Hence by Cauchy's theorem

(1.12.10)

$$\int_{r}^{R} F(x)\, dx + \int_{C_R} F(z)\, dz$$

$$+ \int_{-R}^{-r} F(x)\, dx + \int_{C_r} F(z)\, dz = 0.$$

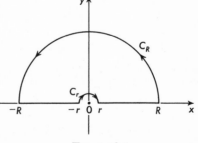

Fɪɢ. 1.12.5

Because $1/z$ satisfies the conditions of Lemma I, we have

$$\lim_{R \to \infty} \int_{C_R} F(z)\, dz = 0.$$

On the semicircle C_r, $z = re^{i\theta}$, $dz = iz\,d\theta$. Therefore

$$\lim_{r\to 0}\int_{C_R}\frac{e^{itz}}{z}\,dz = \lim_{r\to 0}\int_\pi^0 e^{i(\cos\theta + i\sin\theta)r}\cdot i\,d\theta$$

$$=\int_\pi^0 \lim_{r\to 0} e^{i(\cos\theta + i\sin\theta)r}\cdot i\,d\theta = i\int_\pi^0 d\theta = -\pi i.$$

The operation of taking the limit under the integral sign is permissible here because of the continuity of the integrand.*

Taking the limit of equation (1.12.10) as $R\to\infty$ and $r\to 0$, we get

$$\int_{-\infty}^\infty \frac{e^{itx}}{x}\,dx = \pi i.$$

Equating the real and imaginary parts, we obtain

$$\int_{-\infty}^\infty \frac{\sin tx}{x}\,dx = \pi, \qquad \int_{-\infty}^\infty \frac{\cos tx}{x}\,dx = 0.$$

The integrand of the first integral is even. Therefore

$$\int_0^\infty \frac{\sin tx}{x}\,dx = \frac{\pi}{2}, \quad t > 0.$$

The last type of integral to be considered is one of the form

(1.12.11) $$\int_0^\infty x^{a-1} f(x)\,dx,$$

where a is a constant different from an integer and $f(z)$ is a rational function having no poles, or only simple poles on the positive real axis.

Since a was assumed non-integral, the function $F(z) = z^{a-1} f(z)$ is in general multiple valued and possesses a branch point at the origin, in addition to possible poles on the positive real axis. To make $F(z)$ single valued a barrier or cut is introduced and the branch point is surrounded by a circle of radius r. Figures 1.12.6 and 1.12.7 illustrate, respectively, the types of contours that can be used if $f(z)$ possesses no poles, or one pole on the positive real axis.

We shall now show that if $\lim_{|z|\to\infty} |z\cdot F(z)| = 0$ and $\lim_{|z|\to 0} |z\cdot F(z)| = 0$, then the integral around the large circle C_R tends to zero as its radius $R\to\infty$, and the integral about the small circle C_r tends to zero as $r\to 0$ (Fig. 1.12.6). For, corresponding to $\epsilon > 0$ there exists an R_0 such that

---

* D. V. Widder, *Advanced Calculus*, Prentice-Hall, New York, 1947, pp. 291–292.

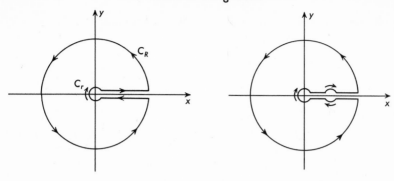

FIG. 1.12.6   FIG. 1.12.7

whenever $R > R_0$, $|z^a f(z)| < \epsilon$. Therefore for points on the circle C_R: $z = Re^{i\theta}$, $dz = zi\,d\theta$, $|dz| = |z|d\theta$ and

$$\left| \int_{C_R} z^{a-1} f(z)\,dz \right| \leqslant \int_{C_R} |z^a f(z)|\,|z|^{-1}|dz| < \epsilon \int_0^{2\pi} d\theta = 2\pi\epsilon,$$

which implies that $\lim_{R\to\infty} \int_{C_R} z^{a-1} f(z)\,dz = 0$. Similarly, for the small circle, corresponding to $\epsilon > 0$ there exists an r_0 such that whenever $r < r_0$, $|z^a f(z)| < \epsilon$. Hence for points on the circle C_r we also have

$$\left| \int_{C_r} z^{a-1} f(z)\,dz \right| < 2\pi\epsilon,$$

which again implies that $\lim_{r\to 0} \int_{C_r} z^{a-1} f(z)\,dz = 0$. Consequently as $R\to\infty$ and $r\to 0$, only the integrals evaluated for the points on the upper and lower sides of the cut remain, and their sum is $2\pi i$ times the sum of the residues of $z^{a-1} f(z)$ inside the contour.

The case for poles on the positive real axis (Fig. 1.12.7) can be treated similarly.

Example 5. Prove $\displaystyle\int_0^\infty \frac{x^{a-1}}{x+1}\,dx = \frac{\pi}{\sin a\pi}$, $0 < a < 1$.

Since there are no poles on the positive real axis, we can integrate around the contour of Fig. 1.12.6. The function $z^{a-1}/(z+1)$ has a branch point at the origin and a pole at $z = -1$. If we use the branch corresponding to $k = 0$, the multiple-valued function z^{a-1} becomes single valued and

$$z^{a-1} = |z|^{a-1}e^{(a-1)i\theta}, \quad 0 \leqslant \theta < 2\pi.$$

For points $z = |z|e^{i\theta}$ on the upper line, $\theta\to 0$ and $|z|\to x$ as the radius of C_r tends to zero. Hence, in the limit, $z^{a-1} = x^{a-1}$ for these points.

For points on the lower line, $\theta \to 2\pi$ and $|z| \to x$ and hence z^{a-1} $= x^{a-1}e^{(a-1)2\pi i} = x^{a-1}e^{2\pi a i}$.   Consequently

$$(1.12.12) \qquad \int_0^\infty \frac{x^{a-1}}{x+1}\,dx + \int_\infty^0 \frac{x^{a-1}e^{2\pi a i}}{x+1}\,dx = 2\pi i \; \text{Res}\,(-1).$$

The residue of $z^{a-1}/(z+1)$ at $z = -1$ is

$$\lim_{z \to -1}\left[(z+1)\frac{z^{a-1}}{z+1}\right] = (-1)^{a-1} = e^{i\pi(a-1)} = -e^{\pi a i}.$$

Therefore from $(1.12.12)$ we get

$$(1 - e^{2\pi a i})\int_0^\infty \frac{x^{a-1}}{x+1}\,dx = -2\pi i e^{\pi a i},$$

or

$$(1.12.13) \qquad \int_0^\infty \frac{x^{a-1}}{x+1}\,dx = \frac{2\pi i}{e^{\pi a i} - e^{-\pi a i}} = \frac{\pi}{\sin \pi a}.$$

PROBLEMS

1. Show that the following relations hold:
   (a) $z\bar{z} = |\bar{z}|^2$,   (b) $\overline{z_1 \pm z_2} = \bar{z}_1 \pm \bar{z}_2$,   (c) $\overline{z_1 z_2} = \bar{z}_1 \cdot \bar{z}_2$,
   (d) $\overline{(z_1/z_2)} = \bar{z}_1/\bar{z}_2$.

2. Prove the inequalities $\big||z_1| - |z_2|\big| \leqslant |z_1 \pm z_2| \leqslant |z_1| + |z_2|$:
   (a) geometrically,   (b) algebraically.

3. In what parts of the plane, or on what curves are the points z satisfying the following relations?
   (a) $|z - 3i| \leqslant 1$,   (b) $\text{Re}(z) \geqslant 3$,   (c) $\text{Im}(z^2 - 1) = 1$,
   (d) $|z - 1| \leqslant 2|z|$,   (e) $\text{Re}\{(z + \bar{z})^2\} \geqslant 4$,   (f) $\text{Re}\{z(\bar{z} + 2)\} = 8$.

4. Show that e^z has the period $2\pi i$.

5. If n is a positive integer, show that:
   (a) $(e^z)^n = e^{nz}$, $(n = 1, 2, 3, \cdots)$
   (b) $e^{ni\theta} = \cos n\theta + i \sin n\theta$,
   (c) $(\cos \theta + i \sin \theta)^n = \cos n\theta + i \sin n\theta$,
   the so-called *de Moivre formula*.

6. From the definition of the hyperbolic sine and cosine functions deduce the following series expansions:
   (a) $\sinh z = z + \dfrac{z^3}{3!} + \dfrac{z^5}{5!} + \cdots = \displaystyle\sum_{n=0}^\infty \dfrac{z^{2n+1}}{(2n+1)!}$,

   (b) $\cosh z = 1 + \dfrac{z^2}{2!} + \dfrac{z^4}{4!} + \cdots = \displaystyle\sum_{n=0}^\infty \dfrac{z^{2n}}{(2n)!}$.

7. Prove that:

    (a) $\sin iz = i \sinh z$, (b) $\cos iz = \cosh z$,

    (c) $\sinh iz = i \sin z$, (d) $\cosh iz = \cos z$.

8. Verify that:

    (a) $\sin (z_1 \pm z_2) = \sin z_1 \cos z_2 \pm \cos z_1 \sin z_2$,

    (b) $\cos (z_1 \pm z_2) = \cos z_1 \cos z_2 \pm \sin z_1 \sin z_2$.

9. Deduce the following formulas:

    (a) $e^z = e^x \cos y + i e^x \sin y$,

    (b) $\sin z = \sin x \cosh y + i \cos x \sinh y$,

    (c) $\cos z = \cos x \cosh y - i \sin x \sinh y$,

    (d) $\sinh z = \sinh x \cos y + i \cosh x \sin y$,

    (e) $\cosh z = \cosh x \cos y + i \sinh x \sin y$.

10. Find the *zeros* of:

    (a) $\sin z$, (b) $\cos z$, (c) $\sinh z$, (d) $\cosh z$.

    A *zero* of a function $f(z)$ is any value of z for which $f(z) = 0$.

    Ans. (a) $z = n\pi$ $(n = 0, 1, 2, \cdots)$.

      (c) $z = n\pi i$ $(n = 0, 1, 2, \cdots)$.

11. Prove:

    (i) $|\sin (x \pm iy)| \leqslant \cosh y$,

    (ii) $|\cos (x \pm iy)| \leqslant \cosh y$.

12. (a) Show that $\sin z$ and $\cos z$ are periodic functions with the period 2π, and

    (b) that $\sinh z$ and $\cosh z$ are periodic functions with the period $2\pi i$.

13. (i) Making use of formula (1.2.12), show that when $b = p/q$,

$$z^{p/q} = r^{p/q} e^{(ip/q)(\theta \pm 2k\pi)}, \quad (0 \leqslant \theta < 2\pi, \, k = 0, 1, 2, \cdots)$$

   where p/q is a fraction in its lowest terms.

   (ii) Deduce from this result that $z^{p/q}$ has exactly q *distinct* values.

   (iii) Find the values of: (a) $2^{3/2}$, (b) $(1 - i)^{-1/2}$.

14. Using the formula mentioned in the previous problem, verify the following results:

    (a) $2^i = e^{\pm 2k\pi}(\cos \ln 2 + \sin \ln 2)$, $(k = 0, 1, 2, \cdots)$

    (b) $(1 + i)^i = e^{-(\frac{1}{4} \pm 2k)\pi}(\cos \ln \sqrt{2} + i \sin \ln \sqrt{2})$ $(k = 0, 1, 2, \cdots)$.

15. Find all the values of:

    (a) $\cos^{-1}(i)$, (b) $\tanh^{-1}(1 - i)$, (c) $\ln (- 2)$, (d) $\ln i$,

    (e) $\sin^{-1} 3$.

16. Prove that $\lim\limits_{z \to z_0} |f(z)| = | \lim\limits_{z \to z_0} f(z)|$.

17. Prove that if $f(z)$ is analytic at $z = z_0$ it is continuous at that point.

18. Show that the following functions:

    (a) e^z, (b) $\sinh z$, (c) $\ln z$, (h) $\tan z$

    satisfy the Cauchy-Riemann equations and Laplace's equation.

19. Calculate $\int_i^1 (z^2 - z + 1)\, dz$:

(a) Along $x + y = 1$,

(b) Along $y = 1$ from $(0,1)$ to $(1,1)$ and then along $x = 1$ from $(1,1)$ to $(1,0)$,

(c) Along the parabola $y = 1 - x^2$,

(d) Along the circle $x^2 + y^2 = 1$.   *Ans.* $\frac{1}{3}(1 - 2i)$.

20. Evaluate $\int_i^1 (1 - \bar{z})^2\, dz$ along the paths of Exercise 19.

21. Evaluate $\int_{-i}^{i} \dfrac{1 + z}{z}\, dz$ along the right half of the circle $x^2 + y^2 = 1$.

          Ans. $i(2 + \pi)$.

22. Show that

$$\int_C (z - z_0)^n\, dz = 0, \quad n \neq -1$$
$$= 2\pi i, \quad n = -1$$

where C is a circle of radius r with center at z_0 and n is an integer.

23. Find the value of $\int_C \dfrac{e^{2iz} - 5z}{z + 2i}\, dz$ if C is

(a) The circle $|z + 1| = 3$,

(b) The circle $|z - \frac{1}{2}i| = 1$.

24. Evaluate the integral $\int_C \dfrac{z - 1}{(z^2 + iz + 2)}\, dz$ if C is the curve $x^4 + y^4 = 4$.

25. Find the Laurent expansion of $f(z) = \dfrac{1}{(z - 1)(z - 3)}$ valid for the ring $1 < |z| < 3$.

26. Find and classify the singularities of the following functions:

(a) $\dfrac{2z - 1}{z^3 + 1}$,   (b) $\sin \dfrac{1}{z - i}$,   (c) $\ln (z^2 - 1)$,

(d) $\sqrt[3]{z^2} + 1$,   (e) $\sqrt[3]{3 - z}$,   (f) $\sec z$,

(g) $\dfrac{1}{\sinh (z - i)}$,   (h) $z - \sqrt{z^2 + 1}$,   (i) $\cos\sqrt{1 - z}$,

(j) $\tan^{-1}(z + i)$,   (k) $\ln \dfrac{z}{z - 4}$,   (l) $\sqrt[5]{z^2 + 3}$.

Ans. (a) Poles: $z = -1$, $\frac{1}{2}(1 \pm i\sqrt{3})$; (b) essential singularity: $z = i$; (c) branch pts.: $z = \pm 1$; (d) branch pt.: $z = 0$; (e) branch pt.: $z = 3$; (f) poles: $z = \pm (2n + 1)\pi/2$, $n = 0, 1, 2, \cdots$; (g) poles: $z = (1 \pm n\pi)i$, $n = 0, 1, 2, \cdots$; (h) branch pts.: $z = \pm i$; (i) no singularities; (j) branch pts.: $z = 0, -2i$; (k) branch pts.: $z = 0, 4$; (l) branch pts.: $z = \pm i\sqrt{3}$.

27. Show that the function $f(z) = \dfrac{1}{(az)^{1/2} + 1}$ has a branch point at $z = 0$. Also show that this is the only singularity of $f(z)$ if the branch of $(az)^{1/2}$ corresponding to $k = 0$ is taken, whereas there is in addition to the branch point a pole at $z = 1/a$ if the branch of $(az)^{1/2}$ corresponding to $k = 1$ is taken.

28. Find the singularities of the following functions (consider all the branches):

(a) $f(z) = \dfrac{1}{\sqrt{z} + i}$,

(b) $f(z) = \dfrac{1}{\sqrt{z} + z}$,

(c) $f(z) = \dfrac{1}{a\sqrt{z} + \sqrt{z} - i}$, discuss the cases: $a \neq \pm 1$, $a = \pm 1$,

(d) $f(z) = \dfrac{1}{(z - 1)\sqrt{z} + 1}$.

29. Determine the values of the residues of the following functions at each of their poles:

(a) $\dfrac{e^{tz}}{z^3 - a^3}$,

(b) $\dfrac{\sin tz}{z^3}$,

(c) $\dfrac{1 + z}{z^2(z - a)^2}$,

(d) $\dfrac{az^2 + bz + c}{(z - z_0)(z - z_1)}$.

30. Evaluate the residues of $\dfrac{1}{1 - \cos z}$ at the poles $z = \pm 2n\pi$, $(n = 0, 1, 2, \cdots)$.

31. Using contour integration, verify that

(a) $\displaystyle\int_0^{2\pi} \dfrac{dx}{a + b \cos x} = \dfrac{2\pi}{\sqrt{a^2 - b^2}}$ $(a > |b|)$,

(b) $\displaystyle\int_0^{\pi} \dfrac{d\theta}{(a + b \cos \theta)^2} = \dfrac{\pi a}{(a^2 - b^2)^{3/2}}$ $(a > |b|)$,

(c) $\displaystyle\int_0^{\pi} \dfrac{d\theta}{1 + \sin^2 \theta} = \dfrac{\pi}{\sqrt{2}}$,

(d) $\displaystyle\int_0^{\infty} \dfrac{dx}{x^4 + a^4} = \dfrac{\pi}{2\sqrt{2}a^3}$,

(e) $\displaystyle\int_{-\infty}^{\infty} \dfrac{x^2\, dx}{x^5 + 1} = \dfrac{\pi}{3}$,

(f) $\displaystyle\int_0^\infty \frac{x \sin x}{x^2 + 4}\, dx = \frac{\pi}{2}\, e^{-2},$

(g) $\displaystyle\int_{-\infty}^\infty \frac{\cos x\, dx}{(x^2 + a^2)(x^2 + b^2)} = \frac{\pi}{a^2 - b^2}\left(\frac{e^{-b}}{b} - \frac{e^{-a}}{a}\right) \quad (a > 0, b > 0),$

(h) $\displaystyle\int_{-\infty}^\infty \frac{\cos tx}{(x - a)^2 + b^2}\, dx = \frac{\pi e^{-tb}\cos ta}{b} \quad (t > 0, b > 0).$

32. By integrating $e^{az}/\cosh \pi z$ around the rectangle of sides $x = \pm R$, $y = 0$, and $y = 1$, show that

$$\int_{-\infty}^\infty \frac{e^{ax}}{\cosh \pi x}\, dx = \sec \frac{a}{2}, \quad -\pi < a < \pi.$$

Making the substitution $- x$ for x and adding the result to the previous one, show finally that

$$\int_{-\infty}^\infty \frac{\cosh ax}{\cosh \pi x}\, dx = \sec \frac{a}{2}, \quad -\pi < a < \pi.$$

33. Show that

$$\int_{-\infty}^\infty \frac{a \cos x + x \sin x}{x^2 + a^2}\, dx = 2\pi e^{-a},\ a > 0.$$

by integrating $e^{iz}/(z - ia)$ over the upper semicircle $|z| = R$, $R > a$.

CHAPTER II

The Laplace Transformation and Its Inverse

2.1 Introduction

The idea of regarding mathematical symbols as operators has been in existence for a long time. A simple example from arithmetic is that of finding the logarithm of numbers. Here the operation of taking the logarithm of the product of two numbers is reduced to that of adding the logarithms of each factor. Similarly, to find the logarithm of a quotient one takes the difference of the logarithms of the dividend and the divisor. The operations of taking the logarithms of products and quotients have thereby been reduced to the simpler operations of addition and subtraction. One observes, however, that the operation of taking the logarithm of a sum or difference cannot be simplified. We may regard the operation of taking logarithms as a *transformation* that transforms numbers into other numbers.

An example of an operator that transforms functions into other functions is that of the differential operator $D \equiv \dfrac{d}{dx}$. Applied to the function $f(x)$, it transforms the given function into another function, i.e., $D f(x) = g(x)$.

A more general operator is the so-called *linear* differential operator $\Phi(D) \equiv a_0 D^n + a_1 D^{n-1} + \cdots + a_n$, where the a's are constants and n is a positive integer indicating the number of times D is to be applied. The study of such operators in detail leads one to an operational calculus that can be used to solve certain types of differential equations.

2.2 Definition of the Laplace Transformation

The operation of multiplying a function $F(t)$ of the real variable t, defined for $t > 0$, by e^{-pt}, where p is the *complex* variable $x + iy$, and integrating the result with respect to t from zero to infinity to generate

47

a new function $f(p)$ is called the *Laplace transformation* of $F(t)$. Symbolically

(2.2.1)
$$f(p) = \int_0^\infty e^{-pt} F(t)\, dt.$$

This operation is often abbreviated by the symbol $L\{F(t)\}$ so that we also write

$$L\{F(t)\} = \int_0^\infty e^{-pt} F(t)\, dt.$$

The function $f(p)$ is called the *Laplace transform* of $F(t)$.

Remark.   In the definition of the Laplace transformation we do not exclude the possibility of $F(t)$ being a complex-valued function of the real variable t, e.g., $F(t) = \sin (a + bi)t$, $F(t) = t + 2it^2$, $F(t) = e^{(3+i)t}$, etc. Such a function can be treated by resolving it into real and imaginary parts, each of which is now a real function of the real variable t.

Since the upper limit of integration defining the $L\{F(t)\}$ is infinite, the integral is a so-called *improper* or *Cauchy* integral.   In addition, it can be improper because $F(t)$ has discontinuities over the range of integration, and in particular at the origin.   Therefore, the integral in (2.2.1) is understood to mean

(2.2.2)
$$\int_0^\infty e^{-pt} F(t)\, dt = \lim_{\substack{b \to \infty \\ a \to 0+}} \int_a^b e^{-pt} F(t)\, dt,$$

where $a \to 0+$ signifies that a tends to zero from the right.

Before we discuss the conditions that $F(t)$ must satisfy in order for its Laplace transform to exist, let us consider the transforms of a few functions.

2.3 Laplace Transforms of Simple Functions

As the first example we shall determine the transform of the step function $F(t) = 1$, $t > 0$ (Fig. 2.3.1).

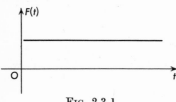

Fig. 2.3.1

The Laplace transform of this function is

$$\int_0^\infty e^{-pt} dt = \lim_{\substack{b \to \infty \\ a \to 0+}} \frac{1}{p}\, (e^{-pa} - e^{-pb}).$$

Now, if the $\mathrm{Re}(p) = x > 0$, then

$$\lim_{b \to \infty} |e^{-pb}| = \lim_{b \to \infty} |e^{-xb} \cdot e^{-iyb}| = \lim_{b \to \infty} e^{-xb}$$

$= 0$, and hence $\lim_{b \to \infty} e^{-pb} = 0$.   Since $\lim_{a \to 0+} e^{-pa}$ is clearly 1, we therefore have

$$L\{1\} = \frac{1}{p}, \text{ when } \mathrm{Re}(p) > 0.$$

The preceding function and in general those that follow will not be defined at the points of finite discontinuity (assumed to be finite in number), since the latter do not affect the value of the integral defining the Laplace transform of a function. Thus, the following functions (Figs. 2.3.2 and 2.3.3) have the same Laplace transform $\frac{1}{p}$, $\mathrm{Re}(p) > 0$.

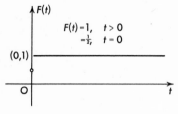

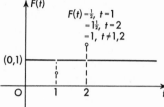

FIG. 2.3.2   FIG. 2.3.3

Let us next calculate the transform of $F(t) = e^{kt}$, where k is a complex number. We have

$$\int_0^\infty e^{kt} \cdot e^{-pt}\, dt = \int_0^\infty e^{-(p-k)t}\, dt = -\frac{e^{-(p-k)t}}{p-k}\bigg]_0^\infty$$

If $\mathrm{Re}(p - k) > 0$, then it is easily seen that

$$L\{e^{kt}\} = \frac{1}{p-k}.$$

Finally, let us consider the transform of $F(t) = \sin kt$, where k is real.

$$\int_0^\infty e^{-pt} \sin kt\, dt = \frac{1}{2i} \int_0^\infty e^{-pt}(e^{ikt} - e^{-ikt})\, dt$$

$$= \frac{1}{2i}\left[-\frac{e^{-(p-ik)t}}{p - ik} + \frac{e^{-(p+ik)t}}{p + ik} \right]_0^\infty$$

Hence, if $\mathrm{Re}(p) > 0$, then

$$L\{\sin kt\} = \frac{1}{2i}\left[\frac{1}{p - ik} - \frac{1}{p + ik} \right] = \frac{k}{p^2 + k^2}.$$

The preceding examples make it clear that the Laplace transformation establishes a correspondence between pairs of functions, one a *real* function, the other a *complex* function. Thus, to the function $F(t) = 1, t > 0$, there corresponds the function $f(p) = \frac{1}{p}$, defined in the half-plane $\mathrm{Re}(p) > 0$. Similarly, the mate of e^{kt} is $\frac{1}{(p - k)}$, when $\mathrm{Re}(p) > \mathrm{Re}(k)$, and of $\sin kt$, $\frac{k}{p^2 + k^2}$, provided $\mathrm{Re}(p) > 0$.

By considering the transforms of many functions a table of transform pairs can be built.   Such a table is given in Appendix C and will facilitate the solution of many problems.

2.4 Existence of Laplace Transforms

The integral defining the Laplace transform of a function may fail to exist for various reasons.   For example, $F(t)$ may have infinite discontinuities in the interval of integration, or it may increase so rapidly that the multiplier e^{-pt} cannot dampen it sufficiently for convergence of the integral to take place.   To insure the convergence of the integral, we shall state certain *sufficient* conditions on $F(t)$ which will be satisfied by most of the functions arising in the solution of physical problems.

A function $F(t)$ is said to be *sectionally continuous* over a finite interval if that interval can be divided into a finite number of sub-intervals over each of which $F(t)$ is continuous and possesses finite limits as t tends to either end of the subinterval from the interior. The function shown in Fig. 2.4.1 is sectionally continuous over the interval $(0, t_3)$.   Since $\lim\limits_{t \to t_1-} F(t) = 1$ and $\lim\limits_{t \to t_1+} F(t) = 2$ (where $t \to t_1-$ and $t \to t_1+$ mean that t tends to t_1 from the left and right,

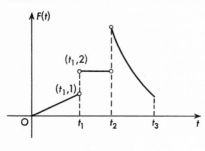

Fɪɢ. 2.4.1

respectively), $F(t)$ is discontinuous at $t = t_1$ and has a so-called *finite jump*.   A similar jump occurs at $t = t_2$.

A function $F(t)$ is said to be of *exponential order* as $t \to \infty$ if there is a constant c such that the product $e^{-ct}|F(t)|$ is bounded for all $t > T$, where T is a finite number.   In other words, if M is a bound,

$$|F(t)| < Me^{ct} \quad \text{for} \quad t > T.$$

When this inequality is satisfied we often say that $F(t)$ is of the order of e^{ct}, and write briefly $F(t) = O(e^{ct})$.

The function $F(t) =$ constant is clearly of exponential order with $c = 0$.   So also are $e^{at} \cos bt$ with $c > a$, t^n $(n \geqslant 0)$ with $c > 0$ and $t^2 \sin t$ with $c > 0$.   All *bounded* functions are clearly of exponential order with $c = 0$.   The function e^{t^2}, however, is not of exponential order.

Suppose now that $F(t)$ is (a) sectionally continuous in any finite interval for which $t \geqslant 0$ and (b) of exponential order as t becomes infinite. Then

$$\int_0^\infty |e^{-pt} F(t)| \, dt = \int_0^\infty e^{-xt} |F(t)| dt$$

$$= \int_0^T e^{-xt} |F(t)| dt + \int_T^\infty e^{-xt} |F(t)| dt$$

$$= \int_0^T e^{-xt} |F(t)| dt + M \int_T^\infty e^{-(x-c)t} \, dt.$$

The first integral on the right exists because it is the sum of integrals over the separate subintervals in which the function is continuous, and the second integral clearly exists if $x = \mathrm{Re}(p) > c$. It follows that $L\{F(t)\}$ converges *absolutely* when $\mathrm{Re}(p) > c$. Thus, the existence of the Laplace transformation is established when the two preceding conditions are satisfied.

We can relax these conditions somewhat by allowing $F(t)$ to have certain infinite discontinuities at $t = 0$. To be precise, if (a) $F(t)$ is sectionally continuous in any finite range for which $t > 0$, (b) $F(t)$ $= O(e^{ct})$ and (c) $t^n F(t)$ is bounded near $t = 0$, where n is a number *less than one*, and then its transform still exists. We leave the justification of this to the reader as an exercise.

2.5 The Inverse Laplace Transform

Thus far we have considered the following problem: given a function $F(t)$ satisfying certain conditions, what is the $L\{F(t)\}$? This is the *direct* problem. In the applications to follow it will be very important to be able to solve the following problem: What is the function $F(t)$ which has a given transform $f(p)$? This is the *inverse* problem. It is customary to denote the *inverse Laplace transform* of $f(p)$ by the symbol $L^{-1}\{f(p)\}$. Thus, if

$$L\{F(t)\} = f(p),$$

then

$$F(t) = L^{-1}\{f(p)\}.$$

For example, we have seen that $L\{e^{at}\} = \dfrac{1}{p-a}.$ Hence

$$L^{-1}\left\{\frac{1}{p-a}\right\} = e^{at}.$$

The problem of determining the inverse transform may be looked upon as one of solving the *integral* equation

(2.5.1) $$\int_0^\infty e^{-pt} F(t) \, dt = f(p),$$

where $f(p)$ is *given* and $F(t)$ is to be *determined*. In solving such an equation it is important to know whether the solution (if there is one) is *unique*. That the inverse transform is not, strictly speaking, unique is suggested by the examples of Figs. 2.3.2 and 2.3.3. All the functions defined there had the same inverse transform, namely, $1/p$. It is clear that the same inverse transform would be obtained if $F(t)$ differed from those functions at a finite number of points.

A theorem by Lerch[*] states that two functions which have the same transform cannot differ over any interval of positive length. Since such functions are in general of no significance in the applications, we can say that the inverse transform is essentially unique.

In order to solve the integral equation (2.5.1), we shall find it convenient to employ the Fourier integral which will be considered in the next section.

2.6 The Fourier Integral

Suppose that $\phi(t)$ is defined arbitrarily in the interval $(-l, l)$ and by the relation $\phi(t + 2l) = \phi(t)$ outside this interval. Furthermore, let $\phi(t)$ and $\phi'(t)$ be sectionally continuous in the interval $(-l, l)$. Then it is well known that $\phi(t)$ can be represented by a series of the form

$$(2.6.1) \qquad \phi(t) = a_0/2 + \sum_{n=1}^{\infty} \left(a_n \cos \frac{n\pi}{l} t + b_n \sin \frac{n\pi}{l} t \right),$$

$$(2.6.2) \qquad a_n = \frac{1}{l} \int_{-l}^{l} \phi(\tau) \cos \frac{n\pi}{l} \tau \, d\tau, \quad b_n = \frac{1}{l} \int_{-l}^{l} \phi(\tau) \sin \frac{n\pi}{l} \tau \, d\tau,$$

$$(n = 0, 1, 2, \cdots)$$

which converges to $\phi(t)$ at all points of continuity and to

$$\frac{\phi(t + 0) - \phi(t - 0)}{2}$$

at points of discontinuity. We say that the function $\phi(t)$ has been expanded in a *Fourier series*.

The number l in the preceding formulas was finite. We now proceed to see what happens to the Fourier series when l becomes infinite. Substituting the expressions (2.6.2) in (2.6.1), we obtain

$$(2.6.3) \qquad \phi(t) = \frac{1}{2l} \int_{-l}^{l} \phi(\tau) \, d\tau + \frac{1}{l} \sum_{n=1}^{\infty} \int_{-l}^{l} \phi(\tau) \cos \frac{n\pi}{l} (t - \tau) \, d\tau.$$

Now, if in addition to the conditions stipulated above on $\phi(t)$, we

---

[*] G. Doetsch, *Theorie und Anwendung der Laplace—Transformation*, p. 35.

assume that $\int_{-\infty}^{\infty} |\phi(\tau)|d\tau$ exists and has the value A, say, then

$$\left| \frac{1}{2l} \int_{-l}^{l} \phi(\tau)\, d\tau \right| \leqslant \frac{1}{2l} \int_{-l}^{l} |\phi(\tau)|d\tau \leqslant \frac{A}{2l},$$

and clearly the first integral tends to zero as $l \to \infty$.

In order to examine the series on the right of (2.6.3), let us denote $n\pi/l$ by y_n and $y_n - y_{n-1} = \pi/l$ by Δy. Then it becomes

$$(2.6.4) \qquad \frac{1}{\pi} \sum_{n=1}^{\infty} \Delta y \int_{-l}^{l} \phi(\tau) \cos y_n(t - \tau)\, d\tau = \frac{1}{\pi} \sum_{n=1}^{\infty} \psi(y_n)\Delta y,$$

where $\psi(y) = \int_{-l}^{l} \phi(\tau) \cos y(t - \tau)\, d\tau$.

Now the sum (2.6.4) is somewhat like that which defines a Riemann integral and it seems plausible that the series (2.6.4) becomes

$$\frac{1}{\pi} \int_{0}^{\infty} dy \int_{-\infty}^{\infty} \phi(\tau) \cos y(t - \tau)\, d\tau,$$

as $\Delta y \to 0$, i.e., as $l \to \infty$, so that (2.6.3) can finally be written as

$$(2.6.5) \qquad \phi(t) = \frac{1}{\pi} \int_{0}^{\infty} dy \int_{-\infty}^{\infty} \phi(\tau) \cos y(t - \tau)\, d\tau.$$

The foregoing discussion can be made rigorous[*] and the integral (2.6.5) is known as the *Fourier integral*.

A form of (2.6.5) more suitable for our purpose is that obtained by making use of the relation

$$\cos y(t - \tau) = \frac{e^{iy(t-\tau)} + e^{-iy(t-\tau)}}{2}.$$

Upon substituting this expression in (2.6.5) and making a simple transformation, we obtain

$$(2.6.6) \qquad \phi(t) = \frac{1}{2\pi} \int_{-\infty}^{\infty} e^{iyt} \left\{ \int_{-\infty}^{\infty} e^{-iy\tau}\phi(\tau)\, d\tau \right\} dy.$$

Summarizing, we have the so-called *Fourier integral theorem*:
If $\phi(t)$ and $\phi'(t)$ are sectionally continuous in every finite interval and
$\int_{-\infty}^{\infty} |\phi(t)|dt$ *exists, then*

$$(2.6.7) \qquad \phi(t) = \frac{1}{2\pi} \lim_{R \to \infty} \int_{-R}^{R} e^{iyt} \int_{-\infty}^{\infty} e^{-iy\tau}\phi(\tau)\, d\tau\, dy$$

at all points of continuity and is equal to $\frac{1}{2}[\phi(t + 0) + \phi(t - 0)]$ at points

---

[*] R. Courant, *Differential and Integral Calculus*, Vol. II, Interscience Publishers, New York, pp. 321–323.

of discontinuity, where $\phi(t + 0)$ and $\phi(t - 0)$ represent the right- and left-hand limits at t.

It is important in many applications (especially in electrical engineering) to have Fourier integral representations of functions. The following example gives such a representation of a well-known function.

Example. Obtain the Fourier integral representation of the D-C pulse

$$\phi(t) = 0, \quad t < 0$$
$$= E_0, \quad 0 < t < a$$
$$= 0, \quad t > a.$$

From (2.6.5), we have

$$\phi(t) = \frac{E_0}{\pi}\int_0^\infty dy \int_0^a \cos y(t - \tau)\, d\tau$$

$$= \frac{E_0}{\pi}\int_0^\infty \left[-\frac{\sin y(t - \tau)}{y}\right]_0^a dy = \frac{E_0}{\pi}\int_0^\infty \frac{\sin yt - \sin y(t - a)}{y}\, dy$$

$$= \frac{2E_0}{\pi}\int_0^\infty \frac{\sin \frac{a}{2}y}{y} \cos (t - \frac{a}{2})y\, dy.$$

2.7 Fourier Transforms

If the expression $\cos y(t - \tau)$ in formula (2.6.5) is expanded, then (2.6.5) can be written in the form

(2.7.1) $\phi(t)$

$$= \frac{1}{\pi}\int_0^\infty \cos yt\, dy \int_{-\infty}^\infty \phi(\tau) \cos y\tau\, d\tau + \frac{1}{\pi}\int_0^\infty \sin yt\, dy \int_{-\infty}^\infty \phi(\tau) \sin y\tau\, d\tau.$$

Suppose, now, that $\phi(t)$ is an *even* function, i.e., $\phi(t) = \phi(-t)$, then $\phi(\tau) \sin y\tau$ is an odd function and formula (2.7.1) becomes

$$\phi(t) = \frac{1}{\pi}\int_0^\infty \cos yt\, dy \int_{-\infty}^\infty \phi(\tau) \cos y\tau\, d\tau,$$

because the second integral vanishes. In addition, $\phi(\tau) \cos y\tau$, being the product of two even functions, is even, and the preceding integral reduces to

(2.7.2) $$\phi(t) = \frac{2}{\pi}\int_0^\infty \cos yt\, dy \int_0^\infty \phi(\tau) \cos y\tau\, d\tau.$$

In a similar manner it can be shown that if $\phi(t)$ is an *odd* function, i.e., $\phi(t) = -\phi(-t)$, then

(2.7.3) $$\phi(t) = \frac{2}{\pi}\int_0^\infty \sin yt\, dy \int_0^\infty \phi(\tau) \sin y\tau\, d\tau.$$

Referring to formula (2.6.6), let us denote the integral within the braces, multiplied by $\dfrac{1}{\sqrt{2\pi}}$, by $\psi(y)$. We then obtain the pair of integrals,

(2.7.4) $$\psi(y) = \frac{1}{\sqrt{2\pi}} \int_{-\infty}^{\infty} e^{-iy\tau} \phi(\tau)\, d\tau,$$

and

(2.7.5) $$\phi(t) = \frac{1}{\sqrt{2\pi}} \int_{-\infty}^{\infty} e^{-iyt} \psi(y)\, dy,$$

which form a reciprocal relation between $\phi(t)$ and $\psi(y)$. They are known as the *Fourier transforms* of one another.

Analogously, from formula (2.7.2) we obtain the reciprocal relations

(2.7.6) $$\chi(y) = \sqrt{\frac{2}{\pi}} \int_{0}^{\infty} \phi(\tau) \cos y\tau\, d\tau, \quad \phi(t) = \sqrt{\frac{2}{\pi}} \int_{0}^{\infty} \chi(y) \cos yt\, dy,$$

known as the *Fourier cosine transforms*, and from formula (2.7.3), the expressions

(2.7.7) $$\theta(y) = \sqrt{\frac{2}{\pi}} \int_{0}^{\infty} \phi(\tau) \sin y\tau\, d\tau, \quad \phi(t) = \sqrt{\frac{2}{\pi}} \int_{0}^{\infty} \theta(y) \sin yt\, dy,$$

known as the *Fourier sine transforms*.

Exercise 1.

Show that the Fourier sine transform of $\phi(t) = \sin t$, $|t| < \pi$; $\phi(t) = 0$, $|t| \geqslant \pi$ is

$$\theta(y) = \sqrt{\frac{2}{\pi}} \frac{\sin y\pi}{1 - y^2}, \quad y^2 \neq 1$$
$$= \sqrt{\pi/2}, \quad y = 1$$
$$= -\sqrt{\pi/2}, \quad y = -1.$$

Sketch the function $\theta(y)$.

Exercise 2.
Show that the Fourier cosine transform of $\phi(t) = \pi - |t|$, $|t| < \pi$; $\phi(t) = 0$, $|t| \geqslant \pi$ is

$$\chi(y) = \sqrt{\frac{2}{\pi}} \left(\frac{\pi}{y} - \frac{\sin y\pi}{y^2} \right), \quad y \neq 0$$
$$= 0, \quad y = 0.$$

Sketch the function $\chi(y)$.

2.8   The Complex Inversion Integral

Suppose that the function $\phi(t)$ appearing in the Fourier integral theorem is defined as follows:

$$\phi(t) = e^{-ct} F(t), \quad t > 0$$
$$= 0, \quad t < 0$$

where $F(t)$ and $F'(t)$ are sectionally continuous for $t \geqslant 0$, $c > 0$ and $F(t) = O(e^{c_0 t})$.   Then

$$\int_0^\infty |\phi(\tau)| d\tau \leqslant M \int_0^\infty e^{-(c-c_0)\tau} d\tau$$

and the last integral exists when $c > c_0$.   Also, $\phi(t)$ and $\phi'(t)$ are clearly sectionally continuous.   Therefore the conditions of the Fourier integral theorem are satisfied and (2.6.7) becomes

$$e^{-ct} F(t) = \frac{1}{2\pi} \lim_{R\to\infty} \int_{-R}^R e^{iyt} \left\{ \int_0^\infty e^{-(c+iy)\tau} F(\tau) \, d\tau \right\} dy.$$

Let $p = c + iy$.   Then, after substituting in the preceding equation, we get

$$(2.8.1) \qquad e^{-ct} F(t) = \frac{1}{2\pi i} \lim_{R\to\infty} \int_{c-iR}^{c+iR} e^{-ct} \cdot e^{pt} \left\{ \int_0^\infty e^{-p\tau} F(\tau) \, d\tau \right\} dp.$$

Dividing (2.8.1) by e^{-ct} and making the substitution $\int_0^\infty e^{-p\tau} F(\tau) \, d\tau = f(p)$, we obtain

$$F(t) = \frac{1}{2\pi i} \lim_{R\to\infty} \int_{c-iR}^{c+iR} e^{pt} f(p) \, dp.$$

Thus, we have shown that if (a) $F(t)$ is defined for $t \geqslant 0$ and $F(t) = O(e^{c_0 t})$, (b) $F(t)$ and $F'(t)$ are sectionally continuous, and (c) $f(p) = \int_0^\infty e^{-pt} F(t) \, dt$, then

$$(2.8.2) \qquad L^{-1}\{f(p)\} = F(t) = \frac{1}{2\pi i} \lim_{R\to\infty} \int_{c-iR}^{c+iR} e^{pt} f(p) \, dp,$$

where the path of integration is the line $x = c$ *and c is any positive constant greater than* c_0.

Formula (2.8.2) is known as the *complex inversion integral* of the Laplace transformation, or the *Bromwich-Wagner integral*.   This integral enables one to find the inverse transforms of many functions and will be the basis of a method for solving differential equations.

2.9   Calculation of Inverse Transforms

In order to see how formula (2.8.2) may be used to determine inverse transforms of functions we shall state without proof* a theorem

---

* For a proof, see P. Franklin, *A Treatise on Advanced Calculus*, p. 503.

which is greatly responsible for the success of the operational method in applied mathematics.

Theorem I.   If $F(t)$ is a sectionally continuous function in any finite range and of exponential order, i.e., $F(t) = 0(e^{ct})$, for $t \geqslant 0$, then

$$f(p) = \int_0^\infty e^{-pt} F(t)\, dt$$

is an analytic function in the half-plane $\operatorname{Re}(p) > c.$

The remarkableness of this theorem lies in the fact that a certain class of *discontinuous* functions is transformed into the more tractable class of *analytic* functions whose properties are well known.

Although $f(p)$, since it is analytic, has no singularities to the right of the line $x = c$, it will have, in general, singularities to the left of this line.   This fact enables us to evaluate the integral of formula (2.8.2) by enclosing the singularities by a suitable contour and making use of Cauchy's residue theorem. The contour we shall select is that shown in Fig. 2.9.1, which consists of a semicircle C of radius R with center at O, two parallel lines BA and DE each of length c and the line EA.

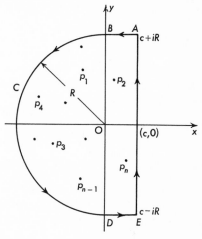

FIG. 2.9.1

Suppose that $f(p)$ has a *finite* number of poles $p_1,\ p_2,\ \cdots,\ p_n$ lying within the contour $ABCDEA$. Then by the Cauchy residue theorem

$$(2.9.1) \qquad \lim_{R \to \infty} \left\{ \int_{c-iR}^{c+iR} e^{pt} f(p)\, dp + \int_{AB} e^{pt} f(p)\, dp + \int_C e^{pt} f(p)\, dp \right.$$

$$\left. + \int_{DE} e^{pt} f(p)\, dp \right\} = 2\pi i \sum_{i=1}^n \operatorname{Res}_{p_i} e^{pt} f(p).$$

In order to show that $\lim\limits_{R \to \infty} \int_C e^{pt} f(p)\, dp = 0$ we shall prove:

Lemma II.   If $|f(p)| \leqslant M/|p|^k$ *when* $|p| > R_0$, *where* $M,\ k$ *are constants and* $k > 0$, *then*

$$\lim_{R \to \infty} \int_C e^{pt} f(p)\, dp = 0, \quad (t > 0)$$

where C *is the left half of the circle* $|p| = R$.

This lemma follows directly from Lemma I by making the substitution $p = iz$ in the integral of Lemma I, namely,

$$(2.9.2) \qquad \lim_{R \to \infty} \int_{C'} e^{izt} F(z)\, dz = 0,$$

where C' is the upper half of the circle $|z| = R$.

Let $z = Re^{i\theta}$ and $p = \rho e^{i\psi}$. Then from $p = iz$ we have

$$\rho e^{i\psi} = iRe^{i\theta} = Re^{i(\theta + \pi/2)},$$

whence

$$\rho = R \quad \text{and} \quad \psi = \theta + \pi/2.$$

The preceding result implies that the upper semicircle C' of Lemma I goes into the semicircle C of Fig. 2.9.1. For the modulus of p is R and as θ goes from 0 to π, ψ goes from $\pi/2$ to $\frac{3}{2}\pi$ so that the directions along the paths are preserved, both semicircles being described in a counterclockwise direction. Furthermore, upon making the substitution $p = iz$ in integral (2.9.2), we obtain

$$\int_{C'} e^{izt} F(z)\, dz = -i \int_C e^{pt} F(p/i)\, dp = -i \int_C e^{pt} f(p)\, dp,$$

where $F(p/i) \equiv f(p)$. The condition $|F(z)| \leqslant M/|z|^k$ of Lemma I is now replaced by $|f(p)| \leqslant M/|p|^k$. Substituting $-i \int_C e^{pt} f(p)\, dp$ for the integral in (2.9.2) and dividing by $-i$, we obtain Lemma II.

Along AB, $p = x + iR$. Hence under the same hypotheses on $f(p)$ as in Lemma II, we have

$$|e^{pt} f(p)| = |e^{t(x+iR)} f(p)| \leqslant \frac{e^{tc} M}{R^k},$$

since $0 \leqslant x \leqslant c$ and $|x + iR| = \sqrt{x^2 + R^2} \geqslant R$. Therefore

$$\left| \int_{AB} e^{pt} f(p)\, dp \right| \leqslant \int_{AB} |e^{pt} f(p)|\, |dp| \leqslant \frac{ce^{tc} M}{R^k},$$

because $|dp| = c$, and consequently

$$\lim_{R \to \infty} \int_{AB} e^{pt} f(p)\, dp = 0.$$

The proof that $\lim_{R \to \infty} \int_{DE} e^{pt} f(p)\, dp = 0$ is similar. Thus we have proved

Lemma III. If $|f(p)| \leqslant M|p|^{-k}$ when $|p| > R_0$, where M, k are constants and $k > 0$, then

$$\lim_{R \to \infty} \int_{\Pi} e^{pt} f(p)\, dp = 0,$$

where Π is the contour $ABCDE$ of Fig. 2.9.1.

Since $\lim\limits_{R\to\infty} \int_{c-iR}^{c+iR} e^{pt} f(p)\, dp = 2\pi i\, F(t)$, we see from (2.9.1) that

(2.9.3) $L^{-1}\{f(p)\} = F(t) = \sum\limits_{i=1}^{n} \text{Residues of } e^{pt} f(p) \text{ at } p = p_i.$

Example 1.   Find $L^{-1}\left\{\dfrac{p}{p^2 + a^2}\right\}.$

Since $|f(p)| \leqslant \dfrac{|p|}{|p|^2 - a^2} < \dfrac{2}{|p|}$ for $|p| > a\sqrt{2}$, the function $f(p)$

$= \dfrac{p}{p^2 + a^2}$ clearly satisfies the conditions of Lemma III.   The poles of $f(p)$ occur at $p_1 = ai$, $p_2 = -ai$.   Now by formula (1.11.9)

$$\text{Res}\left[\frac{pe^{pt}}{p^2 + a^2}\right]_{p=ai} = \frac{aie^{ait}}{2ai} = \frac{e^{ait}}{2},$$

and

$$\text{Res}\left[\frac{pe^{pt}}{p^2 + a^2}\right]_{p=-ai} = \frac{-aie^{-ait}}{-2ai} = \frac{e^{-ait}}{2}.$$

Hence

$$L^{-1}\left\{\frac{p}{p^2 + a^2}\right\} = \sum_{i=1}^{2} \text{Res}_{p_i} \frac{pe^{pt}}{p^2 + a^2} = \frac{e^{ait} + e^{-ait}}{2} = \cos at.$$

Example 2.   Determine $L^{-1}\left\{\dfrac{1}{p^{n+1}}\right\}$, $n = 1, 2, 3, \cdots .$

Here again the function $f(p) = \dfrac{1}{p^{n+1}}$ satisfies the conditions of Lemma III.   The singularity of $f(p)$ consists of an $(n + 1)$-tuple pole at $p = 0$.   Therefore by formula (1.11.7)

$$\text{Res}\left[\frac{e^{pt}}{p^{n+1}}\right]_{p=0} = \frac{1}{n!}\lim_{p\to 0}\frac{d^n}{dp^n}\left(e^{pt}\right) = \lim_{p\to 0}\left(\frac{t^n e^{pt}}{n!}\right) = \frac{t^n}{n!}.$$

and

$$L^{-1}\left\{\frac{1}{p^{n+1}}\right\} = \frac{t^n}{n!},   n = 1, 2, 3, \cdots .$$

Thus far we have assumed that $f(p)$ has a *finite* number of poles—a situation that frequently arises in the solution of *ordinary differential equations*.   However, in the solution of some ordinary differential equations (section 4.7) and especially in the solution of *partial differential equations* an *infinite* number of poles is involved.   In that case we select the contour of Fig. 2.9.2 enclosing n poles and selecting a sequence of radii $\{R_n\}$ we pass to the limit as $n \to \infty$. The radii R_n are so chosen that the contours associated with them do not pass through any poles. Hence, for the case of a function $f(p)$ having an *infinite* number of poles and satisfying the conditions of Lemma III we have the formula

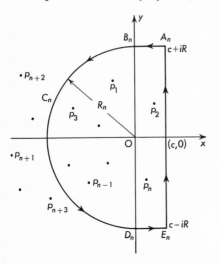

FIG. 2.9.2

$(2.9.4)$

$$L^{-1}\{f(p)\} = F(t)$$

$$= \sum_{i=1}^{\infty} \mathrm{Res}_{p_i}[e^{pt} f(p)].$$

Before proceeding with the determination of the inverse transform of the rational function, we shall make use of the following two properties which are direct consequences of the definition of the Laplace transformation:

(i) $L\{A_1 F_1(t) + A_2 F_2(t) + \cdots + A_n F_n(t)\}$
$$= A_1 L\{F_1(t)\} + A_2 L\{F_2(t)\} + \cdots + A_n L\{F_n(t)\}$$

and

(ii) $L^{-1}\{A_1 f_1(p) + A_2 f_2(p) + \cdots + A_n f_n(p)\}$
$$= A_1 L^{-1}\{f_1(p)\} + A_2 L^{-1}\{f_2(p)\} + \cdots + A_n L^{-1}\{f_n(p)\},$$

where $A_1, A_2, \cdots, A_n$ are constants.

We leave the verification of the preceding two properties to the reader as exercises. They state that the Laplace transformation and its inverse are *linear*.

2.10 The Inverse Transform of the Fractional Rational Function

The residue theorem enables us to express the inverse transform of a rational function, i.e., the quotient of two polynomials in a very convenient form.   Let,

$$f(p) = \frac{A(p)}{B(p)},$$

where $A(p)$ and $B(p)$ are polynomials having no common factors, and the degree of $B(p)$ is greater than the degree of $A(p)$.

Case I. $B(p)$ *has* n *distinct zeros* $p_1, p_2, \cdots, p_n$.   Since $f(p)$ satisfies the conditions of Lemma III, we have by (2.9.2)

$$(2.10.1) \qquad L^{-1}\left\{\frac{A(p)}{B(p)}\right\} = \sum \text{Res}_{p_i} \frac{e^{pt}A(p)}{B(p)}.$$

The residue at the simple pole $p = p_r$ is

$$\frac{e^{p_r t}A(p_r)}{B'(p_r)},$$

where $B'(p_r)$ is the derivative of $B(p)$ evaluated at $p = p_r$.   Hence, from (2.10.1) it follows that

$$(2.10.2) \qquad L^{-1}\left\{\frac{A(p)}{B(p)}\right\} = \sum_{r=1}^{n} \frac{e^{p_r t}A(p_r)}{B'(p_r)}.$$

The result just proved is often called Heaviside's expansion theorem or the "partial fraction" rule.

Example.   Find $L^{-1}\left\{\dfrac{p}{(p+1)(p+3)}\right\}$.   Since the zeros of the denominator occur at $p = -1$ and $p = -3$, while $B'(p) = 2p + 4$, we have

$$L^{-1}\left\{\frac{p}{(p+1)(p+3)}\right\} = \frac{-e^{-t}}{2} + \frac{3e^{-3t}}{2}.$$

Case II. $B(p)$ *is of degree* n *and has a zero* p_s *of multiplicity* m, i.e., a factor $(p - p_s)^m$ *and the remaining* $n - m$ *zeros are distinct.*   As before

$$L^{-1}\left\{\frac{A(p)}{B(p)}\right\} = \sum \text{Res}_{p_i} \frac{e^{pt}A(p)}{B(p)}.$$

The residue at the multiple pole $p = p_s$ is

$$\frac{1}{(m-1)!} \lim_{p \to p_s} \frac{d^{m-1}}{dp^{m-1}}\left[(p - p_s)^m \frac{e^{pt}A(p)}{B(p)}\right].$$

Therefore

$$(2.10.3) \qquad L^{-1}\left\{\frac{A(p)}{B(p)}\right\} = \sum_{r=1}^{n-m} \frac{e^{p_r t}A(p_r)}{B'(p_r)}$$

$$+ \frac{1}{(m-1)!} \lim_{p \to p_s} \frac{d^{m-1}}{dp^{m-1}}\left[(p - p_s)^m \frac{e^{pt}A(p)}{B(p)}\right].$$

The case in which $B(p)$ has more than one multiple zero is treated similarly.

Example.   Determine $L^{-1}\left\{\dfrac{1}{p^2(p+1)}\right\}$. $p = -1$ is a simple pole,

$p = 0$ is a pole of order $m = 2$ and $B'(p) = 3p^2 + 2p$. At $p = 0$,

$$\lim_{p \to 0} \frac{d}{dp} \left[\frac{e^{pt}}{p+1} \right] = t - 1. \quad \text{Therefore by (2.10.3)}$$

$$L^{-1} \left\{ \frac{1}{p^2(p+1)} \right\} = e^{-t} + t - 1.$$

2.11 The Inverse Transform of $e^{-a\sqrt{p}}/p \ (a \geqslant 0)$

In the solution of certain linear partial differential equations to be considered later on, it is necessary to determine the inverse transforms of certain important functions. One of these is

$$(2.11.1) \qquad f(p) = e^{-a\sqrt{p}}/p, \quad (a \geqslant 0)$$

whose transform we shall now determine by means of contour integration.

By the complex inversion integral, we have

$$(2.11.2) \qquad F(t) = L^{-1}\{e^{-a\sqrt{p}}/p\} = \frac{1}{2\pi i} \lim_{R \to \infty} \int_{c-iR}^{c+iR} e^{pt - a\sqrt{p}} \frac{dp}{p}.$$

Since the integrand has a branch point at the origin, we must introduce a cut or barrier to render it single valued and then select an appropriate path to evaluate this integral. There are many ways in which this can be done. We shall choose the negative real axis as the cut. By so doing, the functions $\sqrt{p}$ and $e^{-a\sqrt{p}}$ become single valued for $-\pi < \theta < \pi$, and a part of the integration can be done in terms of real variables.

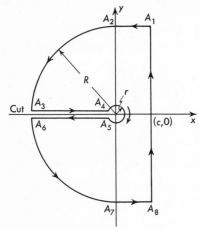

The problem now is to evaluate

$$\frac{1}{2\pi i} \int e^{pt - a\sqrt{p}} \frac{dp}{p}$$

over the closed circuit shown in Fig. 2.11.1. By Cauchy's theorem this integral is zero.

Since for any point p on either of the arcs $A_2 A_3$ and $A_6 A_7$ we have

FIG. 2.11.1

$$p = Re^{i\theta} \text{ and } \sqrt{p} = R^{\frac{1}{2}}e^{i(\theta/2)}, \text{ where}$$

$\pi/2 \leqslant \theta < \pi$ when p is on arc $A_2 A_3$ and $-\pi < \theta \leqslant -\pi/2$ when p is on arc $A_6 A_7$, then

$$\left| \frac{e^{-a\sqrt{p}}}{p} \right| = \frac{e^{-aR^{\frac{1}{2}} \cos(\theta/2)}}{R}.$$

Furthermore, because $a \geqslant 0$ and $\cos(\theta/2) > 0$ in the intervals mentioned above, $e^{-aR^{\frac{1}{2}}\cos(\theta/2)} \leqslant 1$ and hence we can write

$$\left| \frac{e^{-a\sqrt{p}}}{p} \right| \leqslant \frac{1}{R}.$$

The conditions of Lemma III are now satisfied and the integrals along the arcs A_2A_3 and A_6A_7 tend to zero as $R \to \infty$.

For a point on A_1A_2 we have $p = x + iR = \sqrt{x^2 + R^2}\, e^{i(\theta/2)}$,

$$0 \leqslant x \leqslant c, \quad \sqrt{p} = \sqrt[4]{x^2 + R^2}\left(\cos\frac{\theta}{2} + i\sin\frac{\theta}{2}\right) \text{ and}$$

$$\left| \frac{e^{-a\sqrt{p}}}{p} \right| = \frac{e^{-a\sqrt[4]{x^2+R^2}\cos(\theta/2)}}{R}.$$

Again, since $0 < \theta \leqslant \pi/2$, $\cos(\theta/2) > 0$ and therefore $|e^{-a\sqrt{p}}/p| \leqslant 1/R$ and the integral along A_1A_2 vanishes as $R \to \infty$.

In the same way we show that for any point $p = x - iR$ on A_7A_8 the integral along A_7A_8 vanishes as $R \to \infty$.

Therefore we have

(2.11.3)
$$\frac{1}{2\pi i}\int_{c-i\infty}^{c+i\infty} e^{pt-a\sqrt{p}}\frac{dp}{p} + \lim_{R\to\infty}\frac{1}{2\pi i}\int_{A_3A_4} e^{pt-a\sqrt{p}}\frac{dp}{p}$$

$$+ \lim_{r\to 0}\frac{1}{2\pi i}\int_{C_r} e^{pt-a\sqrt{p}}\frac{dp}{p} + \lim_{R\to\infty}\frac{1}{2\pi i}\int_{A_5A_6} e^{pt-a\sqrt{p}}\frac{dp}{p} = 0,$$

where C_r is the circle of radius r enclosing the branch point at the origin. In the limit as $r \to 0$, $p = \rho e^{i\pi}$ and $p = \rho e^{-i\pi}$ on the lines A_3A_4 and A_6A_5, respectively.

Hence for A_3A_4: $\sqrt{p} = \sqrt{\rho}\, e^{i(\pi/2)} = i\sqrt{\rho}$ and

$$\lim_{R\to\infty}\frac{1}{2\pi i}\int_{A_3A_4} e^{pt-a\sqrt{p}}\frac{dp}{p} = \frac{1}{\pi}\int_{\infty}^{0} e^{-\rho t}\left(\frac{e^{-ai\sqrt{\rho}}}{2i}\right)\frac{d\rho}{\rho},$$

while for A_5A_6: $\sqrt{p} = \sqrt{\rho}\, e^{-i(\pi/2)} = -i\sqrt{\rho}$ and

$$\lim_{R\to\infty}\frac{1}{2\pi i}\int_{A_5A_6} e^{pt-a\sqrt{p}}\frac{dp}{p} = \frac{1}{\pi}\int_{0}^{\infty} e^{-\rho t}\left(\frac{e^{ai\sqrt{\rho}}}{2i}\right)\frac{d\rho}{\rho}.$$

The sum of the integrals on the right side of the preceding two equalities gives:

$$\frac{1}{\pi}\int_{0}^{\infty} e^{-\rho t}\cdot\frac{e^{ai\rho}-e^{-ai\rho}}{2i}\,\frac{d\rho}{\rho} = \frac{1}{\pi}\int_{0}^{\infty} e^{-\rho t}\sin a\sqrt{\rho}\,\frac{d\rho}{\rho},$$

which becomes

(2.11.4)
$$\frac{2}{\pi}\int_{0}^{\infty} e^{-tv^2}\sin av\,\frac{dv}{v}$$

when the substitution $\sqrt{\rho} = v$ is made.

From a table of integrals* we find that

(2.11.5) $$\int_0^\infty e^{-tv^2} \cos av \, dv = \frac{\sqrt{\pi} e^{-a^2/4t}}{2\sqrt{t}}, \quad t > 0.$$

If we multiply both sides of (2.11.5) by $\dfrac{2}{\pi}$ and integrate from 0 to a, then

(2.11.6) $$\frac{\pi}{2}\int_0^\infty e^{-tv^2}\left\{\int_0^a (\cos av)(v)\, da\right\}\frac{dv}{v} = \frac{2}{\sqrt{\pi}}\int_0^a e^{-a^2/4t}\frac{da}{2\sqrt{t}},$$

and, after carrying out the integration on the left side, we arrive at the following result

(2.11.7) $$\frac{2}{\pi}\int_0^\infty e^{-tv^2} \sin av \, \frac{dv}{v} = \frac{2}{\sqrt{\pi}}\int_0^{a/2\sqrt{t}} e^{-\xi^2}\, d\xi = \mathrm{erf}\left(\frac{a}{2\sqrt{t}}\right),$$

where $\mathrm{erf}\, x = \dfrac{2}{\sqrt{\pi}}\displaystyle\int_0^x e^{-\xi^2}\, d\xi$ is the so-called *error function*.

In order to obtain (2.11.7) it was necessary to change the order of integration in the left member of (2.10.6) from $\int_0^a \int_0^\infty$ to $\int_0^\infty \int_0^a$. This interchange is valid because of the continuity of $e^{-tv^2}\cos av$ with respect to a as well as v and the uniform convergence of $\int_0^\infty e^{-tv^2}\cos av \, dv$.†

The integral along the small circle C_r can be evaluated by making the substitution $p = re^{i\theta}$, $dp = rie^{i\theta}\, d\theta$ in the third integral of equality (2.11.3). Thus
(2.11.8)

$$\lim_{r\to 0}\frac{1}{2\pi i}\int_{C_r} e^{pt-a\sqrt{p}}\frac{dp}{p} = \frac{1}{2\pi i}\int_\pi^{-\pi}\lim_{r\to 0} e^{rte^{i\theta}-a\sqrt{r}\, e^{i(\theta/2)}}i\, d\theta = \frac{1}{2\pi}\int_\pi^{-\pi}d\theta = -1.$$

The operation of taking the limit inside the integral sign is valid because the integrand is a continuous function of r and θ. Substituting this result and that of (2.11.7) in (2.11.3) and transposing, we finally obtain

(2.11.9) $$L^{-1}\{e^{-a\sqrt{p}}/p\} = \frac{1}{2\pi i}\int_{c-i\infty}^{c+i\infty} e^{pt-a\sqrt{p}}\frac{dp}{p} = 1 - \mathrm{erf}\left(\frac{a}{2\sqrt{t}}\right)$$

$$= \mathrm{erfc}\left(\frac{a}{2\sqrt{t}}\right), \quad a \geqslant 0, \, t > 0$$

where $\mathrm{erfc}\, x = 1 - \mathrm{erf}\, x = \dfrac{2}{\sqrt{\pi}}\displaystyle\int_x^\infty e^{-\xi^2}\, d\xi$ is the so-called *complementary error function*.

* See e.g., *Mathematical Tables from the Handbook of Chemistry and Physics*, Seventh Edition.
† I. S. Sokolnikoff, *Advanced Calculus*, McGraw-Hill Book Co., New York, 1939, p. 356.

Exercise. By contour integration show that

$$L^{-1}\{e^{-a\sqrt{p}}\} = \frac{a}{2\sqrt{\pi t^3}} \exp\left(-\frac{a^2}{4t}\right), \quad a > 0, t > 0.$$

PROBLEMS

1. Verify the following transformations (a, b, and c are real numbers):

(a) $L\{\sinh at\} = \dfrac{a}{p^2 - a^2}$, $\mathrm{Re}(p) > |a|$,

(b) $L\{\cosh at\} = \dfrac{p}{p^2 - a^2}$, $\mathrm{Re}(p) > |a|$,

(c) $L\{t^n\} = \dfrac{n!}{p^{n+1}}$, $n = 1, 2, 3, \cdots$; $\mathrm{Re}(p) > 0$,

(d) $L\{t^n e^{at}\} = \dfrac{n!}{(p - a)^{n+1}}$, $n = 1, 2, 3, \cdots$; $\mathrm{Re}(p) > a$,

(e) $L\{e^{-at} \sin bt\} = \dfrac{b}{(p + a)^2 + b^2}$, $\mathrm{Re}(p) > -a$,

(f) $L\{e^{-at} \cos bt\} = \dfrac{p + a}{(p + a)^2 + b^2}$, $\mathrm{Re}(p) > -a$.

2. Verify the following inverse transforms:

(a) $L^{-1}\left\{\dfrac{1}{p^2 + a^2}\right\} = \dfrac{\sin at}{a}$,

(b) $L^{-1}\left\{\dfrac{1}{p^2 - a^2}\right\} = \dfrac{\sinh at}{a}$,

(c) $L^{-1}\left\{\dfrac{p}{p^2 - a^2}\right\} = \cosh at$,

(d) $L^{-1}\left\{\dfrac{1}{(p + a)^2 + b^2}\right\} = \dfrac{e^{-at} \sin bt}{b}$,

(e) $L^{-1}\left\{\dfrac{p + a}{(p + a)^2 + b^2}\right\} = e^{-at} \cos bt$,

(f) $L^{-1}\left\{\dfrac{1}{(p - a)^{n+1}}\right\} = \dfrac{t^n e^{-at}}{n!}$, $n = 1, 2, 3, \cdots$.

3. Find the inverse transforms of the following:

(a) $\dfrac{1}{p(p+a)(p+b)}$,

(b) $\dfrac{p+a}{(p+b)(p+c)^2}$,

(c) $\dfrac{1}{p^4-a^4}$,

(d) $\dfrac{1}{(p^2+a^2)^2}$,

(e) $\dfrac{p^2-a^2}{(p^2+a^2)^2}$,

(f) $\dfrac{1}{p^2(p^2+a^2)}$.

Check your results by referring to the Table of Laplace Transforms in Appendix C.

CHAPTER III

Properties of the Laplace Transformation

3.1 Transforms of Derivatives

One operational property of the Laplace transform was already given in the previous chapter, namely, that it is linear. In this chapter we shall derive further operational properties of great usefulness and importance in the solution of problems in applied mathematics.

Theorem 1. *Let $F(t)$ be continuous and $F'(t)$ sectionally continuous in every finite interval $0 \leqslant t \leqslant T$. If $F(t)$ is, in addition, of the order $e^{c_0 t}$ as $t \to \infty$, then when* $\mathrm{Re}(p) > c_0$.

$$(3.1.1) \qquad L\{F'(t)\} = pf(p) - F(0+).$$

Making use of the integration by parts formula, we have

$$(3.1.2) \qquad L\{F'(t)\} = \lim_{T \to \infty} e^{-pt} F(t) \Big]_{0+}^{T} + \lim_{T \to \infty} p \int_{0}^{T} e^{-pt} F(t)\, dt.$$

Now, since $F(t)$ is of $0(e^{-c_0 t})$ as $t \to \infty$,

$$|e^{-pT} F(t)| < M e^{-(c-c_0)T},$$

where $c = \mathrm{Re}(p)$. Hence, when $c > c_0$ the right-hand side of the inequality vanishes as $T \to \infty$. Consequently $\lim\limits_{T \to \infty} e^{-pt} F(t) \Big]_{0+}^{T} = -F(0+)$

and $\lim\limits_{T \to \infty} \int_{0}^{T} e^{-pt} F(t)\, dt = L\{F(t)\} = f(p)$. From this we get formula (1). It is this property that will be of great use to us when we come to solve differential equations.

Suppose now that $F'(t)$ is continuous (which implies that $F(t)$ is continuous) and $F''(t)$ is sectionally continuous. Then integrating by parts as before, we get

$$L\{F''(t)\} = e^{-pt} F'(t) \Big]_{0+}^{T} + pL\{F'(t)\}.$$

If $F'(t)$ and $F(t)$ are assumed to be of exponential order, then $\lim_{t\to\infty} e^{-pt} F'(t) = 0$ and this combined with (3.1.1) gives

$$L\{F''(t)\} = p^2 f(p) - pF(0+) - F'(0+).$$

By considering

$$L\{F^{(n)}(t)\} = pL\{F^{(n-1)}(t)\} - F^{(n-1)}(0+)$$

and proceeding by induction, we obtain the following

Theorem 2. If $F(t)$, $F'(t)$, $\cdots$, $F^{(n-1)}(t)$ are continuous over every interval $0 \leqslant t \leqslant T$, $F^{(n)}(t)$ is sectionally continuous over the same interval and $F(t)$, $F'(t)$, $\cdots$, $F^{(n)}(t)$ are of the order $e^{-c_0 t}$ as t becomes infinite, then when $\mathrm{Re}(p) > c_0$
(3.1.3)

$$L\{F^{(n)}(t)\} = p^n f(p) - p^{n-1}F(0+) - p^{n-2}F'(0+) - \cdots - F^{(n-1)}(0+).$$

Although the conditions on $F(t)$ of the preceding theorem are somewhat restrictive in character, the usefulness of the theorem is not greatly impaired because most of the functions arising in the applications satisfy these conditions.

Example. Let $F(t) = \cos at$. Since $F(t)$ and $F'(t) = -a\sin at$ are bounded, they are of exponential order. Also $L\{\cos at\} = \dfrac{p}{p^2 + a^2}$, therefore

$$L\{-a\sin at\} = p \cdot \frac{p}{p^2 + a^2} - F(0+)$$

or

$$-aL\{\sin at\} = \frac{p^2}{p^2 + a^2} - 1 = \frac{a^2}{p^2 + a^2},$$

from which

$$L\{\sin at\} = \frac{a}{p^2 + a^2}.$$

Exercise. Find the formula that would replace (3.1.1) if $F(t)$ were assumed continuous, except at $t = T_0 (0 < T_0 < T)$, where it has a finite discontinuity.

3.2 Transform of an Integral

The following theorem establishes an operational property which involves an integral.

Theorem 3. If $F(t)$ is sectionally continuous and of exponential order, then the transform of the integral of $F(t)$ evaluated between 0 and t is equal to the transform of $F(t)$ divided by p.

Making use of the integration by parts formula, we obtain

$$L\left\{\int_0^t F(\tau)\,d\tau\right\} = \int_0^\infty e^{-pt}\left\{\int_0^t F(\tau)\,d\tau\right\}dt$$

$$= -\frac{e^{-pt}}{p}\int_0^t F(\tau)\,d\tau\Big]_0^\infty + \frac{1}{p}\int_0^\infty e^{-pt}\,F(t)\,dt.$$

Since $F(t)$ is sectionally continuous and of exponential order, $\int_0^t F(\tau)\,d\tau$ is *continuous* and also of exponential order, say of $O(e^{c_0 t})$.   (Prove this.) Hence, if $\mathrm{Re}(p) = x > c_0$, then the integrated part will vanish as $t \to \infty$ and as $t \to 0+$.   Therefore,

(3.2.1) $$L\left\{\int_0^t F(\tau)\,d\tau\right\} = \frac{f(p)}{p},$$

or

(3.2.2) $$L^{-1}\left\{\frac{f(p)}{p}\right\} = \int_0^t F(\tau)\,d\tau.$$

A repeated use of this formula yields

(3.2.3) $$L^{-1}\left\{\frac{f(p)}{p^2}\right\} = \int_0^t\int_0^{t_1} F(t_2)dt_2\,dt,$$

(3.2.4) $$L^{-1}\left\{\frac{f(p)}{p^3}\right\} = \int_0^t\int_0^{t_1}\int_0^{t_2} F(t_3)dt_3\,dt_2\,dt_1,\ \text{etc.}$$

Remark.   We have noted that if $F(t)$ is sectionally continuous and of exponential order then $\int_0^t F(\tau)\,d\tau$ is continuous and also of ex-

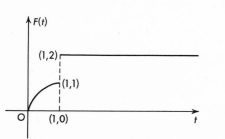

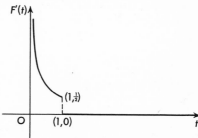

FIG. 3.2.1   FIG. 3.2.2

ponential order.   This cannot be said in general of the derivative of $F(t)$.   For instance, the sectionally continuous function (Fig. 3.2.1)

$$F(t) = \sqrt{t},\ \ 0 \leqslant t \leqslant 1$$
$$= 2,\ \ t > 1$$

has as its derivative the function (Fig. 3.2.2)

$$F'(t) = \frac{1}{2\sqrt{t}}, \quad 0 < t \leqslant 1$$
$$= 0, \quad t > 1,$$

which has an infinite discontinuity at $t = 0$.

The function $\cos e^{t^2}$ is clearly bounded and therefore of exponential order. However, its derivative $- 2te^{t^2} \sin e^{t^2}$ is *not* of exponential order.

Nevertheless, many of the functions arising in the practical applications are such that not only they, but their derivatives are sectionally continuous and of exponential order.

Exercise. Show that

$$L\left\{\int_{t_0}^{t} F(\tau) \, d\tau\right\} = \frac{1}{p} f(p) - \frac{1}{p} \int_0^{t_0} F(\tau) \, d\tau, \quad t_0 > 0.$$

3.3 The Unit Step Function

A function that will play a useful role in the further development of the operational method is the unit step function (Fig. 3.3.1) defined as follows:

$$(3.3.1) \qquad\qquad 1(t - t_0) = 0, \quad t < t_0$$
$$= 1, \quad t \geqslant t_0.$$

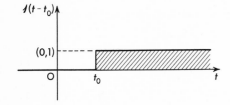

FIG. 3.3.1   FIG. 3.3.2

Its transform is

(3.3.2)

$$L\{1(t - t_0)\} = \int_{t_0}^{\infty} e^{-pt} \, dt = \frac{e^{-pt_0}}{p}.$$

In particular, if $t_0 = 0$ we have

$$(3.3.3) \qquad\qquad 1(t) = 0, \quad t < 0$$
$$= 1, \quad t \geqslant 0.$$

This function (Fig. 3.3.2), which was much used by Heaviside, is known as Heaviside's unit function. From (3.3.2) its transform is seen to be

$$(3.3.4) \qquad\qquad L\{1(t)\} = \frac{1}{p}.$$

By compounding the unit step function appropriately, many functions can be expressed analytically in terms of it. For example, the function shown in (Fig. 3.3.3) can be represented as

$$F(t) = a\{\, 1(t) - 1(t - a)$$
$$+\ 1(t - 2a) - 1(t - 3a) + \cdots \}$$
$$= a \sum_{n=0}^{\infty} (-1)^n 1(t - na).$$

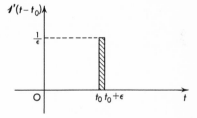

FIG. 3.3.3

Exercise. Assuming that the order of the operators $\sum\limits_{0}^{\infty}$ and $\int_{0}^{\infty}$ can be interchanged, show that the transform of the preceding function is $\dfrac{a}{p(1 + e^{-ap})}$, $\mathrm{Re}(p) > 0$.

3.4 The Unit Impulse

In many of the problems in applied mathematics, electrical and mechanical systems are encountered in which the forces acting on them are of an impulsive character, i.e., forces which act on the system for a very short duration of time. For example, in mechanics problems occur in which a system is set in motion by blows and in electrical systems impulsive voltages are often applied to circuits. In other applications it is desirable to have a representation of a force distributed over a small interval as a concentrated force and vice versa.

A function that is very large in a very small region, zero outside it, and such that its integral over the region is finite serves to characterize adequately the situations encountered in the solution of certain physical problems. Many such functions have been constructed and one of the simplest is the *unit impulse* (Fig. 3.4.1) defined as follows:

$$1'(t - t_0) = \lim_{\epsilon \to 0} \frac{1(t - t_0) - 1(t - t_0 - \epsilon)}{\epsilon}.$$

As is seen, the area of the shaded region is unity. The unit impulse function was extensively used by Dirac and is known among physicists as the Dirac $\delta(t)$-function.

It should be observed that the unit impulse $1'(t - t_0)$ is not a function in the usual mathematical sense. It has been introduced simply because a *formal* use of it leads to results that are capable of being interpreted physically.* Thus, suppose that a mechanical system is given an impulse of magnitude I (lb sec) at time $t = t_0$. Then we can think of the impulsive force F (lb) as given by

$$F = \lim_{\epsilon \to 0} I \cdot \frac{1(t - t_0) - 1(t - t_0 - \epsilon)}{\epsilon} = I \cdot 1'(t - t_0).$$

It is clear from the preceding relation that $1'(t - t_0)$ has the dimensions of $(\text{time})^{-1}$.

Similarly, in dealing with a concentrated load F (lb) acting on a beam at $x = x_0$, we consider it as being replaced by the limit of the distributed load F/ϵ (lb per unit length) acting over the distance ϵ, i.e., by

$$\lim_{\epsilon \to 0} F \frac{1(x - x_0) - 1(x - x_0 - \epsilon)}{\epsilon} = F 1'(x - x_0).$$

Let us compute the Laplace transform of $1'(t - t_0)$. Using L'Hospital's rule, we have

$$L\{1'(t - t_0)\} = \int_0^\infty e^{pt} 1'(t - t_0) \, dt = \lim_{\epsilon \to 0} \frac{1}{\epsilon} \int_{t_0}^{t_0+\epsilon} e^{-pt} \, dt$$

$$= \lim_{\epsilon \to 0} \frac{e^{-pt_0} - e^{-p(t_0+\epsilon)}}{p\epsilon} = \lim_{\epsilon \to 0} e^{-p(t_0+\epsilon)} = e^{-pt_0}.$$

Therefore

(3.4.1) $$L\{1'(t - t_0)\} = e^{-pt_0}.$$

In particular, for $t_0 = 0$

(3.4.2) $$L\{1'(t)\} = 1.$$

A result that will be useful later on is the following:

If $F(t)$ is a continuous function in the closed interval $(0, t)$, then

(3.4.3) $$\int_0^t F(\tau) 1'(\tau - t_0) \, d\tau = F(t_0) 1(t - t_0).$$

(a) When $t < t_0$ it is clear that

$$\int_0 F(\tau) 1'(\tau - t_0) \, d\tau = 0.$$

(b) In the interval $t_0 \leqslant t \leqslant t_0 + \epsilon$, we have

$$\int_0^t F(\tau) 1'(\tau - t_0) \, d\tau = \lim_{\epsilon \to 0} \frac{1}{\epsilon} \int_{t_0}^{t_0+\epsilon} F(\tau) \, d\tau.$$

Now by the mean value theorem of the integral calculus

$$\int_{t_0}^{t_0+\epsilon} F(\tau) \, d\tau = \epsilon F(\xi), \quad \text{where } t_0 \leqslant \xi \leqslant t_0 + \epsilon.$$

---

* For a method that justifies not only the use of the δ-function, but also the use of all its derivatives see Laurent Schwartz, *Théorie des distributions*, Hermann, Paris, 1950.

Therefore

$$\lim_{\epsilon \to 0} \frac{1}{\epsilon} \int_{t_0}^{t_0+\epsilon} F(\tau)\, d\tau = \lim_{\epsilon \to 0} \frac{1}{\epsilon} \cdot \epsilon F(\xi) = F(t_0),$$

since $\xi \to t_0$ as $\epsilon \to 0$.

(c) When $t > t_0 + \epsilon$, the integral in (3.4.3) will be the sum of the results obtained in (a) and (b). Consequently, in all cases

$$\int_0^t F(\tau) 1'(\tau - t_0)\, d\tau = F(t_0) 1(t - t_0), \text{ q.e.d.}$$

For the infinite interval $(0, \infty)$ it is clear that we have simply

$$\int_0^\infty F(\tau) 1'(\tau - t_0)\, d\tau = F(t_0).$$

It is possible to define successive derivatives of $1'(t - t_0)$. For example,

$$1''(t - t_0) = \lim_{\epsilon \to 0} \frac{1'(t - t_0) - 1'(t - t_0 - \epsilon)}{\epsilon},$$

and in general

$$1^{(n)}(t - t_0) = \lim_{\epsilon \to 0} \frac{1^{(n-1)}(t - t_0) - 1^{(n-1)}(t - t_0 - \epsilon)}{\epsilon}.$$

However, beyond $n = 2$ these occur infrequently in practice and will not be treated here.

Exercise. The function $1''(x - x_0)$ is often called the *unit doublet*. Draw its graph and interpret it as a couple of unit moment applied at $x = x_0$ in a counterclockwise direction which will be construed as a *positive* moment. Thus, if a couple of moment M_0 is applied to a beam at the point $x = x_0$, then it may be represented as a distributed load $M_0 1''(x - x_0)$. Show that

$$L\{1''(x - x_0)\} = pe^{-x_0 p}.$$

3.5 Translation Theorem I

If $L\{F(t)\} = f(p)$, *then for any real constant $a > 0$,*
$$(3.5.1) \qquad L^{-1}\{e^{-ap} f(p)\} = F(t - a) 1(t - a).$$
For,

$$L\{F(t - a) 1(t - a)\} = \int_0^\infty e^{-pt} F(t - a) 1(t - a)\, dt = \int_a^\infty e^{-pt} F(t - a)\, dt.$$

Making the substitutions $t - a = \tau$, $dt = d\tau$, we have

$$L\{F(t - a) 1 t - a)\} = \int_0^\infty e^{-p(\tau+a)} F(\tau)\, d\tau$$
$$= e^{-ap} \int_0^\infty e^{-p\tau} F(\tau)\, d\tau = e^{-ap} f(p),$$

and hence by taking the inverses of both sides we obtain (3.5.1).

Thus we see that the multiplication of the transform of $F(t)$ by e^{-ap} gives the Laplace transform of the function $F(t-a)1(t-a)$ which is identically equal to zero for $t < a$ and $F(t)$ for $t \geqslant a$. This result can

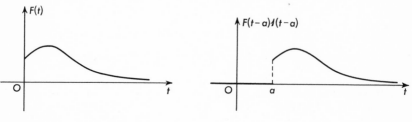

Fig. 3.5.1   Fig. 3.5.2

therefore be interpreted as a translation of $F(t)$ a units to the right (Figs. 3.5.1 and 3.5.2).

Example. Since

$$L^{-1}\left\{\frac{p}{p^2 - k^2}\right\} = \cosh kt,$$

we have

$$L^{-1}\left\{\frac{pe^{-ap}}{p^2 - k^2}\right\} = \cosh k(t-a)1(t-a).$$

Translation Theorem II. *If $L\{F(t)\} = f(p)$, then for any constant a,*

(3.5.2) $L^{-1}\{f(p+a)\} = e^{-at} F(t), \quad \mathrm{Re}(p+a) > c_0.$

Let us assume that $F(t)$ is of $O(e^{-c_0 t})$ as t becomes infinite. Then

$$L\{e^{-at} F(t)\} = \int_0^\infty e^{-pt} e^{-at} F(t) \, dt = \int_0^\infty e^{-(p+a)t} F(t) \, dt$$
$$= f(p+a), \quad \mathrm{Re}(p+a) > c_0.$$

From this result we immediately have (3.5.2).

It will be observed that whereas multiplying the function $f(p)$ by e^{-ap} corresponds to a translation of the function $F(t)$ in the real plane, the multiplication of $F(t)$ by e^{-at} corresponds to a translation of the function $f(p)$ in the complex plane.

Example. Since

$$L^{-1}\left\{\frac{1}{p^2 + a^2}\right\} = \frac{\sin at}{a},$$

then

$$L^{-1}\left\{\frac{1}{(p-a)^2 + a^2}\right\} = \frac{e^{at} \sin at}{a}.$$

3.6 Derivatives of Transforms

Theorem 4. If $F(t)$ is sectionally continuous and of the order $e^{c_0 t}$ as $t \to \infty$, then when $\text{Re}(p) > c_0$.

$$(3.6.1) \qquad f^{(n)}(p) = L\{(-t)^n F(t)\}, \quad n = 1, 2, \cdots.$$

For the type of function $F(t)$ being considered here, it can be shown that differentiating $f(p) = \int_0^\infty e^{-pt} F(t)\, dt$ with respect to p under the integral sign is a valid operation. Therefore, we have

$$f'(p) = \int_0^\infty \frac{\partial}{\partial p}[e^{-pt} F(t)]\, dt = \int_0^\infty - t e^{-pt} F(t)\, dt = L\{-tF(t)\},$$

$$f^{(2)}(p) = \int_0^\infty \frac{\partial}{\partial p}[- t e^{-pt} F(t)]\, dt = \int_0^\infty t^2 e^{-pt} F(t)\, dt = L\{t^2 F(t)\},$$

$$\cdot \quad \cdot \quad \cdot \quad \cdot \quad \cdot \quad \cdot \quad \cdot \quad \cdot \quad \cdot \quad \cdot \quad \cdot \quad \cdot \quad \cdot \quad \cdot$$

$$f^{(n)}(p) = \int_0^\infty \frac{\partial}{\partial p}[(-t)^{n-1} e^{-pt} F(t)]\, dt = \int_0^\infty (-t)^n e^{-pt} F(t)\, dt$$

$$= L\{(-t)^n F(t)\}.$$

This result is useful in the solution of differential equations whose coefficients are polynomials in the variable t.

Example. Determine $L\{t^n e^{at}\}$.
We have

$$\frac{1}{p - a} = L\{e^{at}\}, \quad \text{Re}(p) > a.$$

Now, by (3.6.1)

$$\frac{d^n}{dp^n}\left(\frac{1}{p - a}\right) = \frac{(-1)^n n!}{(p - a)^{n+1}} = L\{(-t)^n e^{at}\}.$$

Therefore

$$L\{t^n e^{at}\} = \frac{n!}{(p - a)^{n+1}}, \quad n = 0, 1, 2, \cdots, \text{Re}(p) > a.$$

3.7 The Convolution or Faltung Theorem

Suppose that $F_1(t)$ and $F_2(t)$ are any two sectionally continuous functions defined for $t \geqslant 0$ and such that $F_1(t)$ and $F_2(t)$ are equal to zero for $t < 0$. Then the integral of $F_1(\tau)F_2(t - \tau)$ from 0 to t is called the *convolution* or *faltung* of $F_1(t)$ and $F_2(t)$, and we denote it by $F_1 * F_2$. Thus, symbolically,

$$(3.7.1) \qquad F_1 * F_2 = \int_0^t F_1(\tau)F_2(t - \tau)\, d\tau.$$

By making the substitution $t - \tau = \mu$ in (3.7.1), we get

$$F_1 * F_2 = - \int_t^0 F_1(t - \mu) F_2(\mu) \, d\mu = \int_0^t F_2(\mu) F_1(t - \mu) \, d\mu = F_2 * F_1.$$

We therefore see that the functions F_1 and F_2 commute in the convolution, i.e.,

$$F_1 * F_2 = F_2 * F_1.$$

Theorem 5. *Let $F_1(t)$ and $F_2(t)$ be sectionally continuous for $t > 0$ and 0 for $t < 0$ and of $O(e^{c_0 t})$ as $t \to \infty$. Then*

$$L\{F_1\} \cdot L\{F_2\} = L\{F_1 * F_2\}, \quad \mathrm{Re}(p) > c_0.$$

Let

(3.7.2) $$L\{F_1\} = f_1(p) = \int_0^\infty e^{-p\tau} F_1(\tau) \, d\tau,$$

(3.7.3) $$L\{F_2\} = f_2(p) = \int_0^\infty e^{-pv} F(v) \, dv.$$

Since the integrals (3.7.2) and (3.7.3) are absolutely convergent when $\mathrm{Re}(p) > c_0$, we can write

$$f_1(p) f_2(p) = \left[\int_0^\infty e^{-p\tau} F_1(\tau) \, d\tau \right] \left[\int_0^\infty e^{-pv} F_2(v) \, dv \right]$$

$$= \int_0^\infty \int_0^\infty e^{-(\tau + v)} F_1(\tau) F_2(v) \, d\tau \, dv$$

$$= \int_0^\infty F_1(\tau) \left\{ \int_0^\infty e^{-p(\tau + v)} F_2(v) \, dv \right\} d\tau.$$

If we make the substitutions $\tau + v = t$, $dv = dt$, then

$$\int_0^\infty e^{-p(\tau + v)} F_2(v) \, dv = \int_\tau^\infty e^{-pt} F_2(t - \tau) \, dt$$

$$= \int_0^\infty e^{-pt} F_2(t - \tau) \, dt,$$

because $F_2(t - \tau) = 0$ for $t < \tau$ and hence $\int_0^\tau e^{-pt} F_1(t - \tau) \, dt = 0$.

Therefore

$$f_1(p) f_2(p) = \int_0^\infty F_1(\tau) \left\{ \int_0^\infty e^{-pt} F_2(t - \tau) \, dt \right\} d\tau$$

$$= \int_0^\infty \int_0^\infty e^{-pt} \{ F_1(\tau) F_2(t - \tau) \, dt \} \, d\tau.$$

But the last double integral is equal to the iterated integral

$$\int_0^\infty e^{-pt} \left\{ \int_0^\infty F_1(\tau) F_2(t - \tau) \, d\tau \right\} dt.$$

Consequently

$$f_1(p)f_2(p) = L\left\{\int_0^\infty F_1(\tau)F_2(t-\tau)\,d\tau\right\}$$

$$= L\left\{\int_0^t F_1(\tau)F_2(t-\tau)\,d\tau\right\},$$

because $F_2(t-\tau) = 0$ when $\tau > t$. Thus we obtain

$$L\{F_1\} \cdot L\{F_2\} = L\{F_1 * F_2\}.$$

The preceding operational rule permits one to determine the inverse transforms of products of transforms, since it is equivalent to the relation

$$L^{-1}\{f_1(p)f_2(p)\} = F_1(t) * F_2(t).$$

Example 1. Determine the inverse Laplace transform of $\dfrac{1}{p(p+1)}$.

We have

$$L^{-1}\left\{\frac{1}{p(p+1)}\right\} = 1 * e^{-t}$$

$$= \int_0^t e^{-\tau}d\tau = 1 - e^{-t}.$$

Example 2. Find the inverse transform of $1/(p^2+1)^2$. As before

$$L^{-1}\left\{\frac{1}{(p^2+1)^2}\right\} = \sin t * \sin t = \int_0^t \sin(t-\tau)\sin\tau\,d\tau$$

$$= \tfrac{1}{2}\int_0^t [\cos(t-2\tau) - \cos t]\,d\tau$$

$$= -\tfrac{1}{4}\sin(t-2\tau)\Big]_0^t - \tfrac{1}{2}\tau\cos t\Big]_0^t$$

$$= \tfrac{1}{2}\sin t - \tfrac{1}{2}t\cos t.$$

3.8 Transforms of Periodic Functions

Let us suppose that $F(t)$ is a periodic function of period T, so that

$$F(t+T) = F(t), \quad t > 0.$$

Furthermore, let $F(t)$ be sectionally continuous over the period $0 < t < T$. Then its Laplace transform is given by

$$(3.8.1) \qquad f(p) = \int_0^\infty e^{-pt}F(t)\,dt = \sum_{n=0}^\infty \int_{nT}^{(n+1)T} e^{-pt}F(t)\,dt.$$

If we make the substitution $t = t' + nT$, then because of the periodicity of $F(t)$, $F(t'+nT) = F(t')$, and from (3.8.1) we get

$$(3.8.2) \qquad f(p) = \sum_{n=0}^\infty e^{-npT}\int_0^T e^{-pt'}F(t')\,dt'.$$

Now $|e^{-pnT}| = e^{-nTRe(p)}$. Taking $\mathrm{Re}(p) > 0$, we have $e^{-nTRe(p)} < 1$ and hence $\sum\limits_{n=0}^{\infty} e^{-npT} = 1/(1 - e^{-pT})$ and from (3.8.2) we obtain the following

Theorem 6.   If $F(t)$ is a periodic function with the period T, then

$$(3.8.3) \qquad L\{F(t)\} = \frac{1}{1 - e^{-pT}} \int_0^T e^{-pt} F(t)\, dt, \quad \mathrm{Re}(p) > 0.$$

Let us apply formula (3.8.3) to obtain the transform of the so-called sawtooth wave (Fig. 3.8.1) given by

$$F(t) = t, \quad 0 < t < T,$$
$$F(t + T) = F(t).$$

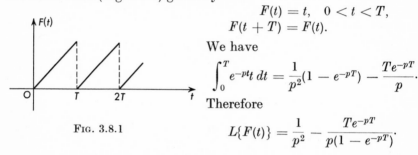

We have

$$\int_0^T e^{-pt} t\, dt = \frac{1}{p^2}(1 - e^{-pT}) - \frac{Te^{-pT}}{p}.$$

Therefore

FIG. 3.8.1

$$L\{F(t)\} = \frac{1}{p^2} - \frac{Te^{-pT}}{p(1 - e^{-pT})}.$$

3.9 The Laplace Transform of $(F(t)/t)$

In order to determine the transforms of certain non-elementary integrals (see section 8.7) we need the following

Theorem 7.   If $F(t)$ is sectionally continuous and of exponential order and $\lim\limits_{t \to 0+} F(t)/t$ exists, then

$$(3.9.1) \qquad\qquad L\{F(t)/t\} = \int_p^{\infty} f(\zeta)\, d\zeta.$$

Integrating both sides of $f(\zeta) = \int_0^{\infty} e^{-\zeta t} F(t)\, dt$ with respect to p from p to ∞ and interchanging the order of integration—a procedure that can be justified under the assumptions made about $F(t)$—we obtain

$$\int_p^{\infty} f(\zeta)\, d\zeta = \int_p^{\infty} \left(\int_0^{\infty} e^{-\zeta t} F(t)\, dt \right) d\zeta$$

$$= \int_0^{\infty} F(t) \left(\int_p^{\infty} e^{-\zeta t}\, d\zeta \right) dt$$

$$= \int_0^{\infty} F(t) \left[-\frac{e^{-\zeta t}}{t} \right]_p^{\infty} dt$$

$$= \int_0^{\infty} \frac{F(t)}{t} e^{-pt}\, dt.$$

Now, although $F(t)$ is sectionally continuous in every finite interval $0 \leqslant t \leqslant T$, $F(t)/t$ need not be, so that the last integral may not exist. For example, $F(t) = 1$ is continuous in every finite interval $0 \leqslant t \leqslant T$, but $F(t)/t = 1/t$ is discontinuous at the origin. However, if we impose the condition that $\lim\limits_{t \to 0+} F(t)/t$ exist, then $F(t)/t$ is sectionally continuous as well as of exponential order and $\displaystyle\int_0^\infty \frac{F(t)}{t} e^{-pt}\, dt$ exists. From this follows (3.9.1).

PROBLEMS

1. Prove that if $L\{F(t)\} = f(p)$, then

$$L\{F(at)\} = \frac{1}{a} f\left(\frac{p}{a}\right), \quad a > 0,$$

and

$$L^{-1}\{f(bp)\} = \frac{1}{b} F\left(\frac{t}{b}\right), \quad b > 0.$$

2. Prove that

$$f(ap - b) = L\left\{\frac{1}{a} e^{(b/a)t} F\left(\frac{t}{a}\right)\right\}, \quad a > 0.$$

3. (a) Represent the function shown in Fig. 3.8.2 in terms of unit step functions.

   (b) Find its Laplace transform.

   Ans. (a) $F(t) = (t - a) \cdot 1(t - a)$
   $- 2(t - 2a) \cdot 1(t - 2a)$
   $+ (t - 3a) \cdot 1(t - 3a)$.

   (b) $L\{F(t)\} = e^{-p}(1 - e^{-p})^2/p$.

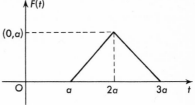

FIG. 3.8.2

4. Use the convolution theorem to determine

$$L^{-1}\left\{\frac{1}{(p - a)(p - b)(p - c)}\right\}.$$

5. Show that the Laplace transform of the *square wave* or *meander* function (Fig. 3.8.3, page 80)
$$F(t) = 1, \quad 0 < t < \tfrac{1}{2}T,$$
$$= -1, \quad \tfrac{1}{2}T < t < T,$$
is $\dfrac{1}{p} \tanh \tfrac{1}{2}pT$.

6. Show that the transform of the *triangular wave* (Fig. 3.8.4, page 80)
$$F(t) = t, \quad 0 < t < T/2,$$
$$= T - t, \quad T/2 < t < T,$$
is $\dfrac{1}{p^2} \tanh \dfrac{pT}{2}$.

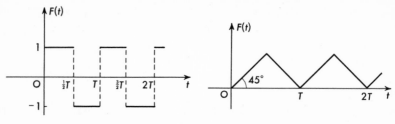

FIG. 3.8.3   FIG. 3.8.4

7. Prove that the transform of the *full-wave rectified sine wave* (Fig. 3.8.5)

$$F(t) = \sin t, \quad 0 < t < \pi,$$
$$F(t + \pi) = F(t),$$

is $\dfrac{\coth (p\pi/2)}{p^2 + 1}$.

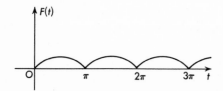
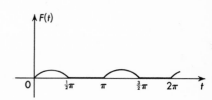

FIG. 3.8.5   FIG. 3.8.6

8. Prove that the transform of a *half-wave rectified sine wave* (Fig. 3.8.6)

$$F(t) = \sin 2t, \quad 0 < t < \pi/2,$$
$$= 0, \quad 0 < t < \pi,$$

is $\dfrac{2}{(p^2 + 4)(1 - e^{p\pi/2})}$.

CHAPTER IV

Ordinary Linear Differential Equations with Constant Coefficients

The properties of the Laplace transform studied in the preceding chapter enable us to solve ordinary and partial differential equations with constant coefficients as well as some types of integral equations and difference equations. In this chapter we shall be concerned with ordinary linear differential equations with constant coefficients, i.e., equations of the form

(I) $\qquad a_0 X^{(n)}(t) + a_1 X^{(n-1)}(t) + \cdots + a_{n-1} X'(t) + a_n X(t) = F(t),$

where $a_0, a_1, \cdots, a_n$ are constants and $F(t)$ is a given function of t.

4.1 Operational Solution of Differential Equations

Let us consider the problem of determining the general solution of the equation

(4.1.1) $\qquad\qquad X''(t) + a^2 X(t) = b, \quad t > 0$

where a and b are constants. Clearly, (4.1.1) is a special case of (I).

Taking the Laplace transform of both sides of the given equation, we have

$$L\{X''(t)\} + a^2 L\{X(t)\} = L\{b\}.$$

Setting $L\{X(t)\} = x(p)$, and making use of Theorem 2 it follows that

$$p^2 x(p) - pX(0) - X'(0) + a^2 x(p) = b/p.$$

Solving the preceding algebraic equation for $x(p)$, we get

$$x(p) = \frac{p^2 X(0) + pX'(0) + b}{p(p^2 + a^2)},$$

the inverse transform of which is

$$X(t) = \frac{1}{2\pi i} \int_{c-i\infty}^{c+i\infty} e^{pt} \frac{p^2 X(0) + pX'(0) + b}{p(p^2 + a^2)} \, dp.$$

Since the coefficient of e^{pt} in the above integrand clearly satisfies the conditions of Lemma III, according to (2.9.3),

$$X(t) = \sum \text{Res } e^{pt} \frac{p^2 X(0) + p X'(0) + b}{p(p^2 + a^2)},$$

at the poles $p = 0$ and $\pm ai$.

Now

$$\text{Res} \left[e^{pt} \frac{p^2 X(0) + p X'(0) + b}{p(p^2 + a^2)} \right]_{p=0} = \frac{b}{a^2},$$

$$\text{Res} \left[e^{pt} \frac{p^2 X(0) + p X'(0) + b}{p(p^2 + a^2)} \right]_{p=ai} = e^{ait} \frac{-a^2 X(0) + ai X'(0) + b}{-2a^2},$$

$$\text{Res} \left[e^{pt} \frac{p^2 X(0) + p X'(0) + b}{p(p^2 + a^2)} \right]_{p=-ai} = e^{-ait} \frac{-a^2 X(0) - ai X'(0) + b}{-2a^2}.$$

Therefore the sum of the residues is

$$X(t) = \frac{(a^2 X(0) - b)}{a^2} \cos at + \frac{X'(0)}{a} \sin at + \frac{b}{a^2},$$

or, setting $(a^2 X(0) - b)/a = A$ and $X'(0)/a = B$, we have

(4.1.2) $$X(t) = A \cos at + B \sin at + b/a^2.$$

In arriving at the above result we have assumed that the unknown function $X(t)$ has the properties necessary for any operational rule that is used to be valid. Under this assumption, therefore, we have shown *only* that $X(t)$ must have the form given in (4.1.2). However, if we succeed in verifying that $X(t)$ satisfies the given differential equation, then it will be the solution of our problem and we need not be concerned about questions of validity. Thus, in our case,

$$X''(t) = -a^2 A \cos at - a^2 B \sin at,$$
$$a^2 X(t) = a^2 A \cos at + a^2 B \sin at + b,$$

and therefore by adding the preceding results

$$X''(t) + a^2 X(t) = b,$$

which shows that (4.1.2) is indeed the solution of the given differential equation.

As another example, let us solve the equation

(4.1.3) $$X''(t) - X'(t) - 2X(t) = t^2, \quad t > 0$$

subject to the initial conditions

(4.1.4) $$X(0) = X'(0) = 1.$$

The transform of (4.1.3) yields

$$p^2 x(p) - p - 1 - p x(p) - 1 - 2x(p) = 2/p^3,$$

from which we obtain

(4.1.5) $$x(p) = \frac{p+2}{p^2 - p - 2} + \frac{2}{p^3(p^2 - p - 2)}.$$

It will be found simpler in most cases not to combine fractions before finding the inverse by means of the residue theory. Thus

$$X(t) = \frac{1}{2\pi i}\int_{c-i\infty}^{c+i\infty} e^{pt}\frac{p+2}{p^2 - p - 2}\, dp + \frac{1}{2\pi i}\int_{c-i\infty}^{c+i\infty} e^{pt}\frac{2}{p^3(p^2 - p - 2)}\, dp.$$

As before

$$X(t) = \sum \text{Res}\left[e^{pt}\frac{p+2}{p^2 - p - 2}\right] + \sum \text{Res}\left[e^{pt}\frac{2}{p^3(p^2 - p - 2)}\right]$$

evaluated at the simple poles $p = -1$ and 2 for the first term on the right of the equal sign and the triple pole $p = 0$ and the simple poles -1 and 2 for the second term. We have

$$\text{Res}\left[e^{pt}\frac{p+2}{(p-2)(p+1)}\right]_{p=2} = \frac{4}{3}e^{2t}, \quad \text{Res}\left[e^{pt}\frac{p+2}{(p-2)(p+1)}\right]_{p=-1}$$
$$= -\frac{1}{3}e^{-t}.$$

Also

$$\text{Res}\left[e^{pt}\frac{2}{p^3(p-2)(p+1)}\right]_{p=2} = \frac{1}{12}e^{2t}, \quad \text{Res}\left[e^{pt}\frac{2}{p^3(p-2)(p+1)}\right]_{p=-1}$$
$$= \frac{2}{3}e^{-t}.$$

$$\text{Res}\left[e^{pt}\frac{2}{p^3(p^2 - p - 2)}\right]_{p=0} = \frac{1}{2!}\lim_{p\to 0}\frac{d^2}{dp^2}\left[e^{pt}\frac{2}{p^2 - p - 2}\right]$$
$$= -t^2/2 + t/2 - 3/4.$$

Therefore, upon adding these results, we get

$$X(t) = \frac{17}{12}e^{2t} + \frac{1}{3}e^{-t} - \frac{t^2}{2} + \frac{t}{2} - \frac{3}{4}$$

which can be easily shown to satisfy the given differential equation and the given initial conditions $X(0) = X'(0) = 1$.

Remark. Another procedure that could be used in finding the inverse of $x(p)$ in (4.1.5) is to combine the fractions, decompose the result into partial fractions and find the inverses of each fraction by looking into a table of transforms. Thus, from (4.1.5) we obtain the following decomposition

$$\frac{p^4 + 2p^3 + 2}{p^3(p^2 - p - 2)} \equiv -\frac{1}{p^3} + \frac{1}{2p^2} - \frac{3}{4p} + \frac{1}{3(p+1)} + \frac{17}{12(p-2)}.$$

Therefore,

$$X(t) = L^{-1}\left\{-\frac{1}{p^3} + \frac{1}{2p^2} - \frac{3}{4p} + \frac{1}{3(p+1)} + \frac{17}{12(p-2)}\right\}$$

and from the table of transforms in the Appendix

$$X(t) = \frac{17}{12}e^{2t} + \frac{1}{3}e^{-t} - \frac{t^2}{2} + \frac{t}{2} - \frac{3}{4},$$

as before.

It may happen that the sought for inverse is already in the table of transforms. In such a case our problem becomes extremely easy to solve. For example, let it be required to find the general solution of

(4.1.6) $X^{(4)}(t) - a^4X(t) = F(t).$

Taking the Laplace transform of both sides of (4.1.6), we obtain

$$x(p) = \frac{p^3X(0)}{p^4 - a^4} + \frac{p^2X'(0)}{p^4 - a^4} + \frac{pX''(0)}{p^4 - a^4} + \frac{X'''(0)}{p^4 - a^4} + \frac{f(p)}{p^4 - a^4},$$

where, as usual, $L\{F(t)\} = f(p)$ and $L\{X(t)\} = x(p)$. The inverses of the first four terms on the right of the equality sign can be found directly from the tables and the inverse of the fifth term can be represented as an integral by making use of the Faltung theorem. We thus find that

$$X(t) = \frac{X(0)}{2}(\cosh at + \cos at) + \frac{X'(0)}{2a}(\sinh at + \sin at)$$

$$+ \frac{X''(0)}{2a^2}(\cosh at - \sin at) + \frac{X'''(0)}{2a^3}(\sinh at - \sin at)$$

$$+ \frac{1}{2a^3}\int_0^t F(\tau)[\sinh a(t - \tau) - \sin a(t - \tau)]\, d\tau,$$

from which, by rearranging terms, we obtain

(4.1.7) $X(t) = \left(\dfrac{X'(0)}{2a} - \dfrac{X''(0)}{2a^2} - \dfrac{X'''(0)}{2a^3}\right)\sin at + \dfrac{X(0)}{2}\cos at$

$$= \left(\frac{X(0)}{2} + \frac{X''(0)}{2a^3}\right)\cosh at + \left(\frac{X'(0)}{2a} + \frac{X'''(0)}{2a^3}\right)\sinh at$$

$$+ \frac{1}{2a^3}\int_0^t F(\tau)[\sinh a(t - \tau) - \sin a(t - \tau)]\, d\tau,$$

or, finally,

(4.1.8) $X(t) = c_1 \sin at + c_2 \cos at + c_3 \cosh at + c_4 \sinh at$

$$+ \frac{1}{2a^3}\int_0^t F(\tau)\,[\sinh a(t - \tau) - \sin a(t - \tau)]\, d\tau,$$

where c_1, c_2, c_3, and c_4 are the coefficients of the corresponding terms in (4.1.7). The preceding result can easily be shown to satisfy (4.1.6).

It has been remarked that in order to make the solution rigorous it is necessary to verify that the result obtained satisfies the differential equation as well as the given initial conditions. In many cases such a verification is extremely tedious. Fortunately, however, it can be shown * that the result of applying the Laplace transformation to the system

$$\sum_{i=0}^{n} a_i X^{(n)}(t) = F(t), \qquad X^{(j)}(0) = X_j, \qquad j = 0, 1, \cdots, n - 1$$

where the a_i's and X_j's are constants, and $F(t)$ is a function whose Laplace transform exists, always gives the desired solution. Moreover, this is also true when the method is applied to systems of simultaneous differential equations with constant coefficients.† By appealing to these theorems, therefore, the necessity for checking each answer is obviated when dealing with such systems.

Exercise 1. Show that the general solution of
$$X''(t) - 2X'(t) + X(t) = t,$$

is
$$X(t) = [X(0) - 2]e^t + [X'(0) - X(0) + 1] te^t + t + 2.$$

Exercise 2. Find the solution of the equation
$$X''(t) + X'(t) + X(t) = e^{2t},$$
subject to the initial conditions $X(0) = X'(0) = 0$.

$$Ans. \ X(t) = -\frac{1}{7}e^{-\frac{1}{2}t}\left(\cos \frac{\sqrt{3}}{2}t + \frac{8}{\sqrt{3}} \sin \frac{\sqrt{3}}{2}t\right) + \frac{1}{7}e^{2t}.$$

4.2 The R-L-C Series Circuit and Two Mechanical Equivalents

The circuit of Fig. 4.2.1 consists of the following components: a *resistor* of resistance R, an *inductor* of inductance L, a *capacitor* of capacitance C and a source of voltage $E(t)$.

If $Q_C(t)$ represents the charge on the capacitor and $I(t)$ represents the current in the circuit, then it is well known from fundamental principles of physics that $Q_C(t)$ and $I(t)$ are related by the equation

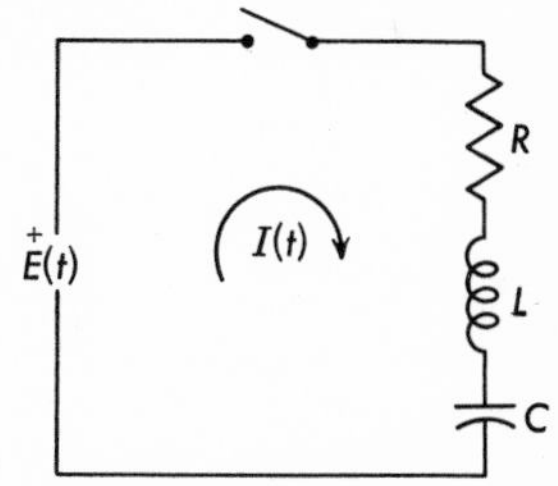

(4.2.1) $$\frac{dQ_C(t)}{dt} = I(t),$$

Fig. 4.2.1

or

(4.2.2) $$Q_C(t) = \int_0^t I(\tau) \, d\tau + Q_0 = Q(t) + Q_0,$$

where $Q(t) = \int_0^t I(\tau) \, d\tau$ is the charge accumulated on the capacitor due

---

* G. Doetsch, *Theorie und Anwendung der Laplace-Transformation*, Julius Springer, Berlin, 1937, p. 327.
† *Ibid.*, p. 330.

to the current and $Q_0 = Q_C(0)$ is the initial charge on the capacitor. Moreover, the voltage drop due to the resistor is equal to

$$RI(t),$$

that due to the inductor

$$L\frac{dI(t)}{dt},$$

and that due to the capacitor

$$\frac{Q_C(t)}{C},$$

where R, L, and C are positive constants.

In order to obtain the voltage equation for the circuit we appeal to *Kirchhoff's voltage law*:

The impressed voltage on any closed circuit is equal to the sum of the voltage drops due to each of the components in the circuit.

Applying this law to the circuit of Fig. 4.2.1 at the instant the switch is closed, we have

$$(4.2.3) \qquad E(t) = RI(t) + L\frac{dI(t)}{dt} + \frac{1}{C}\int_0^t I(\tau)\,d\tau + \frac{Q_0}{C},$$

which is termed an *integro-differential* equation because it contains not only the derivative, but the integral of the unknown function $I(t)$.

Another equation, this one in terms of the charge $Q_C(t)$, is obtained by making use of equations (4.2.1) and (4.2.2). By direct substitution we obtain

$$(4.2.4) \quad L\frac{d^2Q_C(t)}{dt^2} + R\frac{dQ_C(t)}{dt} + \frac{Q_C(t)}{C} = E(t).$$

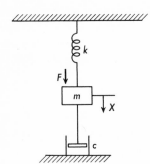

FIG. 4.2.2

Let us now derive the differential equations which describe the oscillations of two important mechanical systems with one degree of freedom.

The first system consists of a mass attached to a coil spring at one end and to a dashpot mechanism at the other end, as shown in Fig. 4.2.2, which produces a damping force.

Let the downward direction be assumed to be positive. If the spring force is proportional to the displacement X, the damping force proportional to the velocity dX/dt and an external force $F(t)$ acts on the mass m which is constrained to move in a linear path, then by Newton's law

$$(4.2.5) \qquad m\frac{d^2X}{dt^2} = -kX - c\frac{dX}{dt} + F(t),$$

or

(4.2.6) $$m\frac{d^2X(t)}{dt^2} + c\frac{dX(t)}{dt} + kX(t) = F(t),$$

where k and c are positive constants, called the spring and damping constants, respectively.

The second system (Fig. 4.2.3) consists of a disk of moment of inertia I attached to a shaft of torsional stiffness K. If the disk is twisted through an angle θ and released it will undergo torsional oscillations.

Suppose that the shaft torque is proportional to the angular displacement θ, the damping torque proportional to the angular velocity $d\theta/dt$ and the external torque is $T(t)$. Since torque $= I\frac{d^2\theta}{dt^2}$, from Newton's law for angular motion it follows that

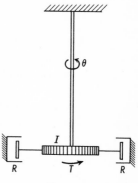

(4.2.7) $$I\frac{d^2\theta}{dt^2} = -K\theta - R\frac{d\theta}{dt} + T(t),$$

or

(4.2.8) $$I\frac{d^2\theta(t)}{dt^2} + R\frac{d\theta(t)}{dt} + K\theta(t) = T(t),$$

FIG. 4.2.3

where R is the damping constant.

An examination of the equations (4.2.4), (4.2.6), and (4.2.8) reveals that the behavior of the electrical, linear, and torsional systems are all governed by the same differential equation. This is an important observation, since the conclusions drawn from the analysis of an electrical system can be applied to the corresponding mechanical systems and conversely.

Table 4.2.1 of analogues will be found useful:

Table 4.2.1

Series Electrical System		Linear System		Torsional System	
Inductance	L	Mass	m	Moment of inertia	I
Elastance	$1/C$	Spring stiffness	k	Torsional stiffness	K
Resistance	R	Damping	c	Torsional damping	R
Impressed voltage	$E(t)$	Impressed Force	$F(t)$	Impressed torque	$T(t)$
Capacitor charge	$Q_C(t)$	Displacement	$X(t)$	Angular displacement	$\theta(t)$
Current $I(t) = \frac{dQ_C(t)}{dt}$		Velocity	$\frac{dX(t)}{dt}$	Angular velocity	$\frac{d\theta(t)}{dt}$

4.3 The L-C Series Circuit

The circuit of Fig. 4.3.1 contains a capacitor, inductor and a switch in series.   The capacitor C has a charge Q_0 and the switch is open when

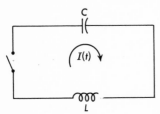

FIG. 4.3.1

$t < 0$.   At $t = 0$ the switch is closed. What is the charge $Q_C(t)$ for $t > 0$?

Since the impressed voltage $E(t) = 0$ and $R = 0$, equation (4.2.4) becomes, after dividing by L,

$$(4.3.1) \qquad Q_C''(t) + \frac{1}{LC} Q_C(t) = 0,$$

with the initial conditions $Q_C(0) = Q_0$ and $Q_C'(0) = 0$.

The transform of (4.3.1) yields

$$(4.3.2) \qquad p^2 q(p) - p Q_0 + \frac{1}{LC} q(p) = 0,$$

where $q(p) = L\{Q_C(t)\}$.   Therefore

$$(4.3.3) \qquad q(p) = \frac{p Q_0}{p^2 + \dfrac{1}{LC}}.$$

Looking up the inverse transform in the tables, or calculating the sum of the residues at the poles $p = \pm \dfrac{i}{\sqrt{LC}}$, we obtain

$$(4.3.4) \qquad Q_C(t) = Q_0 \cos \frac{t}{\sqrt{LC}} = Q_0 \cos \omega_0 t,$$

where $\omega_0 = 1/\sqrt{LC}$ is the so-called natural frequency of the system.

Exercise I.   From the table of analogues write the solutions to the linear and torsional systems corresponding to the above L-C series circuit.

Exercise 2.   In the circuit of section 4.3 obtain the current $I(t)$ directly by using the integro-differential equation (4.2.3).

Ans. $I(t) = -\omega_0 Q_0 \sin \omega_0 t$.

Exercise 3.   A series circuit contains the elements R and C. Initially there is a charge Q_0 on the capacitor.   Find $I(t)$ for $t > 0$.

Ans. $I(t) = -\dfrac{Q_0}{RC} e^{-t/(RC)}$.

Exercise 4.   A series circuit for which $Q_C(0) = Q_0$ contains the elements R and C.   A constant voltage E_0, supplied by a battery, is suddenly switched into the circuit.   Find $I(t)$ for $t > 0$ and draw its graph.   *Ans.* $I(t) = (E_0 C - Q_0)e^{-t/(RC)}$.

4.4 An R-L-C Series Circuit

Consider the circuit of Fig. 4.4.1. If there is a charge Q_0 on the capacitor initially, it is required to find the current $I(t)$ at any time t after the switch is closed.

We are required to solve the equation

(4.4.1)

$$RI(t) + \frac{1}{C}\int_0^t I(\tau)\,d\tau + \frac{Q_0}{C} + L\frac{dI(t)}{dt} = 0$$

subject to the initial conditions $Q_C(0)$ $= Q_0$, $I(0) = 0$. Upon taking the transform of both sides of (4.4.1) we obtain

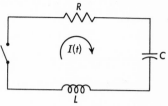

Fig. 4.4.1

$$Ri(p) + \frac{i(p)}{Cp} + \frac{Q_0}{Cp} + Lpi(p) = 0,$$

from which

(4.4.2) $\quad i(p) = -\dfrac{Q_0/(LC)}{p^2 + \dfrac{R}{L}p + \dfrac{1}{LC}} = -\dfrac{Q_0/(LC)}{(p+b)^2 + (\omega_0{}^2 - b^2)},$

where $b = R/(2L)$ and $\omega_0{}^2 = 1/(LC)$.

Three cases can be distinguished, namely, when $\omega_0{}^2 = b^2$, $\omega_0{}^2 > b^2$ and $\omega_0{}^2 < b^2$.

Case I: $\omega_0{}^2 = b^2$. When this condition is satisfied (4.4.2) reduces to

$$i(p) = -\frac{Q_0/(LC)}{(p+b)^2},$$

and directly from the table we get

$$I(t) = -\frac{Q_0}{LC}te^{-bt}.$$

Case II: $\omega_0{}^2 > b^2$. Here, since $\omega_0{}^2 - b^2 > 0$, we find that the inverse of equation (4.4.2) from the table is

$$I(t) = -\frac{Q_0}{LC\sqrt{\omega_0{}^2 - b^2}}\,e^{-bt}\sin t\sqrt{\omega_0{}^2 - b^2}.$$

Case III: $\omega_0{}^2 < b^2$. In this instance (4.4.2) may be written

$$i(p) = -\frac{Q_0/(LC)}{(p+b)^2 - (b^2 - \omega_0{}^2)},$$

where $b^2 - \omega_0{}^2 > 0$ and from the table we have

$$I(t) = -\frac{Q_0}{LC\sqrt{b^2 - \omega_0{}^2}}\,e^{-bt}\sinh t\sqrt{b^2 - \omega_0{}^2}.$$

Exercise I.   Draw the graphs for the current $I(t)$ in each of the preceding three cases.

Exercise 2.   Solve the problem of section 4.4 if a constant potential E_0 supplied by a battery is impressed on the circuit.   Draw graphs in each case.

$$Ans. \text{ to Case I: } I(t) = \left(\frac{E_0}{L} - \frac{Q_0}{LC}\right)te^{-Rt/2L}.$$

4.5 A Sinusoidal Voltage Applied to an R-L-C Circuit

A voltage of the form $E(t) = E_0 \sin \omega t$ is impressed on the circuit of Fig. 4.5.1.   On the assumption that $Q_C(0) = 0$ and $I(0) = 0$ it is required to find the current at any time $t > 0$.

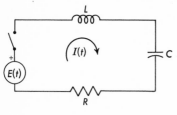

FIG. 4.5.1

The integro-differential equation in this case is

(4.5.1)

$$RI(t) + \frac{1}{C}\int_0^t I(\tau)\,d\tau + L\frac{dI(t)}{dt} = E_0 \sin \omega t,$$

and its transform is

(4.5.2) $$Ri(p) + \frac{i(p)}{Cp} + Lpi(p) = E_0\frac{\omega}{p^2 + \omega^2}.$$

Solving this equation for $i(p)$ we obtain

(4.5.3) $$i(p) = \frac{E_0\omega}{L} \frac{p}{(p^2 + \omega^2)\left(p^2 + \frac{R}{L}p + \frac{1}{CL}\right)}$$

$$= \frac{E_0\omega}{L} \frac{p}{(p^2 + \omega^2)[(p + b)^2 + (\omega_0^2 - b^2)]},$$

where, as before, $b = R/(2L)$ and $\omega_0^2 = 1/(LC)$.   Therefore

(4.5.4) $$I(t) = \sum \text{Res} \frac{E_0\omega}{L} \frac{pe^{pt}}{(p^2 + \omega^2)[(p + b)^2 + (\omega_0^2 - b^2)]}$$

at the poles of $i(p)$.

We shall now consider the three cases that arise.

Case I: $\omega_0^2 = b^2$.   We have from (4.5.3)

$$i(p) = \frac{E_0\omega}{L} \frac{p}{(p^2 + \omega^2)(p + b)^2}$$

and therefore

$$I(t) = \frac{E_0\omega}{L} \sum \text{Res} \frac{pe^{pt}}{(p^2 + \omega^2)(p + b)^2}$$

at the double pole $p = -b$ and the poles $p = \pm i\omega$.

Now

$$\text{Res} \left[\frac{pe^{pt}}{(p^2 + \omega^2)(p + b)^2} \right]_{p=-b} = \lim_{p \to -b} \frac{d}{dp} \left[\frac{pe^{pt}}{p^2 + \omega^2} \right]$$

$$= -\frac{e^{-bt}}{(\omega^2 + b^2)^2}[bt(\omega^2 + b^2) + (b^2 - \omega^2)]$$

$$\text{Res} \left[\frac{pe^{pt}}{(p^2 + \omega^2)(p + b)^2} \right]_{p=+i\omega} = \lim_{p \to i\omega} \frac{pe^{pt}}{(p + i\omega)(p + b)^2}$$

$$= \frac{e^{i\omega t}}{2(i\omega + b)^2}$$

$$\text{Res} \left[\frac{pe^{pt}}{(p^2 + \omega^2)(p + b)^2} \right]_{p=-i\omega} = \lim_{p \to -i\omega} \frac{pe^{pt}}{(p - i\omega)(p + b)^2}$$

$$= \frac{e^{-i\omega t}}{2(-i\omega + b)^2}$$

Adding the preceding residues and simplifying, we obtain

$$I(t) = \frac{E_0\omega/L}{(\omega^2 + b^2)}\{2b\omega \sin \omega t + (b^2 - \omega^2) \cos \omega t$$
$$- e^{-bt}[bt(\omega^2 + b^2) + (b^2 - \omega^2)]\}.$$

Case II: $\omega_0^2 > b^2$.   In this instance

$$I(t) = \frac{E_0\omega}{L} \sum \text{Res} \frac{pe^{pt}}{(p^2 + \omega^2)[(p + b)^2 + (\omega_0^2 - b^2)]}$$

at the poles $p = -b \pm i\sqrt{\omega_0^2 - b^2}$ and $p = \pm i\omega$.

We have

$$\text{Res} \left[\frac{pe^{pt}}{(p^2 + \omega^2)[(p + b)^2 + (\omega_0^2 - b^2)]} \right]_{p=-b+i\sqrt{\omega_0^2-b^2}}$$

$$= \lim_{p \to -b+i\sqrt{\omega_0^2-b^2}} \frac{pe^{pt}}{(p^2 + \omega^2)(p + b + i\sqrt{\omega_0^2 - b^2})}$$

$$= \frac{(-b + i\sqrt{\omega_0^2 - b^2})e^{(-b+i\sqrt{\omega_0^2-b^2})t}}{2i\sqrt{\omega_0^2 - b^2}(2b^2 + \omega^2 - \omega_0^2 - 2bi\sqrt{\omega_0^2 - b^2})}$$

$$\text{Res} \left[\frac{pe^{pt}}{(p^2 + \omega^2)[(p + b)^2 + (\omega_0{}^2 - b^2)]} \right]_{p=-b-i\sqrt{\omega_0{}^2-b^2}}$$

$$= \lim_{p \to -b-i\sqrt{\omega_0{}^2-b^2}} \frac{pe^{pt}}{(p^2 + \omega^2)(p + b - i\sqrt{\omega_0{}^2 - b^2})}$$

$$= - \frac{(-b - i\sqrt{\omega_0{}^2 - b^2})e^{(-b-i\sqrt{\omega_0{}^2-b^2})t}}{2i\sqrt{\omega_0{}^2 - b^2}(2b^2 + \omega^2 - \omega_0{}^2 + 2bi\sqrt{\omega_0{}^2 - b^2})}$$

$$\text{Res} \left[\frac{pe^{pt}}{(p^2 + \omega^2)[(p + b)^2 + (\omega_0{}^2 - b^2)]} \right]_{p=i\omega}$$

$$= \lim_{p \to i\omega} \frac{pe^{pt}}{(p + i\omega)(p^2 + 2bp + \omega_0{}^2)}$$

$$= \frac{e^{i\omega t}}{2(\omega_0{}^2 - \omega^2 + 2ib\omega)}$$

$$= \frac{\cos \omega t + i \sin \omega t}{2(\omega_0{}^2 - \omega^2 + 2ib\omega)}$$

$$\text{Res} \left[\frac{pe^{pt}}{(p^2 + \omega^2)[(p + b)^2 + (\omega_0{}^2 - b^2)]} \right]_{p=-i\omega}$$

$$= \lim_{p \to -i\omega} \frac{pe^{pt}}{(p - i\omega)(p^2 + 2bp + \omega_0{}^2)}$$

$$= \frac{\cos \omega t - i \sin \omega t}{2(\omega_0{}^2 - \omega^2 - 2ib\omega)}.$$

The result of adding these residues is

$$(4.5.5) \quad I(t) = \frac{E_0\omega/L}{(\omega_0{}^2 - \omega^2)^2 + 4b^2\omega^2} \left\{ e^{-bt} \left[(\omega^2 - \omega_0{}^2) \cos t\sqrt{\omega_0{}^2 - b^2} \right. \right.$$

$$\left. - \frac{b(\omega^2 + \omega_0{}^2)}{\sqrt{\omega_0{}^2 - b^2}} \sin t\sqrt{\omega_0{}^2 - b^2} \right] + (\omega_0{}^2 - \omega^2) \cos \omega t + 2b\omega \sin \omega t \bigg\}.$$

Case III: $\omega_0{}^2 < b^2$. Although the current $I(t)$ in this case can be found by proceeding as above, it is more easily obtained by making use of the identities established in Chapter I connecting the trigonometric functions with the hyperbolic functions. Thus

$$\cos t\sqrt{\omega_0{}^2 - b^2} = \cos it\sqrt{b^2 - \omega_0{}^2} = \cosh t\sqrt{b^2 - \omega_0{}^2}$$

and

$$\sin t\sqrt{\omega_0{}^2 - b^2} = \sin it\sqrt{b^2 - \omega_0{}^2} = i \sinh t\sqrt{b^2 - \omega_0{}^2}.$$

Making use of these relations and $\sqrt{\omega_0{}^2 - b^2} = i\sqrt{b^2 - \omega_0{}^2}$, we have by direct substitution in (4.5.5)

$$I(t) = \frac{E_0\omega/L}{(\omega_0{}^2 - \omega^2)^2 + 4b^2\omega^2}\left\{e^{-bt}\left[(\omega^2 - \omega_0{}^2)\cosh t\sqrt{b^2 - \omega_0{}^2}\right.\right.$$

$$\left.\left. - \frac{b(\omega^2 + \omega_0{}^2)}{\sqrt{b^2 - \omega_0{}^2}}\sinh t\sqrt{b^2 - \omega_0{}^2}\right] + (\omega_0{}^2 - \omega^2)\cos\omega t + 2b\omega\sin\omega t\right\}.$$

Exercise. Verify the result (4.5.5).

4.6 A Finite Pulse Applied to a Series R-C Circuit

Let us suppose that a constant voltage E_0, lasting for a short period of time (Fig. 4.6.1) and known as a *potential* pulse, is applied to the circuit of Fig. 4.6.2 at the time $t = 0$. It is desired to know the current I in the circuit for $t > 0$ if, initially, $Q(0) = Q_0$.

The differential equation is

(4.6.1)
$$RI(t) + \frac{1}{C}\int_0^t I(\tau)\,d\tau + \frac{Q_0}{C} = E(t),$$

where
$E(t) = E_0[1(t - t_0) - 1(t - t_1)].$

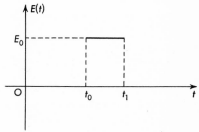

FIG. 4.6.1

Taking the Laplace transform of both sides of (4.6.1), we get

$$Ri(p) + \frac{i(p)}{Cp} + \frac{Q_0}{Cp} = E_0\left[\frac{e^{-pt_0} - e^{-pt_1}}{p}\right]$$

from which
(4.6.2)
$$i(p) = -\frac{Q_0/(RC)}{p + 1/(RC)} + \frac{E_0}{R}\frac{e^{-pt_0} - e^{-pt_1}}{p + 1/(RC)}.$$

Since $L^{-1}\left\{\dfrac{1}{p + 1/(RC)}\right\} = e^{-t/(RC)}$,

from this and Translation Theorem I, we have

(4.6.3)

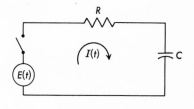

FIG. 4.6.2

$$I(t) = -\frac{Q_0}{RC}e^{-t/(RC)} + \frac{E_0}{R}\left[e^{-(t-t_0)/(RC)}1(t - t_0) - e^{-(t-t_1)/(RC)}1(t - t_1)\right],$$

whose graph is shown in Fig. 4.6.3.

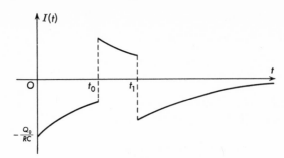

FIG. 4.6.3

Remark. It should be observed that the inverse of the function $f(p) = (e^{-pt_0} - e^{-pt_1})/(p + 1/RC)$ cannot be computed by means of residues because, as is easily verified, $f(p)$ does not satisfy the conditions of Lemma III. Thus, in finding the inverse transforms of functions such as $e^{-ap}\phi(p)(a > 0)$, one finds the inverse transform of $\phi(p)$ from the tables or by the complex inversion integral and then one employs Translation Theorem I.

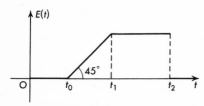

FIG. 4.6.4

Exercise. Solve the problem of section 4.6 if the pulse of Fig. 4.6.4 is impressed on the circuit. Draw a graph of $I(t)$.

4.7 Response of a Series R-L Circuit to a Periodic Voltage

We now suppose that the periodic voltage given in Fig. 4.7.1 is impressed on the series R-L circuit of Fig. 4.7.2. If the circuit is

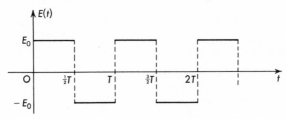

FIG. 4.7.1

dead, initially, what is the current and the voltage across the inductor for $t > 0$?

The differential equation is

(4.7.1) $LI'(t) + RI(t) = E(t),$

where

$$E(t) = E_0, \quad 0 < t < T/2,$$
$$= -E_0, \quad T/2 < t < T,$$
$$E(t + T) = E(t).$$

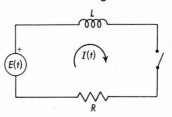

FIG. 4.7.2

Upon taking the transform of (4.7.1) we have, since $E(t)$ is periodic and $I(0) = 0$,

(4.7.2) $$(Lp + R)i(p) = \int_0^T \frac{e^{-pt}E(t)\,dt}{1 - e^{-pT}}.$$

Now

$$\int_0^T e^{-pT}E(t)\,dt = E_0\frac{(1 - e^{-pT/2})^2}{p}.$$

Therefore, substituting this result in (4.7.2) and solving for $i(p)$, we obtain

(4.7.3) $$i(p) = \frac{E_0}{L}\frac{(1 - e^{-pT/2})^2}{p(p + R/L)(1 - e^{-pT})} = \frac{E_0}{L}\frac{1 - e^{-pT/2}}{p(p + R/L)(1 + e^{-pT/2})}.$$

An examination of this function shows that the only singularities are poles at the points $p = -R/L$ and $p = \pm(2n + 1)2\pi i/T$, $n = 0, 1, 2, \cdots$.

Therefore, by the inversion theorem

$$I(t) = \frac{1}{2\pi i}\lim_{R\to\infty}\int_{c-iR}^{c+iR}\frac{E_0}{L}\frac{(1 - e^{-pT/2})e^{pT}}{p(p + R/L)(1 + e^{-pT/2})}\,dp.$$

Using a contour similar to that of Fig. 2.9.2 and observing that $i(p)$ satisfies the conditions of Lemma III, we have from formula (2.9.4):

(4.7.4) $$I(t) = \sum_{n=0}^{\infty}\text{Res}_{p_n}[e^{pt}i(p)].$$

Now

$$\text{Res}\,(-R/L) = \lim_{p\to -R/L}\frac{E_0}{L}\frac{1 - e^{-pT/2}}{p(1 + e^{-pT/2})}e^{pt} = \frac{E_0}{R}\frac{e^{RT/2L} - 1}{e^{RT/2L} + 1}e^{(-R/L)t}.$$

Also

$$\text{Res}\,[(2n + 1)2\pi i/T] = \lim_{p\to(2n+1)2\pi i/T}\frac{E_0}{L}\frac{(1 - e^{-pT/2})e^{pt}}{p(p + R/L)d(1 + e^{-pT/2})/dp}$$

$$= \frac{2E_0}{(2n + 1)\pi L}\frac{e^{(2n+1)2\pi it/T}}{-(2n + 1)2\pi/T + Ri/L},$$

and similarly

$$\text{Res}\,[-(2n + 1)2\pi i/T] = \frac{2E_0}{(2n + 1)\pi L}\frac{e^{-(2n+1)2\pi it/T}}{-(2n + 1)2\pi/T - Ri/L}.$$

Therefore

$$\mathrm{Res}\,[(2n+1)2\pi i/T] + \mathrm{Res}\,[-(2n+1)2\pi i/T]$$

$$= \frac{2E_0}{(2n+1)\pi L}\left\{\frac{e^{(2n+1)2\pi it/T}}{-(2n+1)2\pi/T + Ri/L} + \frac{e^{-(2n+1)2\pi it/T}}{-(2n+1)2\pi/T - Ri/L}\right\}$$

$$= \frac{4E_0}{(2n+1)\pi L}$$

$$\left\{\frac{(R/L)\sin\,[(2n+1)2\pi t/T] - [(2n+1)2\pi/T]\cos\,[(2n+1)2\pi t/T]}{4(2n+1)^2\pi^2/T^2 + R^2/L^2}\right\}.$$

Hence from (4.7.4)

$$I(t) = \frac{E_0}{R}\frac{e^{RT/(2L)} - 1}{e^{RT/(2L)} + 1}e^{-(R/L)t}$$

(4.7.5)

$$+ \frac{4E_0}{\pi L}\sum_{n=0}^{\infty}\frac{(R/L)\sin\,[(2n+1)2\pi t/T] - [2(2n+1)\pi/T]\cos\,[(2n+1)2\pi t/T]}{(2n+1)[4(2n+1)^2\pi^2/T^2 + R^2/L^2]}.$$

The first term constitutes the *transient* term and the second, the *steady state* periodic solution. It should be observed that if only the latter is required it is necessary to consider only the residues at the poles lying along the imaginary axis, namely, $p = \pm(2n+1)2\pi i/T$, $n = 0, 1, 2, \cdots$.

For the voltage E_L across the inductor we have

$$E_L(t) = L\,dI(t)/dt = E_0\frac{1 - e^{RT/(2L)}}{1 + e^{RT/(2L)}}e^{-(R/L)t}$$

(4.7.6)

$$+ \frac{8E_0}{T}\sum_{n=0}^{\infty}\frac{(R/L)\cos\,[(2n+1)2\pi t/T] + [2(2n+1)\pi/T]\sin\,[(2n+1)2\pi t/T]}{4(2n+1)^2\pi^2/T^2 + R^2/L^2}.$$

Exercise. Using (4.7.5), show that $I(0) = 0$. [*Hint*: Make use of the fact that

$$\frac{e^z - 1}{e^z + 1} = \sum_{n=0}^{\infty}\frac{4z}{(2n+1)^2\pi^2 + z^2},$$

for $z \neq k\pi i$ (k is a positive or negative integer or zero).]

Although the preceding solutions for $I(t)$ and $E_L(t)$ make evident by inspection the transient and steady state terms, they do not lend themselves easily to graphical representations. It is therefore instructive to consider solutions which can be more easily graphed. Unfortunately, they suffer the defect that the transient and steady state terms are blended and hence indistinguishable.

Returning to equation (4.7.3), we have

$$i(p) = \frac{E_0}{L} \frac{(1 - e^{-pT/2})(1 + e^{-pT/2})^{-1}}{p(p + R/L)}$$

$$= \frac{E_0}{L} \frac{1 - e^{-pT/2}}{p(p + R/L)} \sum_{n=0}^{\infty} (-1)^n e^{-npT/2}$$

$$= \frac{E_0}{L} \frac{1 + 2 \sum_{n=1}^{\infty} (-1)^n e^{-npT/2}}{p(p + R/L)}.$$

Hence, upon taking inverses of both sides,

(4.7.7)

$$I(t) = \frac{E_0}{R}(1 - e^{-Rt/L}) + \frac{2E_0}{R} \sum_{n=1}^{\infty} (-1)^n (1 - e^{-R(t-nT/2)/L}) 1(t - nT/2).$$

We also have

(4.7.8)

$$E_L(t) = L \, dI(t)/dt = E_0 e^{-Rt/L} + 2E_0 \sum_{n=1}^{\infty} (-1)^n e^{-R(t-nT/2)/L} 1(t - nT/2).$$

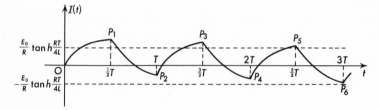

Fig. 4.7.3

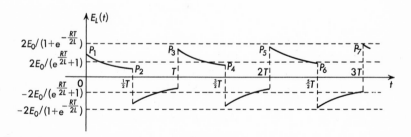

Fig. 4.7.4

The graphs of (4.7.7) and (4.7.8) are shown in Figs. 4.7.3 and 4.7.4, respectively.

In Fig. 4.7.3 the sequence of points $\{P_{2n+1}\}$, $n = 0, 1, 2, \cdots$ tends to the value $(E_0/R)\tanh(RT/4L)$ as $t \to \infty$ and the sequence of points $\{P_{2n}\}$, $n = 1, 2, 3, \cdots$ tends to the value $-(E_0/R)\tanh(RT/4L)$ as $t \to \infty$.

Similarly, in Fig. 4.7.4 the sequence $\{P_{2n+1}\} \to 2E_0/(1 + e^{-RT/(2L)})$ and $\{P_{2n}\} \to 2E_0/(e^{RT/(2L)} + 1)$. The trend in the lower half of the graph is easily discernible.

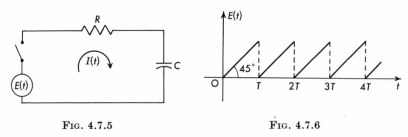

FIG. 4.7.5   FIG. 4.7.6

Exercise. For the circuit and voltage shown (Figs. 4.7.5 and 4.7.6), find $I(t)$ and the voltage across the capacitor $E_C(t)$ in two different ways if $Q(0) = Q_0$ and draw their graphs.

4.8 Deflection of Beams

Suppose that OA represents a straight beam supported as shown in Fig. 4.8.1. Let the x-axis be taken *positive* to the *right* and the Y-axis

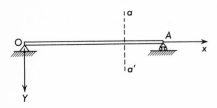

FIG. 4.8.1

positive downward. We shall consider the problem of determining the deflection of the beam OA if it is subjected to a distributed load intensity $W(x)$ (load per unit length of the beam) taken *positive downward*.

Let aa' represent a plane cutting the beam OA at a distance x units from the left end of the beam and consider the left portion as a free body (Fig. 4.8.2). Then from mechanics it is known that the forces

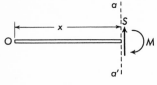

FIG. 4.8.2

acting on this portion of the beam before it was cut can be replaced by a vertical *shearing force* S and a *bending moment* M acting at x. We shall assume that S is taken *positive upward* and M *positive* when *clockwise*.

Consider now a small portion of the beam OA between the distances x and $x + \Delta x$. Then this portion is in equilibrium under the action of the forces and couples shown in

Fig. 4.8.3.   Applying the conditions of equilibrium, we have

$$\Delta S + W\Delta x = 0, \qquad \Delta M - S\Delta x = 0,$$

where differentials of order higher than one have been neglected. Dividing by Δx and passing to the limit we obtain the following relations between load, shear, and moment:

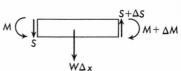

(4.8.1) $\dfrac{dS}{dx} = -W(x),$

(4.8.2) $\dfrac{dM}{dx} = S(x).$

FIG. 4.8.3

By eliminating S between these two equations we have

(4.8.3) $$\frac{d^2M}{dx^2} = -W(x).$$

If the deflections are small, then the elementary theory of bending leads to the equation

(4.8.4) $$EI\frac{d^2W(x)}{dx^2} = -M(x),$$

where E is *Young's modulus* and I is the moment of inertia of the cross-sectional area of the beam with respect to the neutral axis of the beam.

From equations (4.8.4) and (4.8.2) we have

(4.8.5) $$\frac{d}{dx}\left(EI\frac{d^2Y(x)}{dx^2}\right) = -S(x),$$

and from equations (4.8.4) and (4.8.3) we get

(4.8.6) $$\frac{d^2}{dx^2}\left(EI\frac{d^2Y(x)}{dx^2}\right) = W(x),$$

which gives the deflection of the beam when it is subjected to a given load $W(x)$. EI, the *flexural rigidity*, may be variable if the cross section of the beam is not uniform. Unless otherwise stated, we shall assume EI to be constant.

A solution of (4.8.6) will contain four arbitrary constants and consequently four boundary conditions must be prescribed. The following conditions occur frequently:

(i) *Hinged End*.   At a support such as this the vertical displacement Y and moment M must vanish and therefore

$$Y = EI(d^2Y/dx^2) = 0.$$

(ii) *Fixed or Clamped End*.   In this case the displacement Y and slope dY/dx must vanish, i.e.,

$$Y = dY/dx = 0.$$

(iii) *Free End*.   On the assumption that no shearing force or moment is applied at such an end, we have from (4.8.4) and (4.8.5)

$$EI \frac{d^2 Y(x)}{dx^2} = \frac{d}{dx}\left(EI \frac{d^2 Y(x)}{dx^2}\right) = 0.$$

Example 1.   A hinged beam of length l carries a uniform load of W_0 lb/ft over half its length and a concentrated load P_0 (Fig. 4.8.4). Find the deflection $Y(x)$.

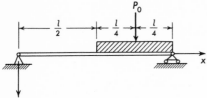

In terms of the unit and impulse functions the load can be represented thus

$$W(x) = W_0[1(x - l/2) - 1(x - l)] + P_0 1'(x - 3l/4),$$
$$0 < x < \infty.$$

Fig. 4.8.4

However, $1(x - l) = 0$ in the interval $0 < x < l$ over which the differential equation governs the deflection of the beam. Therefore equation (4.8.6) becomes

(4.8.7)
$$EI\, d^4 Y(x)/dx^4 = W_0 1(x - l) + P_0 1'(x - 3l/4), \quad 0 < x < l$$

with the boundary conditions

(4.8.8) $Y(0) = Y''(0) = 0, \qquad Y(l) = Y''(l) = 0.$

The transform of (4.8.7) is

$$EI[p^4 y(p) - p^3 Y(0) - p^2 Y'(0) - p Y''(0) - Y'''(0)]$$
$$= W_0 e^{-lp/2}/p + P_0 e^{-3lp/4},$$

from which, after applying the first two boundary conditions in (4.8.8), we get

(4.8.9) $$y(p) = \frac{Y'(0)}{p^2} + \frac{Y'''(0)}{p^4} + \frac{W_0}{EI}\frac{e^{-lp/2}}{p^5} + \frac{P_0}{EI}\frac{e^{-3lp/4}}{p^4}.$$

The result of taking the inverse transform of (4.8.9) is

(4.8.10) $Y(x) = Y'(0)x + Y'''(0)x^3/3!$
$$+ W_0(x - l/2)^4 1(x - l/2)/(4!EI)$$
$$+ P_0(x - 3l/4)^3 1(x - 3l/4)/(3!EI).$$

Making use of the last two boundary conditions (4.8.8), we obtain the two equations

$$Y'(0) + Y'''(0)l^2/3! + W_0 l^3/(4!2^4 EI) + P_0 l^2/(3!4^3 EI) = 0,$$
$$Y'''(0) + W_0 l/(2!4EI) + P_0/(4EI) = 0,$$

from which

$$Y'''(0) = -(W_0 l + 2P_0)/(8EI),$$
$$Y'(0) = (7W_0 l/384 + 5P_0/128)l^2/(EI).$$

These values when substituted in (4.8.10) give the deflection $Y(x)$ at any point in the interval $0 < x < l$.

Example 2.   A cantilever beam of length l, whose left end is clamped so that it remains horizontal, carries a uniformly distributed load of W_0 lb/ft over three-fourths of its length (Fig. 4.8.5).   Determine the deflection $Y(x)$.

Clearly, the load can be represented by the function

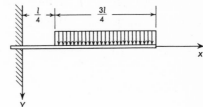

$$W(x) = W_0[1(x - l/4) - 1(x - l)],$$
$$0 < x < \infty.$$

In the interval $0 < x < l$, however, $1(x - l) = 0$.   Therefore the deflection is governed by the equation

FIG. 4.8.5

(4.8.11) $EI\ Y^{(4)}(x) = W_0 1(x - l/4), \quad 0 < x < l.$

For boundary conditions we have

$$Y(0) = Y'(0) = 0, \qquad Y'''(l) = Y''(l) = 0.$$

Taking the transform of (4.8.11) and solving for $y(p)$, we find that

$$y(p) = Y''(0)/p^3 + Y'''(0)/p^4 + W_0 e^{-lp/4}/(p^5 EI),$$

and by inversion

(4.8.12) $Y(x) = Y''(0)x^2/2! + Y'''(0)x^3/3!$
$$+ W_0(x - l/4)^4 1(x - l/4)/(4!EI), \quad 0 < x < l.$$

Taking the second and third derivatives of this equation and making use of the boundary conditions $Y''(l) = Y'''(l) = 0$, we obtain the equations

$$Y''(0) + Y'''(0)l + 9W_0 l^2/(32EI) = 0,$$
$$Y'''(0) + 3W_0 l/(4EI) = 0,$$

from which

$$Y'''(0) = -3W_0 l/(4EI),$$
$$Y''(0) = 15W_0 l^2/(32EI).$$

Substituting these values in (4.8.12) we finally get

$$Y(x) = W_0 l x^2 (15l - 8x)/(64EI)$$
$$+ W_0(x - \tfrac{1}{4}l)^4 1(x - \tfrac{1}{4}l)/(4!EI),$$
$$0 < x < l.$$

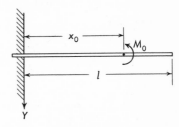

FIG. 4.8.6

Example 3.   A counterclockwise couple
of moment M_0 is applied at the point $x = x_0$ of a cantilever beam of length l (Fig. 4.8.6).   Find the curve of deflection.

The couple applied at $x = x_0$ can be represented by the distributed load $M_0 1''(x - x_0)$ (section 3.4). Hence the differential equation governing deflection is

$$EI \ Y^{(4)}(x) = M_0 1''(x - x_0),$$

with the boundary conditions

$$Y(0) = Y'(0) = 0, \qquad Y''(l) = Y'''(l) = 0.$$

As in the previous examples we find that

$$y(p) = Y''(0)/p^3 + Y'''(0)/p^4 + M_0 e^{-x_0 p}/(p^3 EI),$$

and

(4.8.13) $Y(x) = x^2 Y''(0)/2 + x^3 Y'''(0)/6$
$$+ M_0(x - x_0)^2 1(x - x_0)/(2EI).$$

Utilizing the conditions at the end $x = l$ we obtain

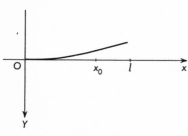

$$Y'''(0) = 0,$$
$$Y''(0) = -M_0/(EI).$$

The substitution of these values in (4.8.12) gives

$$Y(x) = -M_0[x^2$$
$$- (x - x_0)^2 1(x - x_0)]/(2EI),$$
$$0 < x < l,$$

F ig. 4.8.7

whose graph is shown in Fig. 4.8.7.

Remark. Each of the preceding three examples required the solution of a differential equation satisfying conditions which were specified at *two* points. In other physical problems the solution may have to satisfy conditions specified at *three* or *more* points. Such problems are called *boundary value* problems in order to distinguish them from *initial value* problems in which all the conditions are given at one point.

Exercise 1. Find the deflection curve for the beam loaded as shown in Fig. 4.8.8.

Ans. $EI \ Y(x) = W_0 x^4/4! + P_0(x - x_0)^3 1(x - x_0)/3!$
$$+ [W_0 l^4 - 4P_0(l - x_0)(x_0 - 2l)x_0]x^2/(16l^2)$$
$$+ [4P_0(l - x_0)(x_0^2 - 2lx_0 - 2l^2) - 5W_0 l^4] \ x^3/(48l^3).$$

Exercise 2. From the answer to exercise 1 deduce the equations of the deflection curves for the beams loaded as shown in Fig. 4.8.9 and Fig. 4.8.10. What principle is involved?

Exercise 3. Determine the curve of deflection for the beam of Fig. 4.8.11.

Ans. $6EI \ Y(x) = M_0 lx(1 - x^2/l^2) - 3M_0 x(l - x_0)^2/l$
$$+ 3M_0(x - x_0)^2 1(x - x_0), \quad 0 \leqslant x_0 \leqslant l.$$

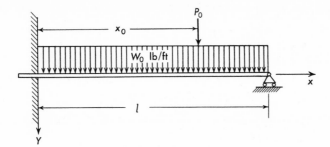

FIG. 4.8.8

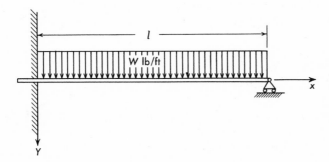

FIG. 4.8.9

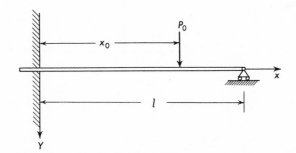

FIG. 4.8.10

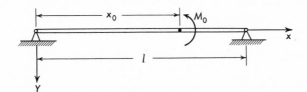

FIG. 4.8.11

4.9 Beams on an Elastic Foundation

An interesting and important problem is that of determining the deflection of a beam attached to an elastic foundation.

Suppose that AB represents a uniform beam attached to the elastic foundation CD which in turn is attached to a fixed base EF (Fig. 4.9.1).

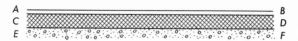

$$A \xrightarrow{\hspace{7cm}} B$$
$$C \hspace{7cm} D$$
$$E \hspace{7cm} F$$

FIG. 4.9.1

If $W(x)$ represents, as before, the load per unit length of the beam, and we assume that the restoring force per unit of length of the elastic medium is $-kY(x)$, acting in a direction opposite to $W(x)$, then from equation (4.8.6)

$$(4.9.1) \hspace{2cm} EI\ Y^{(4)}(x) = W(x) - kY(x),$$

where k is the so-called *modulus of the foundation*.

Example.   A uniform beam of length l, clamped at both ends, is attached to an elastic foundation and carries a uniform load of W_0 lb/ft (Fig. 4.9.2).   Find the deflection of the beam.

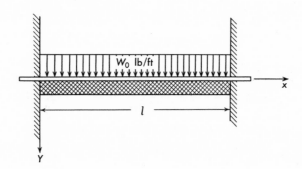

FIG. 4.9.2

In this case $W(x) = W_0$, so that equation (4.9.1) becomes (after transposing $kY(x)$ and dividing by EI):

$$(4.9.2) \hspace{2cm} Y^{(4)}(x) + kY(x)/EI = W_0/EI, \quad 0 < x < l.$$

For convenience, let us define $k/EI = 4a^4$.   Then equation (4.9.2) can be written as

$$(4.9.3) \hspace{2cm} Y^{(4)}(x) + 4a^4 Y(x) = W_0/EI.$$

Since the beam is clamped at both ends, the following conditions obtain

$$Y(0) = Y'(0) = 0, \qquad Y(l) = Y'(l) = 0.$$

The Laplace transform of (4.9.3) yields the equation

(4.9.4) $$y(p) = \frac{W_0}{EI} \frac{1}{p(p^4 + 4a^4)} + \frac{pY''(0)}{p^4 + 4a^4} + \frac{Y'''(0)}{p^4 + 4a^4},$$

and the inverse transform of (4.9.4) gives

(4.9.5) $$Y(x) = \frac{W_0}{EI} L^{-1}\left\{\frac{1}{p(p^4 + 4a^4)}\right\} + Y''(0) L^{-1}\left\{\frac{p}{p^4 + 4a^4}\right\}$$
$$+ Y'''(0) L^{-1}\left\{\frac{1}{p^4 + 4a^4}\right\}.$$

From the tables

$$L^{-1}\{1/(p^4 + 4a^4)\} = (\sin ax \cosh ax - \cos ax \sinh ax)/(4a^3),$$
$$L^{-1}\{p/(p^4 + 4a^4)\} = \sin ax \sinh ax/(2a^2),$$

and from (3.2.2)

$$L^{-1}\{1/[p(p^4 + 4a^4)]\} = \int_0^x (\sin a\xi \cosh a\xi - \cos a\xi \sinh a\xi)\, d\xi/(4a^3).$$

Therefore

(4:9.6) $$Y(x) = W_0 \int_0^x (\sin a\xi \cosh a\xi - \cos a\xi \sinh a\xi)\, d\xi/(4EIa^3)$$
$$+ Y''(0) \sin ax \sinh ax/(2a^2)$$
$$+ Y'''(0) (\sin ax \cosh ax - \cos ax \sinh ax)/(4a^3).$$

As before, $Y''(0)$ and $Y'''(0)$ are obtained by solving the two simultaneous equations that result when the conditions $Y(l) = Y'(l) = 0$ are used in (4.9.6).

Exercise 1. Obtain the simultaneous equations mentioned above and solve for $Y''(0)$ and $Y'''(0)$.

Ans. $$Y''(0) = \frac{W_0}{2aEI} \frac{\sinh al - \sin al}{\sin al + \sinh al},$$

$$Y'''(0) = \frac{W_0}{EI} \frac{\cos al - \cosh al}{\sin al + \sinh al}.$$

Exercise 2. (a) Find the deflection of the beam in the preceding illustrative example if it carries only a concentrated load P_0 at the midpoint of the beam.

(b) How would you find the deflection of this beam from the results thus far obtained if the load is that of the illustrative example plus the concentrated load P_0?

$$Ans. \ (a) \ \ Y(x) = \frac{W_0}{4a^3EI}[\sin a(x - \tfrac{1}{2}l) \cosh a(x - \tfrac{1}{2}l)$$

$$- \cos a(x - \tfrac{1}{2}l) \sinh a(x - \tfrac{1}{2}l)] \, 1(x - \tfrac{1}{2}l) + Y''(0) \sin ax \sinh ax/(2a^2)$$
$$+ \ Y'''(0)(\sin ax \cosh ax - \cos ax \sinh ax)/(4a^3),$$

where

$$Y''(0) = \frac{W_0}{aEI} \frac{\sinh (al/2) \sin (al/2)}{\sinh al + \sin al},$$

$$Y'''(0) = - \frac{W_0}{EI} \frac{\sin (al/2) \cosh (al/2) + \sinh (al/2) \cos (al/2)}{\sinh al + \sin al}.$$

4.10 Motion of a Particle in a Straight Line

Suppose that F represents the resultant of all the forces acting on a particle of constant mass m and a denotes its acceleration. Then Newton's second law states that

$$F = kma,$$

where k is a constant of proportionality depending on the system of units used. The systems in common use are the so-called *cgs* (cm-gm-sec) and *fps* (ft-lb-sec) systems. In the former, $k = 1$ if the mass is measured in grams, the force in dynes and the acceleration in cm/sec², whereas in the latter, $k = 1/g$ if the mass is measured in pounds, the acceleration in ft/sec² and the force in poundals. The gravitational constant g has the approximate value of 32·2 ft/sec² or 980·5 cm/sec².

We shall now illustrate the use of the Laplace transform method in solving ordinary differential equations with constant coefficients that arise in dynamics.

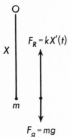

FIG. 4.10.1

Example 1.   A particle of mass m falls under gravity in a resisting medium whose resistance is proportional to its velocity. Find the motion of the particle if it starts from rest.

Let the position of rest be denoted by O and let X represent the distance of the particle from O at the time t. The forces acting on the particle are: the force of gravity F_g acting downward, and the force of resistance F_R acting upward (Fig. 4.10.1). If the downward direction be assumed *positive* and the upward direction *negative*, then the equation of motion is

(4.10.1) $mX''(t) = mg - kX'(t),$

where k is a positive constant.

Equation (4.10.1) must be solved subject to the initial conditions
$$X(0) = X'(0) = 0.$$
The transform of (4.10.1) gives

$$x(p) = \frac{mg}{p^2(mp + k)} = \frac{g}{p^2(p + k/m)},$$

and for the inverse, we have

(4.10.2) $$X(t) = \sum \text{Residues of } \frac{e^{pt}}{p^2(p + k/m)}$$

at the double pole $p = 0$ and the simple pole $p = -k/m$.

Computing these residues, we obtain

(4.10.3) $$X(t) = \frac{mg}{k} t + \frac{m^2 g}{k^2} (e^{(-k/m)t} - 1).$$

The velocity of the particle at any time t is

(4.10.4) $$X'(t) = \frac{mg}{k} (1 - e^{(-k/m)t}).$$

From (4.10.4) we see that as $t \to \infty$ the velocity $X'(t)$ approaches the so-called *limiting velocity* mg/k.

Example 2. A particle of mass m rests in equilibrium on a line joining two fixed centers of attraction. Each center attracts the particle with a force proportional to the distance of the particle from the corresponding center (the constants of proportionality are assumed to be different). Determine the motion if the particle is displaced a distance d_0 from the position of equilibrium and released from rest.

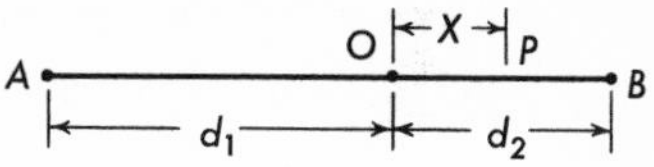

Let O be the position of equilibrium, $AO = d_1$, $OB = d_2$, and $OP = X$ the position of the particle at any time $t > 0$ (Fig. 4.10.2). If the direction from O to P is assumed *positive*, then the forces of attraction are

Fig. 4.10.2

$$F_A = -k_1(X + d_1) \quad \text{and} \quad F_B = k_2(d_2 - X).$$

Also, since O is a position of equilibrium

(4.10.5) $$k_1 d_1 = k_2 d_2.$$

Therefore, Newton's law gives
$$mX'' = -k_1(d_1 + X) + k_2(d_2 - X),$$
which in virtue of (4.10.5) becomes

(4.10.6) $$mX''(t) + (k_1 + k_2)X(t) = 0.$$

This equation must be solved subject to the initial conditions
$$X(0) = d_0, \qquad X'(0) = 0.$$

The transform of (4.10.6) is

$$x(p) = \frac{p d_0}{p^2 + (k_1 + k_2)/m}$$

and its inverse is

$$X(t) = d_0 \cos \sqrt{\frac{k_1 + k_2}{m}}\, t.$$

Thus the particle oscillates about the position of equilibrium O with simple harmonic motion of period $2\pi \sqrt{m/(k_1 + k_2)}$.

4.11 Motion of a Particle in a Plane

In mechanics it is shown that if a particle of mass m moves in space, then the equations governing its motion are given by

$$(4.11.1) \qquad m a_x = F_x, \qquad m a_y = F_y, \qquad m a_z = F_z,$$

where F_x, F_y, F_z, and a_x, a_y, a_z are the components along the coordinate axes X, Y, and Z, respectively, of the force $\bar{F}$ and the acceleration $\bar{a}$ (both vectors).

If the motion of the particle is confined to the plane, then there are only two equations:

$$(4.11.2) \qquad m a_x = F_x, \qquad m a_y = F_y.$$

Suppose that a particle of mass m (whose motion is restricted to the XY-plane) is always acted upon by a force $\bar{F}$ whose components along the coordinate axes are given by

$$F_x = -\lambda_1{}^2 X, \qquad F_y = -\lambda_2{}^2 Y,$$

where $\lambda_1{}^2$ and $\lambda_2{}^2$ are constants. Then equations (4.11.2) assume the form:

$$(4.11.3) \qquad m X'' = -\lambda_1{}^2 X, \qquad m Y'' = -\lambda_2{}^2 Y.$$

Putting $k_1{}^2 = \lambda_1{}^2/m$ and $k_2{}^2 = \lambda_2{}^2/m$, we obtain

$$(4.11.4) \qquad X'' + k_1{}^2 X = 0, \qquad Y'' + k_2{}^2 Y = 0.$$

If the particle is projected at $t = 0$ from the point $(0, d)$ with a velocity v whose components are (v_1, v_2), then the initial conditions are

$$(4.11.5) \quad X(0) = 0, \quad X'(0) = v_1, \qquad Y(0) = d, \quad Y'(0) = v_2.$$

We find that the transforms of (4.11.4) yield the algebraic equations

$$(4.11.6) \qquad (p^2 + k_1{}^2) x(p) = v_1, \qquad (p^2 + k_2{}^2) y(p) = p d + v_2,$$

and by taking the inverses of (4.11.6), we obtain

$$(4.11.7) \quad X(t) = \frac{v_1}{k_1} \sin k_1 t, \qquad Y(t) = \frac{v_2}{k_2} \sin k_2 t + d \cos k_2 t.$$

These are the parametric equations of the paths described by the

particle for various values of k_1 and k_2. The paths are called *Lissajous'*
curves which play a very important role in acoustics.

We shall now consider two special cases.

Case I. $k_1 = k_2 = k$. In this instance the equations (4.11.7)
become

$$X(t) = \frac{v_1}{k} \sin kt, \qquad Y(t) = \frac{v_2}{k} \sin kt + d \cos kt.$$

Eliminating the parameter t and simplifying, we get

$$(v_2{}^2 + d^2)X^2 - 2v_1v_2XY + v_1{}^2Y^2 = v_1{}^2d^2,$$

which is readily verified to be the equation of an ellipse with oblique
axes (Fig. 4.11.1). This motion is called *elliptic harmonic motion*.

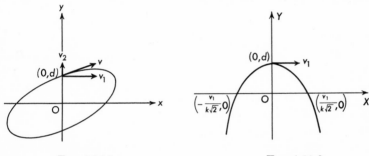

FIG. 4.11.1 FIG. 4.11.2

Case II. $k_1 = k$, $k_2 = 2k$, and $v_2 = 0$, so that initially the particle
is projected horizontally from the point $(0,d)$. Here, we have

$$X(t) = \frac{v_1}{k} \sin kt, \quad Y(t) = d \cos 2kt.$$

From trigonometry, $\cos 2kt = 1 - 2 \sin^2 kt$, and hence

$$Y = \frac{d}{v_1{}^2}(v_1{}^2 - 2k^2X^2),$$

which is a parabola (Fig. 4.11.2).

Exercise. Draw the graph of the Lissajous curve given by equation
(4.11.7) for the constants $k_1 = 2$, $k_2 = 3$, $v_1 = v_2 = 2$, $d = \frac{2}{3}$.

PROBLEMS

Solve the following differential equations and verify each solution:

1. $X''(t) + 3X'(t) + 2X(t) = 0$.
   Ans. $X(t) = - [X'(0) + X(0)]e^{2t} + [2X(0) + X'(0)]e^{-t}$.
2. $X''(t) + X(t) = t$.
   Ans. $X(t) = t - \sin t + X(0) \cos t + X'(0) \sin t$.

3. $X''(t) - X'(t) - 2X(t) = t$.
   Ans. $X(t) = [-1 - X'(0) + 2X(0)]e^{-t}/3 + [1 + 4X(0)$
   $$+ 4X'(0)]e^{2t}/12 - \frac{t}{2} + \frac{1}{4}.$$

4. $X''(t) + \omega^2 X(t) = F(t)$.   Ans. $X(t) = X(0)\cos \omega t + \dfrac{X'(0)}{\omega}\sin \omega t$
   $$+ \frac{1}{\omega}\int_0^t F(\tau)\sin \omega(t - \tau)\,d\tau.$$

5. $X'''(t) + X(t) = a$, $X(0) = X'(0) = X''(0) = 0$.

   Ans. $X(t) = \dfrac{a}{3}(3 - e^{-t} - 2e^{t/2}\cos \dfrac{\sqrt{3}}{2}t)$.

6. $X^{(4)}(t) + X''(t) = e^{at}$, $X(0) = X'(0) = 0$, $X''(0) = 1$, $X'''(0) = -1$.

   Ans. $X(t) = -\dfrac{a+1}{a}t + \dfrac{a^2 - 1}{a^2} + \dfrac{e^{at}}{a^2(a^2 + 1)} + \dfrac{a^2 + a + 1}{a^2 + 1}\sin t$
   $$- \frac{a^2}{a^2 + 1}\cos t.$$

7. $X'''(t) + 3X''(t) + 2X'(t) = 1 - t^2$, $X(0) = X'(0) = X''(0) = 0$.
   Ans. $X(t) = \frac{9}{8} - \frac{5}{4}t + \frac{3}{4}t^2 - \frac{1}{6}t^3 - \frac{1}{8}e^{-2t} - e^{-t}$.

8. $X^{(4)}(t) - 2X^{(2)}(t) + X(t) = \cos t$, $X(0) = X'(0) = 0$,
   $$X''(0) = X'''(0) = 1.$$
   Ans. $X(t) = (3t - 2)(\sinh t)/4 + (2t - 1)(\cosh t)/4 + (\cos t)/4$.

9. Find the current $I(t)$ in a series $R\text{-}C$ circuit for $t > 0$ if, initially, $Q(0) = Q_0$ and the applied voltage $E(t)$ has the following representations:
   (i) $E(t) = E_1[1(t) - 1(t - t_0)] + E_2[1(t - t_0) - 1(t - t_1)]$
   $$+ E_1[1(t + t_1) - 1(t - t_2)], \quad t_0 < t_1 < t_2, \quad E_1 < E_2.$$
   (ii) $E(t) = [1(t) - 1(t - \pi)]\sin t$.
   (iii) $E(t) = t[1(t) - 1(t - t_0)] + (2t_0 - t)[1(t - t_0) - 1(t - 2t_0)]$.
   (iv) $E(t) = t^2[1(t - t_0) - 1(t - t_1)]$, $t_0 < t_1$.
   (v) $\quad E(t) = E_0, \quad 0 < t < T_1$,
   $\qquad\quad = 0, \quad T_1 < t < T_2$,
   $\qquad\quad = E_0, \quad T_2 < t < T$,
   $E(t + T) = E(t)$.
   (vi) $\quad E(t) = 2E_0 t/T, \quad 0 < t < T/2$
   $\qquad\qquad = -2E_0(t - T)/T, \quad T/2 < t < T$
   $E(t + T) = E(t)$.

10 Find the current $I(t)$ in a series $R\text{-}C\text{-}L$ circuit for $t > 0$ if, initially, $Q(0) = Q_0$, $I(0) = 0$ and the voltage $E(t)$ has the representations given in problem 9.

11. If the applied voltage $E(t)$ has the representations given in problem 9, find the current $I(t)$ and the voltage $E(t)$ for $t > 0$ in a series $R\text{-}L$ circuit if, initially, $I(0) = 0$.

12. When a stretched horizontal perfectly flexible cable (cord, string) of length l is subjected to vertical loads which do not cause large deflections, then it can be shown that the differential equation* governing the deflections is given by

$$HY''(x) = -W(x), \quad 0 < x < l$$

where H is the horizontal tension, $W(x)$ is the load per unit length and $Y(x)$ is the deflection. Both $W(x)$ and $Y(x)$ are measured *positive downward*.

Making use of the preceding equation, find the deflection curves for the cables carrying the following loads:

(a) $W(x) = W_0, \quad 0 < x < \frac{3}{4}l,$
$\qquad = 0, \quad \frac{3}{4}l < x < l.$

Ans. $Y(x) = \dfrac{15}{32} \dfrac{W_0}{H} xl - \dfrac{W_0}{2H} [x^2 - (x - \frac{3}{4}l)^2 1(x - \frac{3}{4}l)].$

(b) $W(x) = 0, \quad 0 < x < \frac{1}{2}l,$
$\qquad = W_0, \quad \frac{1}{2}l < x < \frac{3}{4}l,$
$\qquad = 0, \quad \frac{3}{4}l < x < l.$

Ans. $Y(x) = \dfrac{3}{32} \dfrac{W_0}{H} xl$

$$- \dfrac{W_0}{2H}\left[\left(x - \dfrac{l}{2}\right)^2 1\left(x - \dfrac{l}{2}\right) - (x - \tfrac{3}{4}l)^2 1(x - \tfrac{3}{4}l)\right].$$

(c) A concentrated load W_0 at $x = x_0$, $\quad 0 < x_0 < l.$

Ans. $Y(x) = \dfrac{W_0}{Hl}(l - x_0)x - \dfrac{W_0}{H}(x - x_0)1(x - x_0).$

(d) Find the general solution of $HY''(x) = -W(x)$ by making use of the Faltung theorem.

Ans. $Y(x) = \dfrac{x}{lH} \displaystyle\int_0^l (l - \xi)W(\xi)\, d\xi - \dfrac{1}{H} \displaystyle\int_0^x (x - \xi)W(\xi)\, d\xi.$

13. Find the deflection curve for a beam of length l, hinged at both ends and carrying the load of problem 12(a).

Ans. $Y(x) = \dfrac{W_0}{EI}\left[\dfrac{x^4}{4!} - \dfrac{(x - x_0)^4}{4!} 1(x - x_0) + \dfrac{75}{8 \cdot 4^4}xl^3 - \dfrac{15}{8 \cdot 4!}x^3 l\right].$

14. Find the deflection curve for a beam of length l, clamped at the left end, hinged at the right end and carrying the load of problem 12(b).

Ans. $Y(x) = \dfrac{W_0}{EI}\Bigg[\dfrac{(x - l/4)^4}{4!} 1(x - l/2) - \dfrac{(x - \frac{3}{4}l)^4}{4!} 1(x - \tfrac{3}{4}l)$

$$+ \dfrac{81l^2x^2}{16^3} - \dfrac{91}{16^3}x^3 l\Bigg].$$

---

* See T. v. Karman and M. A. Biot, *Mathematical Methods in Engineering*, p. 261, for a derivation of this equation.

15. Find the deflection curve for a beam of length l, clamped at both ends and carrying the concentrated load of problem 12(c).

$$\text{Ans.}\quad Y(x) = \frac{W_0}{6EIl^3}x^2(l-x_0)^2[3x_0l-(l+2x_0)x]$$

$$+\frac{W_0}{6EI}(x-x_0)^3 1(x-x_0).$$

16. Find the general solution of the beam equation $EI\,Y^{(4)}(x) = W(x)$ for clamped ends by making use of the convolution theorem.

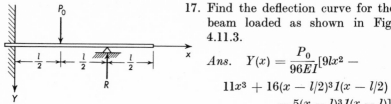

FIG. 4.11.3

17. Find the deflection curve for the beam loaded as shown in Fig. 4.11.3.

$$\text{Ans.}\quad Y(x) = \frac{P_0}{96EI}[9lx^2 -$$

$$11x^3 + 16(x-l/2)^3 1(x-l/2)$$
$$-5(x-l)^3 1(x-l)].$$

18. A light beam of length l, clamped at both ends, is attached to an elastic foundation and carries a concentrated load W_0 at $x = \frac{1}{2}l$. Find the deflection of the beam.

$$\text{Ans.}\quad Y(x) = \frac{W_0}{4EIa^3}\left[\sin a\left(x-\frac{l}{2}\right)\cosh a\left(x-\frac{l}{2}\right)\right.$$

$$\left.-\cos a\left(x-\frac{l}{2}\right)\sinh a\left(x-\frac{l}{2}\right)\right]1\left(x-\frac{l}{2}\right)$$

$$+\frac{Y''(0)}{2a^2}\sin ax\sinh ax$$

$$+\frac{Y'''(0)}{4a^3}[\sin ax\cosh ax - \cos ax\sinh ax],$$

where

$$Y''(0) = \frac{W_0}{aEI}\frac{[F(A-B)-C(D-E)]}{(D^2-E^2-2F^2)},$$

$$Y'''(0) = -\frac{W_0}{EI}\frac{[(A-B)(D+E)-2CF]}{(D^2-E^2-2F^2)},$$

$$k/EI = a^4,$$

$$A = \cos\frac{al}{2}\cosh\frac{al}{2},\qquad B = \cos\frac{al}{2}\sinh\frac{al}{2},\qquad C = \sin\frac{al}{2}\sinh\frac{al}{2},$$

$$D = \sin al\cosh al,\qquad E = \cos al\sinh al,\qquad F = \sin al\sinh al.$$

19. A chain a ft long, weighing w_0 lb/ft, begins to move with $(1/5)a$ ft hanging over a table. If the motion is resisted by a constant force of F_0 lb, find the time required for it to fall off.

$$\text{Ans.}\quad t = \sqrt{\frac{a}{g}}\,\cosh^{-1}\frac{5(aw_0-F_0)}{aw_0-5F_0}.$$

20. A weight of 8 lb extends a spring 1 in. The weight is then given a downward displacement of 3 in. from the position of equilibrium and released. If the resistance of the medium is 10 lb for a velocity of 1 ft/sec, find the position of the body at any time t.

21. A cylindrical buoy, 10 in. in diameter and weighing 200 lb, stands vertically in fresh water. Assuming that the resistance of the water to its motion is proportional to its velocity and equals 4 lb when the velocity is 2 ft/sec, find the period of oscillation and the damping constant when the buoy is given a vertical displacement and released.

CHAPTER V

Matrix Algebra and Systems of Linear Differential Equations

When mechanical systems having more than one degree of freedom are studied or when multi-mesh electrical networks are analyzed, it is found that simultaneous systems of differential equations must be solved. As such systems usually involve many equations it is desirable to have a method that will facilitate not only the writing down of these equations but also their solution. The elements of matrix algebra which we shall study will enable us to express complicated systems compactly and by employing the Laplace transform theory to them we shall eliminate much of the drudgery associated with systems of equations.

5.1 Matrix Algebra

A collection of elements arranged in rows and columns is said to form an *array*. The individual elements may represent, e.g., real or complex numbers. An array consisting of m rows and n columns will be denoted by

$$\mathbf{A} = \begin{bmatrix} a_{11} & a_{12} \cdots a_{1n} \\ a_{21} & a_{22} \cdots a_{2n} \\ \cdot & \cdot \quad \cdot \quad \cdot \\ a_{m1} & a_{m2} \quad a_{mn} \end{bmatrix} = [a_{ij}]$$

and called a *matrix* of order $(m \times n)$.

In particular, the matrix $\mathbf{A}$ may consist of one row

$$\mathbf{A} = [a_1 \quad a_2 \cdots a_n],$$

in which case it is often referred to as a *row matrix*. Or, it may consist of one column

$$\mathbf{A} = \begin{bmatrix} a_1 \\ a_2 \\ \vdots \\ a_n \end{bmatrix},$$

in which case it is called a *column matrix*.

When $m = n$, we have the particularly important case of a *square* matrix.

Two matrices $\mathbf{A}$ and $\mathbf{B}$ of the same order are said to be equal if the corresponding elements are equal, i.e.,

$$\mathbf{A} = \mathbf{B} \quad \text{if} \quad a_{ij} = b_{ij}.$$

Multiplication of a matrix $\mathbf{A}$ by the *scalar k* is defined by the relation

$$k[a_{ij}] = [ka_{ij}] = [a_{ij}]k.$$

Thus

$$k \begin{bmatrix} a_{11} & a_{12} \\ a_{21} & a_{22} \end{bmatrix} = \begin{bmatrix} ka_{11} & ka_{12} \\ ka_{21} & ka_{22} \end{bmatrix} = \begin{bmatrix} a_{11} & a_{12} \\ a_{21} & a_{22} \end{bmatrix} k.$$

The *sum* or *difference* of two matrices of the same order is the matrix each of whose elements is the sum or difference of the corresponding elements of the two given matrices, i.e.,

$$[a_{ij}] \pm [b_{ij}] = [a_{ij} \pm b_{ij}].$$

It is easy to verify that the *commutative* and *associative* laws of addition are valid. Thus

$$\mathbf{A} + \mathbf{B} = \mathbf{B} + \mathbf{A},$$

and

$$\mathbf{A} + (\mathbf{B} + \mathbf{C}) = (\mathbf{A} + \mathbf{B}) + \mathbf{C}.$$

The *product* of two matrices $\mathbf{A}$ and $\mathbf{B}$ in the order $\mathbf{AB}$ is defined only if $\mathbf{A}$ has the same number of *columns* as $\mathbf{B}$ has *rows*. If this condition is satisfied, then by definition

$$[a_{ij}][b_{ij}] = c_{ij},$$

where

$$c_{ij} = \sum_{k=1}^{l} a_{ik} b_{kj},$$

and the orders of $\mathbf{A}$, $\mathbf{B}$, and $\mathbf{C}$ are $(m \times l)$, $(l \times n)$ and $(m \times n)$, respectively. Thus from the definition, we have

$$\mathbf{AB} = \begin{bmatrix} a_{11} & a_{12} & a_{13} \\ a_{21} & a_{22} & a_{23} \end{bmatrix} \begin{bmatrix} b_{11} & b_{12} \\ b_{21} & b_{22} \\ b_{31} & b_{32} \end{bmatrix}$$

$$= \begin{bmatrix} a_{11}b_{11} + a_{12}b_{21} + a_{13}b_{31} & a_{11}b_{12} + a_{12}b_{22} + a_{13}b_{32} \\ a_{21}b_{11} + a_{22}b_{21} + a_{23}b_{31} & a_{21}b_{12} + a_{22}b_{22} + a_{23}b_{32} \end{bmatrix}.$$

Since

$$\mathbf{BA} = \begin{bmatrix} b_{11} & b_{12} \\ b_{21} & b_{22} \\ b_{31} & b_{32} \end{bmatrix} \begin{bmatrix} a_{11} & a_{12} & a_{13} \\ a_{21} & a_{22} & a_{23} \end{bmatrix}$$

$$= \begin{bmatrix} b_{11}a_{11} + b_{12}a_{21} & b_{11}a_{12} + b_{12}a_{22} & b_{11}a_{13} + b_{12}a_{23} \\ b_{21}a_{11} + b_{22}a_{21} & b_{21}a_{12} + b_{22}a_{22} & b_{21}a_{13} + b_{22}a_{23} \\ b_{31}a_{11} + b_{32}a_{21} & b_{31}a_{12} + b_{32}a_{22} & b_{31}a_{13} + b_{32}a_{23} \end{bmatrix},$$

we see that the matrices $\mathbf{A}$ and $\mathbf{B}$ do not commute in general, i.e.,

$$\mathbf{AB} \neq \mathbf{BA}.$$

On the other hand, the *associative* law for matrix products holds, i.e.,

$$(\mathbf{AB})\mathbf{C} = \mathbf{A}(\mathbf{BC}).$$

This follows from the fact that the order of summation in the expression

$$\sum_{j=1}^{n} \sum_{k=1}^{m} a_{ik}b_{kj}c_{jl}$$

for the product of the three matrices $\mathbf{A}$, $\mathbf{B}$, $\mathbf{C}$ is immaterial.

It can easily be verified that the *distributive* law of multiplication holds for matrices. Thus

$$\mathbf{A}(\mathbf{B} + \mathbf{C}) = \mathbf{AB} + \mathbf{AC}.$$

A matrix each of whose elements is zero is called a *zero* matrix and we shall denote it by $\mathbf{O}$. Clearly,

$$\mathbf{O} + \mathbf{A} = \mathbf{A} + \mathbf{O} = \mathbf{A}.$$

A *square* matrix such that the a_{ii}'s are 1's and such that the a_{ij}'s $(i \neq j)$ are zero is called a *unit* or *identity* matrix and we shall denote it by **I**.   It has the property that

$$\mathbf{IA} = \mathbf{AI} = \mathbf{A}.$$

If the rows and columns of the matrix **A** are interchanged, then the resulting matrix is called the *transpose* of matrix **A** and it is denoted by **A**'.   Thus, if $\mathbf{A} = [a_{ij}]$, then $\mathbf{A}' = [a_{ji}]$.

The following relations are readily proved:

$$\mathbf{(A + B)}' = \mathbf{A}' + \mathbf{B}',$$
$$\mathbf{(AB)}' = \mathbf{B}'\mathbf{A}',$$

or, more generally,

$$\mathbf{(A_1 + A_2 + \cdots + A_n)}' = \mathbf{A}_1' + \mathbf{A}_2' + \cdots + \mathbf{A}_n',$$
$$\mathbf{(A_1 A_2 \cdots A_n)}' = \mathbf{A}_n' \cdots \mathbf{A}_2' \mathbf{A}_1'.$$

If a matrix is equal to its transpose, then it is said to be *symmetric*, i.e., symbolically

$$\mathbf{A} = \mathbf{A}'$$

for a symmetric matrix.   Clearly, only a square matrix can be symmetric.

Suppose, now, that the elements a_{ij} of a matrix **A** are functions of the variable t and that the interval over which each function is defined is $t_0 \leqslant t \leqslant t_1$.   Then the matrix **A** will depend on t and we may write

$$\mathbf{A}(t) = \begin{bmatrix} a_{11}(t) & a_{12}(t) & \cdots & a_{1n}(t) \\ a_{21}(t) & a_{22}(t) & \cdots & a_{2n}(t) \\ \cdot & \cdot & \cdots & \cdot \\ a_{m1}(t) & a_{m2}(t) & \cdots & a_{mn}(t) \end{bmatrix}.$$

By the derivative of a matrix we mean the matrix each of whose elements is the derivative of the corresponding element of the given matrix.   Thus

$$\frac{d}{dt}\mathbf{A}(t) = \begin{bmatrix} \dfrac{d}{dt}a_{11}(t) & \dfrac{d}{dt}a_{12}(t) & \cdots & \dfrac{d}{dt}a_{1n}(t) \\ \dfrac{d}{dt}a_{21}(t) & \dfrac{d}{dt}a_{22}(t) & \cdots & \dfrac{d}{dt}a_{2n}(t) \\ \cdot & \cdot & \cdots & \cdot \\ \dfrac{d}{dt}a_{m1}(t) & \dfrac{d}{dt}a_{m2}(t) & \cdots & \dfrac{d}{dt}a_{mn}(t) \end{bmatrix}.$$

Similarly, the integral of a matrix is the matrix each of whose elements is the integral of the corresponding element of the given matrix. Thus

$$\int \mathbf{A}(t)dt = \begin{bmatrix} \int a_{11}(t)dt & \int a_{12}(t)dt & \cdots & \int a_{1n}(t)dt \\ \int a_{21}(t)dt & \int a_{22}(t)dt & \cdots & \int a_{2n}(t)dt \\ \cdot & \cdot & \cdot & \cdot \\ \int a_{m1}(t)dt & \int a_{m2}(t)dt & \cdots & \int a_{mn}(t)dt \end{bmatrix}$$

Exercise 1. Prove the following relations for matrices **A**, **B**, and **C**:

(i) $\mathbf{A} + \mathbf{B} = \mathbf{B} + \mathbf{A}$,
(ii) $\mathbf{A} + (\mathbf{B} + \mathbf{C}) = (\mathbf{A} + \mathbf{B}) + \mathbf{C}$,
(iii) $\mathbf{A}(\mathbf{B}\mathbf{C}) = (\mathbf{A}\mathbf{B})\mathbf{C}$,
(iv) $\mathbf{A}(\mathbf{B} + \mathbf{C}) = \mathbf{A}\mathbf{B} + \mathbf{A}\mathbf{C}$.

Exercise 2. Prove that:

(i) $(\mathbf{A}')' = \mathbf{A}$,   (ii) $(\mathbf{A}\mathbf{B})' = \mathbf{B}'\mathbf{A}'$.

Exercise 3. Show that the following formulas hold:

(i) $\dfrac{d}{dt}[\mathbf{A}(t) + \mathbf{B}(t)] = \dfrac{d\mathbf{A}(t)}{dt} + \dfrac{d\mathbf{B}(t)}{dt}$,

(ii) $\dfrac{d}{dt}[\mathbf{A}(t)\mathbf{B}(t)] = \mathbf{A}(t)\dfrac{d\mathbf{B}(t)}{dt} + \dfrac{d\mathbf{A}(t)}{dt}\mathbf{B}(t)$,

(iii) $\int[\mathbf{A}(t) + \mathbf{B}(t)]dt = \int \mathbf{A}(t)dt + \int \mathbf{B}(t)dt$.

5.2 Inverse of Matrix

Let **A** denote a square matrix and $|\mathbf{A}|$ the determinant formed from the elements of **A**. If $|\mathbf{A}| \neq 0$, then **A** is said to be a *non-singular* matrix, otherwise it is *singular*.

The matrix $\mathbf{A}^{-1}$ having the property that

$$\mathbf{A}\mathbf{A}^{-1} = \mathbf{A}^{-1}\mathbf{A} = \mathbf{I}$$

is defined as the *inverse* of matrix **A**. We shall see that the inverse of a matrix exists if the matrix is non-singular.

In order to determine an expression for the inverse of a matrix, we make use of some results from the elementary theory of determinants. If A_{ij} is the cofactor (signed minor) of the element a_{ij} in the determinant $|\mathbf{A}|$, then it is known that

$$\sum_{j=1}^{n} a_{ij}A_{kj} = |\mathbf{A}| \text{ when } i = k,$$
$$= 0 \text{ when } i \neq k.$$

Now, if $\mathbf{A}$ is non-singular, $|\mathbf{A}| \neq 0$ and we may divide by $|\mathbf{A}|$ and the preceding relation can be written as

$$\sum_{j=1}^{n} a_{ij} \frac{A_{kj}}{|\mathbf{A}|} = 1 \text{ when } i = k,$$
$$= 0 \text{ when } i \neq k.$$

But this is equivalent to the relation

$$\mathbf{A} \frac{[A_{ji}]}{|\mathbf{A}|} = \mathbf{I}.$$

Therefore

(5.2.1)
$$\mathbf{A}^{-1} = \frac{[A_{ji}]}{|\mathbf{A}|} = \frac{[A_{ij}]'}{|\mathbf{A}|}.$$

The matrix $[A_{ji}] = [A_{ij}]'$ is called the *adjoint* of the matrix $[a_{ij}]$. Thus, to find the inverse of the matrix

$$\mathbf{A} = \begin{bmatrix} 1 & -2 & 0 \\ 3 & 4 & -1 \\ 5 & 0 & -3 \end{bmatrix},$$

we form the matrix whose elements are the cofactors of the corresponding elements of $\mathbf{A}$, namely,

$$[A_{ij}] = \begin{bmatrix} -12 & 4 & -20 \\ -6 & -3 & -10 \\ 2 & 1 & 10 \end{bmatrix}.$$

The adjoint matrix is the transpose of this matrix and hence

$$[A_{ji}] = [A_{ij}]' = \begin{bmatrix} -12 & -6 & 2 \\ 4 & -3 & 1 \\ -20 & -10 & 10 \end{bmatrix}.$$

Now, since $|\mathbf{A}| = -20$, we finally have

$$\mathbf{A}^{-1} = \frac{\begin{bmatrix} -12 & -6 & 2 \\ 4 & -3 & 1 \\ -20 & -10 & 10 \end{bmatrix}}{-20} = \begin{bmatrix} \frac{3}{5} & \frac{3}{10} & -\frac{1}{10} \\ -\frac{1}{5} & \frac{3}{20} & -\frac{1}{20} \\ 1 & \frac{1}{2} & -\frac{1}{2} \end{bmatrix}.$$

One of the most frequently occurring problems in applied mathematics is that of solving a system of linear equations. With the aid of matrix algebra concepts it is possible to write such systems and their solutions in compact form. For, consider the system of equations

$$Y_1 = a_{11}X_1 + a_{12}X_2 + \cdots + a_{1n}X_n,$$
$$Y_2 = a_{21}X_1 + a_{22}X_2 + \cdots + a_{2n}X_n,$$
$$\cdot \quad \cdot \quad \cdot \quad \cdot \quad \cdot \quad \cdot \quad \cdot \quad \cdot \quad \cdot \quad \cdot \quad \cdot \quad \cdot$$
$$Y_n = a_{n1}X_1 + a_{n2}X_2 + \cdots + a_{nn}X_n.$$

If we let

$$\mathbf{Y} = \begin{bmatrix} Y_1 \\ Y_2 \\ \vdots \\ Y_n \end{bmatrix} \quad \text{and} \quad \mathbf{X} = \begin{bmatrix} X_1 \\ X_2 \\ \vdots \\ X_n \end{bmatrix},$$

then evidently the above system can be written as

$$\mathbf{Y} = \mathbf{AX},$$

where $\mathbf{A} = [a_{ij}]$. Now, if we multiply both sides on the left by $\mathbf{A}^{-1}$, then, provided the matrix $\mathbf{A}$ is non-singular, we obtain

$$\mathbf{X} = \mathbf{A}^{-1}\mathbf{Y},$$

which is the symbolic solution of our system.

As an example, let us solve the system of equations

$$3 = X_1 - 2X_2,$$
$$-2 = 3X_1 + 4X_2 - X_3,$$
$$-1 = 5X_1 - 3X_3.$$

The matrix of this system of equations is

$$\mathbf{A} = \begin{bmatrix} 1 & -2 & 0 \\ 3 & 4 & -1 \\ 5 & 0 & -3 \end{bmatrix},$$

and its inverse is

$$\mathbf{A}^{-1} = \begin{bmatrix} \frac{3}{5} & \frac{3}{10} & -\frac{1}{10} \\ -\frac{1}{5} & \frac{3}{20} & -\frac{1}{20} \\ 1 & \frac{1}{2} & -\frac{1}{2} \end{bmatrix},$$

as was shown above. Therefore

$$\begin{bmatrix} X_1 \\ X_2 \\ X_3 \end{bmatrix} = \begin{bmatrix} \frac{3}{5} & \frac{3}{10} & -\frac{1}{10} \\ -\frac{1}{5} & \frac{3}{20} & -\frac{1}{20} \\ 1 & \frac{1}{2} & -\frac{1}{2} \end{bmatrix} \begin{bmatrix} 3 \\ -2 \\ -1 \end{bmatrix} = \begin{bmatrix} \frac{13}{10} \\ -\frac{17}{20} \\ \frac{5}{2} \end{bmatrix}$$

and $X_1 = \frac{13}{10}$, $X_2 = -\frac{17}{20}$, $X_3 = \frac{5}{2}$.

Exercise I. Prove the following relations:

(a) $(\mathbf{A}')^{-1} = (\mathbf{A}^{-1})'$,   (b) $(\mathbf{AB})^{-1} = \mathbf{B}^{-1}\mathbf{A}^{-1}$.

Exercise 2. Solve the following system of equations by matrix methods

$$3X_1 - X_2 + 5X_3 = 7,$$
$$X_1 + 2X_2 - 4X_3 = -4,$$
$$2X_2 - 3X_2 + X_3 = 1.$$

Exercise 3. Using the relation $\mathbf{A}^{-1}(t)\mathbf{A}(t) = \mathbf{I}$ and the formula for the derivative of the product of two matrices, show that

$$\frac{d}{dt}\mathbf{A}^{-1}(t) = -\mathbf{A}^{-1}(t)\frac{d\mathbf{A}(t)}{dt}\mathbf{A}^{-1}(t).$$

Exercise 4. If

$$\mathbf{A} = \begin{bmatrix} a_{11} & a_{12} \cdots a_{1n} \\ a_{21} & a_{22} \cdots a_{2n} \\ \cdot & \cdot \quad \cdot \quad \cdot \\ a_{n1} & a_{n2} \cdots a_{nn} \end{bmatrix} \quad \text{and} \quad \mathbf{Y}(t) = \begin{bmatrix} Y_1(t) \\ Y_2(t) \\ \vdots \\ Y_n(t) \end{bmatrix},$$

verify that

$$L\{\mathbf{A}\mathbf{Y}(t)\} = \mathbf{A}L\{\mathbf{Y}(t)\}.$$

5.3 A System of First Order Linear Ordinary Differential Equations

In many applications it is required to find the solution of the following system of differential equations

(5.3.1)
$$a_{11}Y_1'(t) + a_{12}Y_2'(t) + \cdots + a_{1n}\,Y_n'(t) + \cdots + b_{11}Y_1(t)$$
$$+ b_{12}Y_2(t) + \cdots + b_{1n}Y_n(t) = F_1(t)$$
$$a_{21}Y_1'(t) + a_{22}Y_2'(t) + \cdots + a_{2n}Y_n'(t) + \cdots + b_{21}Y_1(t)$$
$$+ b_{22}Y_2(t) + \cdots + b_{2n}Y_n(t) = F_2(t)$$
$$\cdot \quad \cdot \quad \cdot \quad \cdot \quad \cdot \quad \cdot \quad \cdot \quad \cdot \quad \cdot \quad \cdot \quad \cdot \quad \cdot$$
$$a_{n1}Y_1'(t) + a_{n2}Y_2'(t) + \cdots + a_{nn}Y_n'(t) + \cdots + b_{n1}Y_1(t)$$
$$+ b_{n2}Y_2(t) + \cdots + b_{nn}Y_n(t) = F_n(t),$$

where the a_{ij}'s are constants. Such a system is termed a system of *first order linear ordinary differential equations.* These equations, which may be written more compactly in the following way,

(5.3.2)
$$\sum_{k=1}^{n} a_{ik}Y_k'\,(t) + \sum_{k=1}^{n} b_{ik}Y_k(t) = F_i(t), \quad i = 1, 2, \cdots, n$$

are to be solved subject to the initial conditions

(5.3.3)
$$Y_1(0) = Y_{10}, \qquad Y_2(0) = Y_{20}, \cdots, \qquad Y_n(0) = Y_{n0}.$$

Now, if we let

$$\mathbf{A} = \begin{bmatrix} a_{11}\, a_{12} \cdots a_{1n} \\ a_{21}\, a_{22} \cdots a_{2n} \\ \cdot\quad\cdot\quad\cdot\quad\cdot \\ a_{n1}\, a_{n2} \cdots a_{nn} \end{bmatrix}, \qquad \mathbf{B} = \begin{bmatrix} b_{11}\, b_{12} \cdots b_{1n} \\ b_{21}\, b_{22} \cdots b_{2n} \\ \cdot\quad\cdot\quad\cdot\quad\cdot \\ b_{n1}\, b_{n2} \cdots b_{nn} \end{bmatrix},$$

$$\mathbf{Y}(t) = \begin{bmatrix} Y_1(t) \\ Y_2(t) \\ \vdots \\ Y_n(t) \end{bmatrix}, \quad \mathbf{F}(t) = \begin{bmatrix} F_1(t) \\ F_2(t) \\ \vdots \\ F_n(t) \end{bmatrix}, \quad \mathbf{Y}(0) = \begin{bmatrix} Y_{10} \\ Y_{20} \\ \vdots \\ Y_{n0} \end{bmatrix},$$

then clearly (5.3.2) can be written as the *matric differential equation*

(5.3.4) $$\mathbf{A}\mathbf{Y}'(t) + \mathbf{B}\mathbf{Y}(t) = \mathbf{F}(t).$$

Furthermore, if $L\{\mathbf{Y}(t)\} = \mathbf{y}(p)$ and $L\{\mathbf{F}(t)\} = \mathbf{f}(p)$, where

$$\mathbf{y}(p) = \begin{bmatrix} L\{Y_1(t)\} \\ L\{Y_2(t)\} \\ \vdots \\ L\{Y_n(t)\} \end{bmatrix} = \begin{bmatrix} y_1(p) \\ y_2(p) \\ \vdots \\ y_n(p) \end{bmatrix} \text{ and } \mathbf{f}(p) = \begin{bmatrix} L\{F_1(t)\} \\ L\{F_2(t)\} \\ \vdots \\ L\{F_n(t)\} \end{bmatrix} = \begin{bmatrix} f_1(p) \\ f_2(p) \\ \vdots \\ f_n(p) \end{bmatrix},$$

then upon taking the Laplace transform of (5.3.4), we obtain

(5.3.5) $$(\mathbf{A}p + \mathbf{B})\mathbf{y}(p) = \mathbf{f}(p) + \mathbf{A}\mathbf{Y}(0),$$

whence, after multiplying on the left by $(\mathbf{A}p + \mathbf{B})^{-1}$,

(5.3.6) $$\mathbf{y}(p) = (\mathbf{A}p + \mathbf{B})^{-1}[\mathbf{f}(p) + \mathbf{A}\mathbf{Y}(0)],$$

provided $\mathbf{A}$ and $\mathbf{B}$ are non-singular.

The inverse transform of this expression gives the solution

(5.3.7) $$\mathbf{Y}(t) = L^{-1}\{(\mathbf{A}p + \mathbf{B})^{-1}[\mathbf{f}(p) + \mathbf{A}\mathbf{Y}(0)]\}.$$

In order to illustrate the mode of procedure we shall consider two examples.

Example 1. Find the functions $Y_1(t)$ and $Y_2(t)$ that satisfy the system of equations

$$Y_1'(t) + 2Y_1(t) + Y_2(t) = 4,$$
$$Y_2'(t) - Y_1(t) - 8Y_2(t) = t,$$

and the conditions

$$Y_1(0) = 0, \qquad Y_2(0) = 1.$$

We have

$$\mathbf{A} = \begin{bmatrix} 1 & 0 \\ 0 & 1 \end{bmatrix}, \quad \mathbf{B} = \begin{bmatrix} 2 & 1 \\ -1 & -8 \end{bmatrix}, \quad \mathbf{Y}(0) = \begin{bmatrix} 0 \\ 1 \end{bmatrix},$$

and

$$\mathbf{A}p + \mathbf{B} = \begin{bmatrix} 1 & 0 \\ 0 & 1 \end{bmatrix} p + \begin{bmatrix} 2 & 1 \\ -1 & -8 \end{bmatrix} = \begin{bmatrix} p+2 & 1 \\ -1 & p-8 \end{bmatrix}.$$

Using formula (5.2.1) for the inverse of a matrix, we obtain

$$(\mathbf{A}p + \mathbf{B})^{-1} = \frac{\begin{bmatrix} p-8 & 1 \\ -1 & p+2 \end{bmatrix}'}{p^2 - 6p - 15} = \frac{\begin{bmatrix} p-8 & -1 \\ 1 & p+2 \end{bmatrix}}{p^2 - 6p - 15}.$$

Furthermore,

$$\mathbf{f}(p) = \begin{bmatrix} L\{4\} \\ L\{t\} \end{bmatrix} = \begin{bmatrix} \dfrac{4}{p} \\ \dfrac{1}{p^2} \end{bmatrix}, \quad \mathbf{A}\mathbf{Y}(0) = \begin{bmatrix} 1 & 0 \\ 0 & 1 \end{bmatrix}\begin{bmatrix} 0 \\ 1 \end{bmatrix} = \begin{bmatrix} 0 \\ 1 \end{bmatrix},$$

and

$$\mathbf{f}(p) + \mathbf{A}\mathbf{Y}(0) = \begin{bmatrix} \dfrac{4}{p} \\ \dfrac{1}{p^2} \end{bmatrix} + \begin{bmatrix} 0 \\ 1 \end{bmatrix} = \begin{bmatrix} \dfrac{4}{p} \\ \dfrac{1}{p^2} + 1 \end{bmatrix}.$$

Therefore

$$(\mathbf{A}p + \mathbf{B})^{-1}[\mathbf{f}(p) + \mathbf{A}\mathbf{Y}(0)] = \frac{\begin{bmatrix} p-8 & -1 \\ 1 & p+2 \end{bmatrix}\begin{bmatrix} 4/p^2 \\ 1/p^2 + 1 \end{bmatrix}}{p^2 - 6p - 15}$$

$$= \begin{bmatrix} \dfrac{3p^2 - 32p - 1}{p^2(p^2 - 6p - 15)} \\[3ex] \dfrac{p^3 + 2p^2 + 5p + 2}{p^2(p^2 - 6p - 15)} \end{bmatrix}$$

and by formula (5.3.7)

$$\mathbf{Y}(t) = \begin{bmatrix} L^{-1}\left\{\dfrac{3p^2 - 32p - 1}{p^2(p^2 - 6p - 15)}\right\} \\[4ex] L^{-1}\left\{\dfrac{p^3 + 2p^2 + 5p + 2}{p^2(p^2 - 6p - 15)}\right\} \end{bmatrix}.$$

The function $Y_1(t)$ is obtained from the formula

$$Y_1(t) = \sum \text{Res} \, \frac{(3p^2 - 32p - 1)e^{pt}}{p^2(p^2 - 6p - 15)}$$

at the double pole $p = 0$ and the simple poles $p = 3 \pm 2\sqrt{6}$.   We have

$$\text{Res}\,(0) = \lim_{p \to 0} \frac{d}{dp} \frac{(3p^2 - 32p - 1)e^{pt}}{p^2 - 6p - 15} = \frac{t}{15} + \frac{474}{225},$$

$$\text{Res}\,(3 + 2\sqrt{6}) = \lim_{p \to 3 + 2\sqrt{6}} \frac{(3p^2 - 32p - 1)e^{pt}}{p^2 \dfrac{d}{dp}(p^2 - 6p - 15)}$$

$$= \frac{948 - 347\sqrt{6}}{900} e^{(3 + 2\sqrt{6})t},$$

$$\text{Res}\,(3 - 2\sqrt{6}) = \lim_{p \to 3 - 2\sqrt{6}} \frac{(3p^2 - 32p - 1)e^{pt}}{p^2 \dfrac{d}{dp}(p^2 - 6p - 15)}$$

$$= \frac{948 + 347\sqrt{6}}{900} e^{(3 - 2\sqrt{6})t},$$

and hence upon adding, we obtain

$$Y_1(t) = \frac{t}{15} + \frac{474}{225} + e^{3t}\left(\frac{79}{75} \cosh 2t\sqrt{6} - \frac{347\sqrt{6}}{900} \sinh 2t\sqrt{6}\right).$$

Similarly,

$$Y_2(t) = \sum \text{Res} \, \frac{(p^3 + 2p^2 + 5p + 2)e^{pt}}{p^2(p^2 - 6p - 15)}$$

at the double pole $p = 0$ and the simple poles $p = 3 \pm 2\sqrt{6}$.   We have

$$\text{Res}\,(0) = \lim_{p \to 0} \frac{d}{dp} \frac{(p^3 + 2p^2 + 5p + 2)e^{pt}}{p^2 - 6p - 15} = -\frac{2}{15}t - \frac{63}{225},$$

$$\text{Res}\,(3 + 2\sqrt{6}) = \lim_{p \to 3 + 2\sqrt{6}} \frac{(p^3 + 2p^2 + 5p + 2)e^{pt}}{p^2 \dfrac{d}{dp}(p^2 - 6p - 15)}$$

$$= -\frac{576 + 161\sqrt{6}}{900} e^{(3 + 2\sqrt{6})t},$$

$$\text{Res}\,(3 - 2\sqrt{6}) = \lim_{p \to 3 - 2\sqrt{6}} \frac{(p^3 + 2p^2 + 5p + 2)e^{pt}}{p^2 \dfrac{d}{dp}(p^2 - 6p - 15)}$$

$$= -\frac{576 - 161\sqrt{6}}{900} e^{(3 - 2\sqrt{6})t},$$

from which, upon combining terms,

$$Y_2(t) = -\frac{2}{15}t - \frac{63}{225} - e^{3t}\left(\frac{16}{25} \cosh 2t\sqrt{6} + \frac{161\sqrt{6}}{900} \sinh 2t\sqrt{6}\right).$$

Remark.   It will have been noticed that

$$\text{Res } (3 - 2\sqrt{6}) = \text{conjugate of Res } (3 + 2\sqrt{6})$$

in each of the above pair of evaluations.   This follows from the relation

$$\overline{R(a + \sqrt{b})e^{(a+\sqrt{b})t}} = \overline{R(a + \sqrt{b})}\,e^{\overline{(a+\sqrt{b})t}},$$

where a and b are rational numbers (b is not a perfect square), $\overline{a + \sqrt{b}} = a - \sqrt{b}$ and $R(p)$ is a rational fractional function, i.e., a quotient of two polynomials.
Similarly,

$$\overline{R(a + ib)e^{(a+ib)t}} = \overline{R(a + ib)}\,e^{\overline{(a+ib)t}},$$

where a and b are real numbers.   Verify these statements.

Example 2.   Solve the following system of differential equations for $Y_1(t)$ and $Y_2(t)$:

$$Y_1'(t) + Y_1(t) - Y_2(t) = 0,$$
$$Y_2'(t) + 2Y_1(t) + 3Y_2(t) = 0,$$
$$Y_1(0) = a, \qquad Y_2(0) = b.$$

We have

$$\mathbf{A} = \begin{bmatrix} 1 & 0 \\ 0 & 1 \end{bmatrix}, \qquad \mathbf{B} = \begin{bmatrix} 1 & -1 \\ 2 & 3 \end{bmatrix},$$

and

$$\mathbf{A}p + \mathbf{B} = \begin{bmatrix} p+1 & -1 \\ 2 & p+3 \end{bmatrix}.$$

From this

$$(\mathbf{A}p + \mathbf{B})^{-1} = \frac{\begin{bmatrix} p+3 & -2 \\ 1 & p+1 \end{bmatrix}'}{p^2 + 4p + 5} = \frac{\begin{bmatrix} p+3 & 1 \\ -2 & p+1 \end{bmatrix}}{(p+2)^2 + 1}.$$

Also,

$$\mathbf{f}(p) = \begin{bmatrix} L\{0\} \\ L\{0\} \end{bmatrix} = \begin{bmatrix} 0 \\ 0 \end{bmatrix}, \qquad \mathbf{Y}(0) = \begin{bmatrix} a \\ b \end{bmatrix},$$

$$\mathbf{AY}(0) = \begin{bmatrix} 1 & 0 \\ 0 & 1 \end{bmatrix}\begin{bmatrix} a \\ b \end{bmatrix} = \begin{bmatrix} a \\ b \end{bmatrix}, \qquad \mathbf{f}(p) + \mathbf{AY}(0) = \begin{bmatrix} a \\ b \end{bmatrix},$$

and

$$(\mathbf{A}p + \mathbf{B})^{-1}[\mathbf{f}(p) + \mathbf{A}\mathbf{Y}(0)] = \cfrac{\begin{bmatrix} p+3 & 1 \\ -2 & p+1 \end{bmatrix}\begin{bmatrix} a \\ b \end{bmatrix}}{(p+2)^2+1}$$

$$= \cfrac{\begin{bmatrix} ap + 3a + b \\ bp + b - 2a \end{bmatrix}}{(p+2)^2+1}.$$

Therefore,

$$\mathbf{Y}(t) = \begin{bmatrix} L^{-1}\left\{ \dfrac{a(p+2) + (a+b)}{(p+2)^2 + 1} \right\} \\ L^{-1}\left\{ \dfrac{b(p+2) - (b+2a)}{(p+2)^2 + 1} \right\} \end{bmatrix},$$

and from the table of transforms and Translation Theorem II,

$$Y_1(t) = L^{-1}\left\{ \frac{a(p+2) + (a+b)}{(p+2)^2 + 1} \right\} = e^{-2t}\,[a \cos t + (a+b) \sin t],$$

$$Y_2(t) = L^{-1}\left\{ \frac{b(p+2) - (b+2a)}{(p+2)^2 + 1} \right\} = e^{-2t}\,[b \cos t - (b+2a) \sin t].$$

Exercise 1.   Solve for $Y_1(t)$ and $Y_2(t)$:

$$Y_1'(t) + 2Y_2'(t) - Y_1(t) + 3Y_2(t) = t,$$
$$Y_1'(t) - 3Y_2'(t) + 2Y_1(t) - Y_2(t) = e^t,$$
$$Y_1(0) = Y_2(0) = 0.$$

Ans. $Y_1(t) = \dfrac{1}{5}\left[t + 2 + \dfrac{5}{3}e^t - \dfrac{e^{-t/2}}{3}(11 \cos \dfrac{\sqrt{3}}{2}t + 5\sqrt{3} \sin \dfrac{\sqrt{3}}{2}t) \right],$

$Y_2(t) = \dfrac{1}{5}\left[2t - 1 + e^{-t/2}(\cos \dfrac{\sqrt{3}}{2}t - \dfrac{5\sqrt{3}}{3} \sin \dfrac{\sqrt{3}}{2}t) \right].$

Exercise 2.   Determine the functions $Y_1(t)$ and $Y_2(t)$ that satisfy the system:

$$Y_1'(t) + 2Y_2'(t) - Y_1(t) = e^{3t},$$
$$2Y_1'(t) - Y_2'(t) + 4Y_1(t) = \sin t,$$
$$Y_1(0) = Y_{10}, \qquad Y_2(0) = Y_{20}.$$

Ans. $Y_1(t) = Y_{10}e^{-\frac{7}{6}t} + \dfrac{e^{3t}}{22} + \dfrac{1}{37}(7 \sin t - 5 \cos t),$

$Y_2(t) = Y_{20} - \dfrac{6}{7}Y_{10}e^{-\frac{7}{6}t} + \dfrac{5}{33}e^{3t} - \dfrac{1}{37}(6 \sin t + \cos t).$

5.4 A System of Second Order Linear Ordinary Differential Equations

A system such as this occurs frequently in dynamics and circuit analysis and is represented by the following simultaneous equations

$$
\begin{aligned}
a_{11} Y_1'' + \cdots + a_{1n} Y_n'' + b_{11} Y_1' + \cdots & \\
+ b_{1n} Y_n' + c_{11} Y_1 + \cdots + c_{1n} Y_n &= F_1(t), \\
(5.4.1) \quad a_{21} Y_1'' + \cdots + a_{2n} Y_n'' + b_{21} Y_1' + \cdots & \\
+ b_{2n} Y_n' + c_{21} Y_1 + \cdots + c_{2n} Y_n &= F_2(t), \\
\cdots \cdots \cdots \cdots \cdots \cdots \cdots \cdots & \\
a_{n1} Y_1'' + \cdots + a_{nn} Y_n'' + b_{n1} Y_1' + \cdots & \\
+ b_{nn} Y_n' + c_{n1} Y_1 + \cdots + c_{nn} Y_n &= F_n(t),
\end{aligned}
$$

where the Y_i's are functions of t and the a_{ij}'s, b_{ij}'s and c_{ij}'s are constants. We shall solve such a system for $Y_1(t)$, $Y_2(t)$, $\cdots$, $Y_n(t)$ satisfying the initial conditions

$$
\begin{aligned}
Y_1(0) &= Y_{10}, & Y_2(0) &= Y_{20}, \cdots, & Y_n(0) &= Y_{n0}, \\
Y_1'(0) &= Y_{10}', & Y_2'(0) &= Y_{20}', \cdots, & Y_n'(0) &= Y_{n0}'.
\end{aligned}
$$

As before, the system (5.4.1) can be written more compactly as follows

$$(5.4.2) \quad \sum_{i=1}^{n} a_{ij} Y_i''(t) + \sum_{i=1}^{n} b_{ij} Y_i'(t) + \sum_{i=1}^{n} c_{ij} Y_i(t) = F_j, \quad j = 1, 2, \cdots, n.$$

Or, if

$$\mathbf{A} = [a_{ij}], \qquad \mathbf{B} = [b_{ij}], \qquad \mathbf{C} = [c_{ij}],$$

$$
\mathbf{Y}(t) = \begin{bmatrix} Y_1(t) \\ Y_2(t) \\ \vdots \\ Y_n(t) \end{bmatrix} \quad \text{and} \quad \mathbf{F}(t) = \begin{bmatrix} F_1(t) \\ F_2(t) \\ \vdots \\ F_n(t) \end{bmatrix}.
$$

then (5.4.2) can be written as the single *matric differential equation*

$$(5.4.3) \qquad \mathbf{A Y}''(t) + \mathbf{B Y}'(t) + \mathbf{C Y}(t) = \mathbf{F}(t).$$

Let

$$
L\{\mathbf{Y}(t)\} = \begin{bmatrix} L\{Y_1(t)\} \\ L\{Y_2(t)\} \\ \vdots \\ L\{Y_n(t)\} \end{bmatrix} = \begin{bmatrix} y_1(p) \\ y_2(p) \\ \vdots \\ y_n(p) \end{bmatrix} = \mathbf{y}(p),
$$

$$L\{\mathbf{F}(t)\} = \begin{bmatrix} L\{F_1(t)\} \\ L\{F_2(t)\} \\ \vdots \\ L\{F_n(t)\} \end{bmatrix} = \begin{bmatrix} f_1(p) \\ f_2(p) \\ \vdots \\ f_n(p) \end{bmatrix} = \mathbf{f}(p).$$

Then, upon taking the Laplace transform of both sides of (5.4.3), we obtain

$$(\mathbf{A}p^2 + \mathbf{B}p + \mathbf{C})\mathbf{y}(p) = (\mathbf{A}p + \mathbf{B})\mathbf{Y}(0) + \mathbf{A}\mathbf{Y}'(0) + \mathbf{f}(p),$$

from which

$$\mathbf{y}(p) = (\mathbf{A}p^2 + \mathbf{B}p + \mathbf{C})^{-1}[(\mathbf{A}p + \mathbf{B})\mathbf{Y}(0) + \mathbf{A}\mathbf{Y}'(0) + \mathbf{f}(p)]$$

and hence

$$\mathbf{Y}(t) = L^{-1}\{(\mathbf{A}p^2 + \mathbf{B}p + \mathbf{C})^{-1}[(\mathbf{A}p + \mathbf{B})\mathbf{Y}(0) + \mathbf{A}\mathbf{Y}'(0) + \mathbf{f}(p)]\}.$$

We shall confine ourselves here to systems of linear ordinary differential equations with constant coefficients of first and second order. However, the problem of analyzing similar systems of higher order offers no difficulty and its formulation is left to the reader.

Example. Determine the functions $Y_1(t)$ and $Y_2(t)$ satisfying the system

$$Y_1''(t) + Y_2''(t) + 2Y_1'(t) - 3Y_2'(t) + Y_1(t) - 4Y_2(t) = 0,$$
$$Y_1''(t) - Y_2''(t) + 4Y_1'(t) + 2Y_2'(t) - 5Y_1(t) - Y_2(t) = 0,$$
$$Y_1(0) = Y_2(0) = 0, \qquad Y_1'(0) = 1, \qquad Y_2'(0) = 2.$$

We have

$$\mathbf{A} = \begin{bmatrix} 1 & 1 \\ 1 & -1 \end{bmatrix}, \qquad \mathbf{B} = \begin{bmatrix} 2 & -3 \\ 4 & 2 \end{bmatrix}, \qquad \mathbf{C} = \begin{bmatrix} 1 & -4 \\ -5 & -1 \end{bmatrix},$$

$$\mathbf{A}p^2 + \mathbf{B}p + \mathbf{C} = \begin{bmatrix} p^2 + 2p + 1 & p^2 - 3p - 4 \\ p^2 + 4p - 5 & -p^2 + 2p - 1 \end{bmatrix},$$

and

$$|\mathbf{A}p^2 + \mathbf{B}p + \mathbf{C}| = (p+1)(p-1)\begin{vmatrix} p+1 & p-4 \\ p+5 & -(p-1) \end{vmatrix}$$

$$= -(p+1)(p-1)(p-3)(2p+7).$$

Therefore,

$$(\mathbf{A}p^2 + \mathbf{B}p + \mathbf{C})^{-1} = \frac{\begin{bmatrix} -p^2 + 2p - 1 & -(p^2 + 4p - 5) \\ -(p^2 - 3p - 4) & p^2 + 2p + 1 \end{bmatrix}'}{-(p+1)(p-1)(p-3)(2p+7)}$$

$$= \frac{\begin{bmatrix} p^2 - 2p + 1 & p^2 - 3p - 4 \\ p^2 + 4p - 5 & -(p^2 + 2p + 1) \end{bmatrix}}{(p+1)(p-1)(p-3)(2p+7)}.$$

Also,

$$\mathbf{Y}(0) = \begin{bmatrix} 0 \\ 0 \end{bmatrix}, \qquad \mathbf{Y}'(0) = \begin{bmatrix} 1 \\ 2 \end{bmatrix}, \qquad \mathbf{f}(p) = \begin{bmatrix} 0 \\ 0 \end{bmatrix}.$$

Consequently,

$$(\mathbf{A}p + \mathbf{B})\mathbf{Y}(0) + \mathbf{A}\mathbf{Y}'(0) + \mathbf{f}(p) = \begin{bmatrix} p+2 & p-3 \\ p+4 & -p+2 \end{bmatrix}\begin{bmatrix} 0 \\ 0 \end{bmatrix}$$

$$+ \begin{bmatrix} 1 & 1 \\ 1 & -1 \end{bmatrix}\begin{bmatrix} 1 \\ 2 \end{bmatrix} + \begin{bmatrix} 0 \\ 0 \end{bmatrix} = \begin{bmatrix} 3 \\ -1 \end{bmatrix},$$

$$\mathbf{y}(p) = \frac{\begin{bmatrix} p^2 - 2p + 1 & p^2 - 3p - 4 \\ p^2 + 4p - 5 & -(p^2 + 2p + 1) \end{bmatrix}\begin{bmatrix} 3 \\ -1 \end{bmatrix}}{(p+1)(p-1)(p-3)(2p+7)},$$

and

$$\mathbf{Y}(t) = \begin{bmatrix} L^{-1}\left\{ \dfrac{2p^2 - 3p + 7}{(p+1)(p-1)(p-3)(2p+7)} \right\} \\ L^{-1}\left\{ \dfrac{2(2p^2 + 7p - 7)}{(p+1)(p-1)(p-3)(2p+7)} \right\} \end{bmatrix}$$

$$= \begin{bmatrix} \sum \text{Res} \dfrac{(2p^2 - 3p + 7)e^{pt}}{(p+1)(p-1)(p-3)(2p+7)} \\ \sum \text{Res} \dfrac{2(2p^2 + 7p - 7)e^{pt}}{(p+1)(p-1)(p-3)(2p+7)} \end{bmatrix}.$$

Now,

$$\text{Res}\,(-1) = \lim_{p \to -1} \frac{(2p^2 - 3p + 7)e^{pt}}{(p-1)(p-3)(2p+7)} = \frac{3}{10}e^{-t},$$

$$\text{Res (1)} = \lim_{p \to 1} \frac{(2p^2 - 3p + 7)e^{pt}}{(p + 1)(p - 3)(2p + 7)} = -\frac{1}{6}e^t,$$

$$\text{Res (3)} = \lim_{p \to 3} \frac{(2p^2 - 3p + 7)e^{pt}}{(p + 1)(p - 1)(2p + 7)} = \frac{2}{13}e^{3t},$$

$$\text{Res}\left(-\frac{7}{2}\right) = \lim_{p \to -\frac{7}{2}} \frac{(2p^2 - 3p + 7)e^{pt}}{(p - 1)(p + 1)(p - 3)} = -\frac{336}{585}e^{-\frac{7}{2}t}.$$

Therefore,

$$Y_1(t) = \frac{3}{10}e^{-t} - \frac{1}{6}e^t + \frac{2}{13}e^{3t} - \frac{336}{585}e^{-\frac{7}{2}t}.$$

Similarly,

$$\text{Res}(-1) = \lim_{p \to -1} \frac{2(2p^2 + 7p - 7)e^{pt}}{(p - 1)(p - 3)(2p + 7)} = -\frac{3}{5}e^{-t},$$

$$\text{Res (1)} = \lim_{p \to 1} \frac{2(2p^2 + 7p - 7)e^{pt}}{(p + 1)(p - 3)(2p + 7)} = -\frac{1}{9}e^t,$$

$$\text{Res (3)} = \lim_{p \to 3} \frac{2(2p^2 + 7p - 7)e^{pt}}{(p + 1)(p - 1)(2p + 7)} = \frac{8}{13}e^{3t},$$

$$\text{Res}\left(-\frac{7}{2}\right) = \lim_{p \to -\frac{7}{2}} \frac{2(2p^2 + 7p - 7)e^{pt}}{(p + 1)(p - 1)(p - 3)} = \frac{112}{585}e^{-\frac{7}{2}t}.$$

Hence,

$$Y_2(t) = -\frac{3}{5}e^{-t} - \frac{1}{9}e^t + \frac{8}{13}e^{3t} + \frac{112}{585}e^{-\frac{7}{2}t}.$$

Exercises. Solve the following systems of differential equations:

1. $Y_1''(t) = Y_2(t) + a, \quad Y_2''(t) = Y_1(t) + b, \quad Y_1(0) = c_1,$
    $Y_2(0) = c_2, \quad Y_1'(0) = c_3, \quad Y_2'(0) = c_3.$

Ans. $Y_1(t) = -b + \frac{1}{2}[(c_1 + c_2 + a + b)\cosh t$
    $+ (c_3 + c_4)\sinh t + (c_1 - c_2 - a + b)\cos t + (c_3 - c_4)\sin t],$
    $Y_2(t) = -a + \frac{1}{2}[(c_1 + c_2 + a + b)\cosh t + (c_3 + c_4)\sinh t$
    $+ (c_2 - c_1 + a - b)\cos t + (c_4 - c_3)\sin t].$

2. $Y_1''(t) + Y_2'(t) + 4Y_1(t) = 0, \quad Y_2''(t) + Y_1'(t) + Y_2(t) = 0,$
    $Y_1(0) = -1, \quad Y_1'(0) = Y_2(0) = Y_2'(0) = 0.$

Ans. $Y_1(t) = \frac{1}{\sqrt{2}} t \sin \sqrt{2} t - \cos \sqrt{2} t,$

    $Y_2(t) = t \cos \sqrt{2} t - \frac{1}{\sqrt{2}} \sin \sqrt{2} t.$

5.5 Multi-Mesh Networks

In the preceding chapter, section 4.2, we considered the behavior of a single-mesh network. For this purpose it was sufficient to use Kirchhoff's voltage law to derive the integro-differential equation which gives the response of a circuit subjected to an impressed voltage. When a multi-mesh network is considered, however, Kirchhoff's voltage law must be used in conjunction with Kirchhoff's *current law*, namely,

The sum of the currents entering any junction of a network is equal to the sum of the currents leaving that junction.

In order to illustrate the classical procedure of deriving the equations governing the behavior of a network, we shall consider the double-mesh network of Fig. 5.5.1 in which the initial charge on each of the capacitors

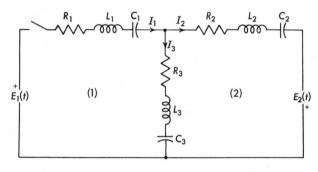

Fig. 5.5.1

C_1, C_2, and C_3 is assumed to be zero. The positive directions of the voltages are indicated by plus signs and the positive directions of the currents are indicated by the arrows. These conventions are purely arbitrary and others could be used just as well.

Assume that at $t = 0$ the switch is closed. Then from Kirchhoff's current law we see that

(5.5.1) $$I_1 = I_2 + I_3,$$

and from Kirchhoff's voltage law applied to meshes (1) and (2), we obtain, respectively,

(5.5.2) $$R_1I_1(t) + L_1I_1'(t) + \frac{1}{C_1}\int_0^t I_1(\tau)d\tau + R_3I_3(t) + L_3I_3'(t)$$
$$+ \frac{1}{C_3}\int_0^t I_3(\tau)d\tau = E_1(t),$$

(5.5.3) $$- L_3I_3'(t) - R_3I_3(t) - \frac{1}{C_3}\int_0^t I_3(\tau)d\tau + R_2I_2(t) + L_2I_2'(t)$$
$$+ \frac{1}{C_2}\int_0^t I_2(\tau)d\tau = E_2(t).$$

The current $I_3(t)$ can be eliminated from these two equations by making use of relation (5.5.1). The result of this elimination yields the following pair of equations

$$(5.5.4)\quad (R_1 + R_3)I_2(t) + (L_1 + L_3)I_1'(t) + \left(\frac{1}{C_1} + \frac{1}{C_3}\right)\int_0^t I_1(\tau)d\tau$$

$$- R_3 I_2(t) - L_3 I_2'(t) - \frac{1}{C_3}\int_0^t I_2(\tau)d\tau = E_1(t),$$

$$(5.5.5)\quad (R_2 + R_3)I_1(t) + (L_2 + L_3)I_2'(t) + \left(\frac{1}{C_2} + \frac{1}{C_3}\right)\int_0^t I_2(\tau)d\tau$$

$$- R_3 I_1(t) - L_3 I_1'(t) - \frac{1}{C_3}\int_0^t I_1(\tau)d\tau = E_2(t).$$

This procedure of obtaining the circuit equations, although perfectly general, becomes unwieldy as the number of meshes increases. Therefore we shall consider another procedure which has a directness lacking in the one just explained. Furthermore, it lends itself readily

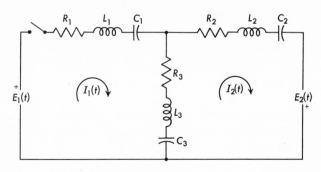

FIG. 5.5.2

to the problem of determining the circuit equations when n meshes are involved.*

We look upon the network of Fig. 5.5.1 now as consisting of two independent meshes, and instead of indicating the *branch* currents I_1, I_2, I_3, we indicate the *mesh* currents $I_1(t)$ and $I_2(t)$, assumed positive in the clockwise sense (Fig. 5.5.2). Applying Kirchhoff's voltage law to each of the meshes in turn we immediately obtain equations (5.5.4) and (5.5.5).

* E. A. Guillemin, *Communication Networks*, Vol. I, John Wiley and Sons, New York, 1931.

Letting $D_i = 1/C_i$ (elastance) and using matrices, these equations can be written as

(5.5.6)

$$\begin{bmatrix} R_1 + R_3 & -R_3 \\ -R_3 & R_2 + R_3 \end{bmatrix} \begin{bmatrix} I_1(t) \\ I_2(t) \end{bmatrix} + \begin{bmatrix} L_1 + L_3 & -L_3 \\ -L_3 & L_2 + L_3 \end{bmatrix} \begin{bmatrix} I_1'(t) \\ I_2'(t) \end{bmatrix}$$

$$+ \begin{bmatrix} D_1 + D_3 & -D_3 \\ -D_3 & D_2 + D_3 \end{bmatrix} \begin{bmatrix} \int_0^t I_1(\tau)d\tau \\ \int_0^t I_2(\tau)d\tau \end{bmatrix} = \begin{bmatrix} E_1(t) \\ E_2(t) \end{bmatrix}$$

Furthermore, setting

$$\mathbf{R} = \begin{bmatrix} R_1 + R_3 & -R_3 \\ -R_3 & R_2 + R_3 \end{bmatrix}, \quad \mathbf{L} = \begin{bmatrix} L_1 + L_3 & -L_3 \\ -L_3 & L_2 + L_3 \end{bmatrix},$$

$$\mathbf{D} = \begin{bmatrix} D_1 + D_3 & -D_3 \\ -D_3 & D_2 + D_3 \end{bmatrix}, \quad \mathbf{I}(t) = \begin{bmatrix} I_1(t) \\ I_2(t) \end{bmatrix}, \quad \mathbf{I}'(t) = \begin{bmatrix} I_1'(t) \\ I_2'(t) \end{bmatrix},$$

$$\int_0^t \mathbf{I}(\tau)d\tau = \begin{bmatrix} \int_0^t I_1(\tau)d\tau \\ \int_0^t I_2(\tau)d\tau \end{bmatrix}, \quad \mathbf{E}(t) = \begin{bmatrix} E_1(t) \\ E_2(t) \end{bmatrix},$$

equation (5 5.6) can be written as the *matric integro-differential equation*

(5.5.7) $$\mathbf{RI}(t) + \mathbf{LI}'(t) + \mathbf{D}\int_0^t \mathbf{I}(\tau)d\tau = \mathbf{E}(t).$$

Now, if

$$L\{\mathbf{I}(t)\} = \begin{bmatrix} L\{I_1(t)\} \\ L\{I_2(t)\} \end{bmatrix} = \begin{bmatrix} i_1(p) \\ i_2(p) \end{bmatrix} = \mathbf{i}(p),$$

and

$$L\{\mathbf{E}(t)\} = \begin{bmatrix} L\{E_1(t) \\ L\{E_2(t) \end{bmatrix} = \begin{bmatrix} e_1(p) \\ e_2(p) \end{bmatrix} = \mathbf{e}(p),$$

then upon applying the Laplace transformation to equation (5.5.7), we get

(5.5.8) $$(\mathbf{R} + \mathbf{L}p + \mathbf{D}/p)\,\mathbf{i}(p) = \mathbf{LI}(0) + \mathbf{e}(p).$$

The coefficient of $\mathbf{i}(p)$ will be called the *impedance* matrix and we shall designate it by the symbol $\mathbf{z}(p)$. Thus

(5.5.9) $$\mathbf{z}(p) = \mathbf{R} + \mathbf{L}p + \mathbf{D}/p,$$

and equation (5.5.8) becomes

$$(5.5.10) \qquad \mathbf{z}(p)\,\mathbf{i}(p) = \mathbf{L}\mathbf{I}(0) + \mathbf{e}(p).$$

In most cases $\mathbf{z}(p)$ is non-singular. In fact, if $\mathbf{z}(p)$ were singular, this would imply that the network equations are not independent, or that the network contains disrupting short circuits. Since such cases must be excluded in practice, we can suppose that $\mathbf{z}(p)$ is non-singular. Hence, multiplying (5.5.10) by $\mathbf{z}^{-1}(p)$, we obtain

$$(5.5.11) \qquad \mathbf{i}(p) = \mathbf{z}^{-1}(p)[\mathbf{L}\mathbf{I}(0) + \mathbf{e}(p)].$$

In circuit analysis, a problem of great importance and frequent occurrence is that of finding the response of a network when no currents are flowing at the time $t = 0$. In such a case the *initial* value matrix $\mathbf{I}(0) = 0$ and equation (5.5.11) becomes

$$(5.5.12) \qquad \mathbf{i}(p) = \mathbf{z}^{-1}(p)\,\mathbf{e}(p),$$

from which

$$(5.5.13) \qquad \mathbf{I}(t) = L^{-1}\{\mathbf{z}^{-1}(p)\,\mathbf{e}(p)\}.$$

In spite of the simplifying assumption we have made that initially the network is dead, i.e., there are no charges on the capacitors and no

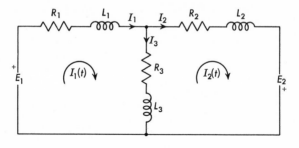

FIG. 5.5.3

currents are flowing at $t = 0$, in most cases it must be expected that a considerable amount of algebra and arithmetic has to be done before the complete solution is obtained.

Example 1.   In the network of Fig. 5.5.3, $R_1 = 1$ ohm, $R_2 = 2$ ohms, $R_3 = 3$ ohms, $L_1 = 6$ henrys, $L_2 = 4$ henrys, and $L_3 = 3$ henrys. Find the branch currents I_1, I_2, and I_3 if (a) $E_1 = 100$ volts, $E_2 = 200$ volts, and (b) $E_1 = \sin t$ volts, $E_2 = 0$.

(a) For this problem we have

$$\mathbf{R} = \begin{bmatrix} 4 & -3 \\ -3 & 5 \end{bmatrix}, \qquad \mathbf{L} = \begin{bmatrix} 9 & -3 \\ -3 & 7 \end{bmatrix}, \qquad \mathbf{D} = \begin{bmatrix} 0 & 0 \\ 0 & 0 \end{bmatrix},$$

$$\mathbf{z}(p) = \begin{bmatrix} 4 & -3 \\ -3 & 5 \end{bmatrix} + \begin{bmatrix} 9 & -3 \\ -3 & 7 \end{bmatrix} p = \begin{bmatrix} 9p+4 & -3p-3 \\ -3p-3 & 7p+5 \end{bmatrix},$$

$$\mathbf{z}^{-1}(p) = \frac{\begin{bmatrix} 7p+5 & 3p+3 \\ 3p+3 & 9p+4 \end{bmatrix}'}{\begin{vmatrix} 9p+4 & -3p-3 \\ -3p-3 & 7p+5 \end{vmatrix}} = \frac{\begin{bmatrix} 7p+5 & 3p+3 \\ 3p+3 & 9p+4 \end{bmatrix}}{54p^2+55p+11},$$

and

$$\mathbf{e}(p) = \begin{bmatrix} L\{100\} \\ L\{200\} \end{bmatrix} = \frac{100}{p} \begin{bmatrix} 1 \\ 2 \end{bmatrix}.$$

Therefore,

$$\mathbf{i}(p) = \mathbf{z}^{-1}(p)\,\mathbf{e}(p) = \frac{\dfrac{100}{p}\begin{bmatrix} 7p+5 & 3p+3 \\ 3p+3 & 9p+4 \end{bmatrix}\begin{bmatrix} 1 \\ 2 \end{bmatrix}}{54p^2+55p+11}$$

$$= \frac{\dfrac{100}{p}\begin{bmatrix} 13p+11 \\ 21p+11 \end{bmatrix}}{54\left(p^2 + \dfrac{55}{54}p + \dfrac{11}{54}\right)}$$

$$= \frac{50}{27}\begin{bmatrix} \dfrac{13p+11}{p(p^2+1\cdot0185p+0\cdot2037)} \\[3mm] \dfrac{21p+11}{p(p^2+1\cdot0185p+0\cdot2037)} \end{bmatrix},$$

and

$$\mathbf{I}(t) = \frac{50}{27}\begin{bmatrix} L^{-1}\left\{\dfrac{13p+11}{p(p+0\cdot274)(p+0\cdot744)}\right\} \\[4mm] L^{-1}\left\{\dfrac{21p+11}{p(p+0\cdot274)(p+0\cdot744)}\right\} \end{bmatrix}$$

$$= \frac{50}{27}\begin{bmatrix} \sum \mathrm{Res}\,\dfrac{(13p+11)e^{pt}}{p(p+0\cdot274)(p+0\cdot744)} \\[4mm] \sum \mathrm{Res}\,\dfrac{(21p+11)e^{pt}}{p(p+0\cdot274)(p+0\cdot744)} \end{bmatrix}.$$

For the branch current $I_1(t)$ the residues at the poles $p = 0$, $p = -0.274$ and $p = -0.744$ are

$$\text{Res}\,(0) = \lim_{p\to 0} \frac{(13p+11)e^{pt}}{p^2+1.0185p+0.2037} = \frac{11}{0.2037}$$
$$= 54.000,$$

$$\text{Res}\,(-0.274) = \lim_{p\to -0.274} \frac{(13p+11)e^{pt}}{p(p+0.744)} = -\frac{7.438}{0.129}e^{-0.274t}$$
$$= -57.658e^{-0.274t},$$

$$\text{Res}\,(-0.744) = \lim_{p\to -0.744} \frac{(13p+11)e^{pt}}{p(p+0.274)} = \frac{1.328}{0.349}e^{-0.744t}$$
$$= 3.805e^{-0.744t}.$$

Consequently,

$$I_1(t) = \frac{50}{27}(54.000 - 57.658e^{-0.274t} + 3.805e^{-0.744t}).$$

For the branch current $I_2(t)$ we similarly have

$$\text{Res}\,(0) = \lim_{p\to 0} \frac{(21p+11)e^{pt}}{p^2+1.0185p+0.2037} = \frac{11}{0.2037}$$
$$= 54.000,$$

$$\text{Res}\,(-0.274) = \lim_{p\to -0.274} \frac{(21p+11)e^{pt}}{p(p+0.744)} = -\frac{5.246}{0.129}e^{-0.274t}$$
$$= -40.667e^{-0.274t},$$

$$\text{Res}\,(-0.744) = \lim_{p\to -0.744} \frac{(21p+11)e^{pt}}{p(p+0.274)} = -\frac{4.624}{0.349}e^{-0.744t}$$
$$= -13.249e^{-0.744t}.$$

Hence,

$$I_2(t) = \frac{50}{27}(54.000 - 40.667e^{-0.274t} - 13.249e^{-0.744t}).$$

For the branch current $I_3(t)$ we obtain

$$I_3(t) = I_1(t) - I_2(t) = \frac{50}{27}(17.054e^{-0.744t} - 16.991e^{-0.274t}).$$

(b) In this case $\mathbf{z}^{-1}(p)$ is the same as before, namely,

$$\mathbf{z}^{-1}(p) = \frac{1}{54}\frac{\begin{bmatrix} 7p+5 & 3p+3 \\ 3p+3 & 9p+4 \end{bmatrix}}{(p+0.274)(p+0.744)}.$$

However,

$$\mathbf{e}(p) = \begin{bmatrix} L\{\sin t\} \\ \\ L\{0\} \end{bmatrix} = \begin{bmatrix} \dfrac{1}{p^2 + 1} \\ \\ 0 \end{bmatrix}.$$

Therefore,

$$\mathbf{i}(p) = \mathbf{z}^{-1}(p)\,\mathbf{e}(p) = \frac{1}{54}\, \frac{\begin{bmatrix} 7p + 5 & 3p + 3 \\ 3p + 3 & 9p + 4 \end{bmatrix}\begin{bmatrix} \dfrac{1}{p^2 + 1} \\ 0 \end{bmatrix}}{(p + 0\cdot274)(p + 0\cdot744)}$$

$$= \frac{1}{54}\, \frac{\begin{bmatrix} \dfrac{7p + 5}{p^2 + 1} \\ \\ \dfrac{3p + 3}{p^2 + 1} \end{bmatrix}}{(p + 0\cdot274)(p + 0\cdot744)},$$

and

$$\mathbf{I}(t) = \frac{1}{54}\begin{bmatrix} L^{-1}\left\{ \dfrac{7p + 5}{(p + i)(p - i)(p + 0\cdot274)(p + 0\cdot744)} \right\} \\ \\ L^{-1}\left\{ \dfrac{3p + 3}{(p + i)(p - i)(p + 0\cdot274)(p + 0\cdot744)} \right\} \end{bmatrix}.$$

Here, the singularities of $i_1(p)e^{pt}$ are simple poles at $p = \pm i$, $p = -0\cdot274$ and $p = -0\cdot744$. Calculating the residues at each of these poles, we have

$$\text{Res}\,(i) = \lim_{p \to i}\, \frac{(7p + 5)e^{pt}}{(p + i)(p^2 + 1\cdot0185p + 0\cdot2037)}$$

$$= \frac{(7i + 5)e^{it}}{2i(1\cdot0185i - 0\cdot7963)}$$

$$= \frac{1}{2}(6\cdot36 + 1\cdot88i)e^{it},$$

$$\text{Res}\,(-i) = \lim_{p \to -i}\, \frac{(7p + 5)e^{pt}}{(p - i)(p^2 + 1\cdot0185p + 0\cdot2037)}$$

$$= \frac{1}{2}(6\cdot36 - 1\cdot88i)e^{-it},$$

$$\text{Res}\,(-0\cdot274) = \lim_{p \to -0\cdot274}\, \frac{(7p + 5)e^{pt}}{(p^2 + 1)(p + 0\cdot744)} = 6\cdot06e^{-0\cdot247t},$$

$$\text{Res}\,(-0\cdot744) = \lim_{p \to -0\cdot744}\, \frac{(7p + 5)e^{pt}}{(p^2 + 1)(p + 0\cdot274)} = 0\cdot285e^{-0\cdot744t}.$$

The result of adding these residues is

$$I_1(t) = \frac{1}{54}(6\cdot36\cos t - 1\cdot88\sin t + 6\cdot06e^{-0\cdot274t} + 0\cdot285e^{-0\cdot744t}).$$

Similarly, for $i_2(p)e^{pt}$ we have

$$\text{Res } (i) = \lim_{p\to i}\frac{(3p+3)e^{pt}}{(p+i)(p^2 + 1\cdot0185p + 0\cdot2037)}$$

$$= \frac{1}{2}(3\cdot25 + 0\cdot398i)e^{it},$$

$$\text{Res } (-i) = \lim_{p\to -i}\frac{(3p+3)e^{pt}}{(p-i)(p^2 + 1\cdot0185p + 0\cdot2037)}$$

$$= \frac{1}{2}(3\cdot25 - 0\cdot398i)e^{-it},$$

$$\text{Res } (-0\cdot274) = \lim_{p\to -0\cdot274}\frac{(3p+3)e^{pt}}{(p^2+1)(p+0\cdot744)} = 4\cdot31e^{-0\cdot274t},$$

$$\text{Res } (-0\cdot744) = \lim_{p\to -0\cdot744}\frac{(3p+3)e^{pt}}{(p^2+1)(p+0\cdot274)} = -1\cdot05e^{-0\cdot744t},$$

and hence

$$I_2(t) = \frac{1}{54}(3\cdot25\cos t - 0\cdot398\sin t + 4\cdot31e^{-0\cdot274t} - 1\cdot05e^{-0\cdot744t}).$$

Also,

$$I_3(t) = I_1(t) - I_2(t) = \frac{1}{54}(3\cdot11\cos t - 1\cdot48\sin t + 1\cdot75e^{-0\cdot274t}$$

$$+ 1\cdot33e^{-0\cdot744t}).$$

In the double-mesh network considered so far the elements of the

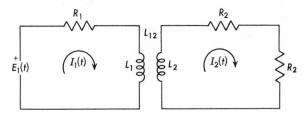

FIG. 5.5.4

circuit were coupled by means of electrical conductors.   It is possible, however, for circuits to be coupled electromagnetically as in Fig. 5.5.4, where L_1 and L_2 refer, respectively, to the inductances of the primary and secondary coils of a transformer and L_{12} is the so-called *mutual* inductance.   The parameter of mutual inductance may be positive or negative depending on whether the magnetic fields due to L_1 and L_2 add or subtract.   Denoting the directions of the voltage and currents as shown and applying Kirchhoff's law to the two closed circuits, the equations and their solution can be determined as before.

Example 2.   At $t = 0$ a constant voltage E_1 is impressed on the circuit of Fig. 5.5.4.   If the currents are zero initially, find $I_1(t)$ and $I_2(t)$ when $t > 0$ and $L_1 = 1$ henry, $L_2 = 3$ henrys, $L_{12} = -1$ henry, $R_1 = 1$ ohm, and $R_2 = 2$ ohms.

Kirchhoff's laws applied to the two circuits give the pair of equations

$$L_1 I_1'(t) + L_{12} I_2'(t) + R_1 I_1(t) = E_1,$$
$$L_{12} I_1'(t) + L_2 I_2'(t) + R_2 I_2(t) = 0,$$

or the single matric equation

(5.5.14) $$\mathbf{L}\mathbf{I}'(t) + \mathbf{R}\mathbf{I}(t) = \mathbf{E}(t),$$

where

$$\mathbf{L} = \begin{bmatrix} L_1 & L_{12} \\ L_{12} & L_2 \end{bmatrix}, \qquad \mathbf{R} = \begin{bmatrix} R_1 & 0 \\ 0 & R_2 \end{bmatrix}, \qquad \mathbf{I}(t) = \begin{bmatrix} I_1(t) \\ I_2(t) \end{bmatrix}, \qquad \mathbf{E}(t) = \begin{bmatrix} E_1 \\ 0 \end{bmatrix}.$$

Taking the Laplace transform of (5.5.14) and making use of the initial conditions, we obtain

$$(\mathbf{L}p + \mathbf{R})\,\mathbf{i}(p) = \mathbf{e}(p),$$

where $\mathbf{e}(p) = L\{\mathbf{E}(t)\}$.   From this it follows that

$$\mathbf{i}(p) = (\mathbf{L}p + \mathbf{R})^{-1}\mathbf{e}(p).$$

Now

$$\mathbf{L}p + \mathbf{R} = \begin{bmatrix} 1 & -1 \\ -1 & 3 \end{bmatrix} p + \begin{bmatrix} 1 & 0 \\ 0 & 2 \end{bmatrix} = \begin{bmatrix} p+1 & -p \\ -p & 3p+2 \end{bmatrix},$$

$$(\mathbf{L}p + \mathbf{R})^{-1} = \frac{\begin{bmatrix} 3p+2 & p \\ p & p+1 \end{bmatrix}'}{\begin{vmatrix} p+1 & -p \\ -p & 3p+2 \end{vmatrix}} = \frac{\begin{bmatrix} 3p+2 & p \\ p & p+1 \end{bmatrix}}{2p^2 + 5p + 2}$$

and $$\mathbf{e}(p) = \frac{E_1}{p} \begin{bmatrix} 1 \\ 0 \end{bmatrix}.$$

Therefore

$$\mathbf{i}(p) = \frac{E_1}{p} \frac{\begin{bmatrix} 3p + 2 & p \\ p & p + 1 \end{bmatrix} \begin{bmatrix} 1 \\ 0 \end{bmatrix}}{(2p + 1)(p + 2)} = E_1 \begin{bmatrix} \dfrac{3p + 2}{p(2p + 1)(p + 2)} \\[2mm] \dfrac{1}{(2p + 1)(p + 2)} \end{bmatrix},$$

and

$$\mathbf{I}(t) = E_1 \begin{bmatrix} L^{-1}\left\{ \dfrac{3p + 2}{p(2p + 1)(p + 2)} \right\} \\[2mm] L^{-1}\left\{ \dfrac{1}{(2p + 1)(p + 2)} \right\} \end{bmatrix}.$$

Since $i_1(p)e^{pt}$ has simple poles at $p = 0$, $p = -\tfrac{1}{2}$, and $p = -2$, we have

$$\operatorname{Res}(0) = \lim_{p \to 0} \frac{(3p + 2)e^{pt}}{(2p + 1)(p + 2)} = 1,$$

$$\operatorname{Res}\left(-\frac{1}{2}\right) = \lim_{p \to -\frac{1}{2}} \frac{(3p + 2)e^{pt}}{p(p + 2)} = -\frac{2}{3}e^{-t/2}$$

$$\operatorname{Res}(-2) = \lim_{p \to -2} \frac{(3p + 2)e^{pt}}{p(2p + 1)} = -\frac{2}{3}e^{-2t},$$

and consequently

$$I_1(t) = E_1(1 - \tfrac{2}{3}e^{-t/2} - \tfrac{2}{3}e^{-2t}).$$

$i_2(p)e^{pt}$ has simple poles at $p = -\tfrac{1}{2}$ and $p = -2$. Hence

$$\operatorname{Res}\left(-\frac{1}{2}\right) = \lim_{p \to -\frac{1}{2}} \frac{e^{pt}}{p + 2} = \frac{2}{3}e^{-t/2},$$

$$\operatorname{Res}(-2) = \lim_{p \to -2} \frac{e^{pt}}{2p + 1} = -\frac{1}{3}e^{-2t},$$

and

$$I_2(t) = \frac{E_1}{3}(2e^{-t/2} - e^{-2t}).$$

Exercise 1.   Find the mesh currents $I_1(t)$ and $I_2(t)$ for the network of Fig. 5.5.5 if initially the network is dead, $C_1 = C_2 = C_3 = 10^{-5}$ farad, $L_1 = 10$ henrys, $L_2 = 20$ henrys, $L_3 = 30$ henrys, and (a) $E_1(t) = 110$ volts, $E_2(t) = 220$ volts; (b) $E_1(t) = \sin 2t$ volts, $E_2(t) = 0$.

Ans.   (a) $I_1(t) = -0{\cdot}011 \sin 62t + 0{\cdot}132 \sin 84t$;
$$I_2(t) = 0{\cdot}038 \sin 62t + 0{\cdot}102 \sin 84t.$$

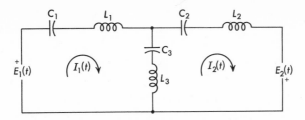

FIG. 5.5.5

Exercise 2. In the network of Fig. 5.5.6, $R_1 = R_2 = 2$ ohms, $L_1 = 2$ henrys, $L_2 = 1$ henry, and $L_{12} = -1$ henry. If the network is dead initially, find $I_1(t)$ and $I_2(t)$ when voltages $E_1(t) = \sin t$ and $E_2(t) = 100$ are impressed on the network at time $t = 0$.

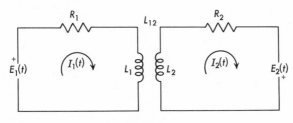

FIG. 5.5.6

5.6 Small Oscillations About an Equilibrium Position

An important problem in dynamics is one in which a system executes *small* vibrations* in the neighborhood of a stable equilibrium position. In deriving the equations of motion for this case all terms higher than the second order in the Taylor expansions of the kinetic energy T and the potential energy U are neglected so that a system with n degrees of freedom has the following expressions for T and U:

$$(5.6.1) \qquad T = \tfrac{1}{2} \sum_{i=1}^{n} \sum_{j=1}^{n} a_{ij} \dot{q}_i \dot{q}_j,$$

$$(5.6.2) \qquad U = \tfrac{1}{2} \sum_{i=1}^{n} \sum_{j=1}^{n} c_{ij} q_i q_j,$$

where a_{ij} and c_{ij} are constants, $(q_1, q_2, \cdots, q_n)$ are the coordinates of the system (the so-called *generalized* coordinates) and the dots refer to differentiation with respect to t. Furthermore, it is *known that* $a_{ij} = a_{ji}$ and $c_{ij} = c_{ji}$.

Now, if a system with n degrees of freedom is *conservative*, i.e., if the work done by the forces acting on the system depends only on the

---

* E. T. Whittaker, *Analytical Dynamics*, Cambridge University Press, 1937.

coordinates of the end points, then the Lagrangian equations of motion for such a system performing *free* oscillations about a position of stable equilibrium are:

(5.6.3)
$$\frac{d}{dt}\left(\frac{\partial T}{\partial \dot{q}_k}\right) - \frac{\partial T}{\partial q_k} + \frac{\partial U}{\partial q_k} = 0, \quad k = 1, 2, \cdots, n.$$

Substituting (5.6.1) and (5.6.2) in (5.6.3), we obtain the following system of linear differential equations with constant coefficients

(5.6.4) $a_{11}\ddot{q}_1 + \cdots + a_{1n}\ddot{q}_n + c_{11}q_1 + \cdots + c_{1n}q_n = 0,$

. . . .

$a_{n1}\ddot{q}_1 + \cdots + a_{nn}\ddot{q}_n + c_{n1}q_1 + \cdots + c_{nn}q_n = 0.$

Let $\mathbf{A} = [a_{ij}]$, $\mathbf{C} = [c_{ij}]$, and

$$\mathbf{Q}(t) = \begin{bmatrix} q_1(t) \\ \vdots \\ q_n(t) \end{bmatrix}.$$

Then the system of equations (5.6.4) can be written as the single matric equation

(5.6.5) $$\mathbf{A}\ddot{\mathbf{Q}}(t) + \mathbf{C}\mathbf{Q}(t) = 0,$$

and it is known that $|\mathbf{A}| \neq 0$ so that the matrix $\mathbf{A}$ is non-singular.   If the initial conditions are now specified, i.e., if

$$\mathbf{Q}(0) = \begin{bmatrix} q_1(0) \\ \vdots \\ q_n(0) \end{bmatrix}, \quad \dot{\mathbf{Q}}(0) = \begin{bmatrix} \dot{q}_1(0) \\ \vdots \\ \dot{q}_n(0) \end{bmatrix},$$

then equation (5.6.5) can easily be solved by the Laplace transform method.   We have

(5.6.6) $$\mathbf{q}(p) = (\mathbf{A}p^2 + \mathbf{C})^{-1}\mathbf{A}[p\mathbf{Q}(0) + \dot{\mathbf{Q}}(0)],$$

where $L\{\mathbf{Q}(t)\} = \mathbf{q}(p)$, and hence

(5.6.7) $$\mathbf{Q}(t) = L^{-1}\{(\mathbf{A}p^2 + \mathbf{C})^{-1}\mathbf{A}[p\mathbf{Q}(0) + \dot{\mathbf{Q}}(0)]\}.$$

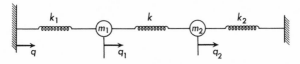

Fig. 5.6.1

Example.   Determine the motion of a system of two coupled masses (Fig. 5.6.1) if at $t = 0$, when the system is in equilibrium, a velocity v_0 in the positive q-direction is imparted to the mass m_1.

The kinetic and potential energies of the system are easily computed to be

$$T = \tfrac{1}{2}(m\dot{q}_1{}^2 + m_2\dot{q}_2{}^2), \qquad U = \tfrac{1}{2}[k_1q_1{}^2 + k(q_1 - q_2)^2 + k_2q_2{}^2].$$

Substituting these values in the Lagrange equations (5.6.3), we obtain

$$m_1\ddot{q}_1 + (k_1 + k)q_1 - kq_2 = 0,$$
$$m_2\ddot{q}_2 - kq_1 + (k + k_2)q_2 = 0.$$

Then

$$\mathbf{A} = \begin{bmatrix} m_1 & 0 \\ 0 & m_2 \end{bmatrix}, \quad \mathbf{C} = \begin{bmatrix} k_1 + k & -k \\ -k & k + k_2 \end{bmatrix}, \quad \mathbf{Q}(t) = \begin{bmatrix} q_1(t) \\ q_2(t) \end{bmatrix},$$

and the initial-value matrices are

$$\mathbf{Q}(0) = \begin{bmatrix} 0 \\ 0 \end{bmatrix}, \quad \dot{\mathbf{Q}}(0) = \begin{bmatrix} v_0 \\ 0 \end{bmatrix}.$$

Furthermore,

$$p\mathbf{Q}(0) + \dot{\mathbf{Q}}(0) = \begin{bmatrix} v_0 \\ 0 \end{bmatrix}, \quad \mathbf{A}[p\mathbf{Q}(0) + \dot{\mathbf{Q}}(0)] = \begin{bmatrix} m_1v_0 \\ 0 \end{bmatrix},$$

and

$$\mathbf{A}p^2 + \mathbf{C} = \begin{bmatrix} m_1p^2 & 0 \\ 0 & m_2p^2 \end{bmatrix} + \begin{bmatrix} k_1 + k & -k \\ -k & k + k_2 \end{bmatrix}$$

$$= \begin{bmatrix} m_1p^2 + k + k_1 & -k \\ -k & m_2p^2 + k + k_2 \end{bmatrix}.$$

The inverse of the last matrix is easily seen to be

$$(\mathbf{A}p^2 + \mathbf{C})^{-1} = \frac{\begin{bmatrix} m_2p^2 + k + k_2 & k \\ k & m_1p^2 + k + k_1 \end{bmatrix}}{(m_1p^2 + k + k_1)(m_2p^2 + k + k_2) - k^2}$$

Therefore

$$\mathbf{q}(p) = (\mathbf{A}p^2 + \mathbf{C})^{-1}\mathbf{A}[p\mathbf{Q}(0) + \dot{\mathbf{Q}}(0)]$$

$$= \frac{\begin{bmatrix} m_1v_0(m_2p^2 + k + k_2) \\ m_1kv_0 \end{bmatrix}}{(m_1p^2 + k + k_1)(m_2p^2 + k + k_2) - k^2},$$

and

$$\mathbf{Q}(t) = \begin{bmatrix} q_1(t) \\ \\ q_2(t) \end{bmatrix} = \begin{bmatrix} L^{-1}\left\{\dfrac{m_1 v_0(m_2 p^2 + k + k_2)}{(m_1 p^2 + k + k_1)(m_2 p^2 + k + k_2) - k^2}\right\} \\ \\ L^{-1}\left\{\dfrac{m_1 k v_0}{(m_1 p^2 + k + k_1)(m_2 p^2 + k + k_2) - k^2}\right\} \end{bmatrix}.$$

Let us analyze the particular case when $m_1 = m$, $m_2 = 2m$, $k_1 = 2k$, $k_2 = 3k$. We must then find the inverse Laplace transforms

(5.6.8)

$$L^{-1}\left\{\frac{m v_0(2mp^2 + 4k)}{2m^2 p^4 + 10mkp^2 + 11k^2}\right\} = \sum \text{Res}\, \frac{m v_0(2mp^2 + 4k)e^{pt}}{2m^2 p^4 + 10mkp^2 + 11k^2},$$

and

(5.6.9)

$$L^{-1}\left\{\frac{mkv_0}{2m^2 p^4 + 10mkp^2 + 11k^2}\right\} = \sum \text{Res}\, \frac{mkv_0 e^{pt}}{2m^2 p^4 + 10mkp^2 + 11k^2}.$$

The poles of the functions whose residues are to be computed occur at $p = \pm\, 1{\cdot}28i\sqrt{k/m}$ and $\pm\, 1{\cdot}83i\sqrt{k/m}$. For the function appearing in (5.6.8) we have

$$\text{Res}\,(1{\cdot}28i\sqrt{k/m}) = \lim_{p \to 1{\cdot}28i\sqrt{k/m}} \frac{m v_0(2mp^2 + 4k)e^{pt}}{\dfrac{d}{dp}(2m^2 p^4 + 10mkp^2 + 11k^2)}$$

$$= \frac{0{\cdot}082}{i} v_0 \sqrt{k/m}\; e^{1{\cdot}28i\sqrt{k/m}\,t},$$

$$\text{Res}\,(-\,1{\cdot}28i\sqrt{k/m}) = \lim_{p \to -1{\cdot}28i\sqrt{k/m}} \frac{m v_0(2mp^2 + 4k)e^{pt}}{\dfrac{d}{dp}(2m^2 p^4 + 10mkp^2 + 11k^2)}.$$

$$= -\,\frac{0{\cdot}082}{i} v_0 \sqrt{k/m}\; e^{-1{\cdot}28i\sqrt{k/m}\,t},$$

$$\text{Res}\,(1{\cdot}83i\sqrt{k/m}) = \lim_{p \to 1{\cdot}83i\sqrt{k/m}} \frac{m v_0(2mp^2 + 4k)e^{pt}}{\dfrac{d}{dp}(2m^2 p^4 + 10mkp^2 + 11k^2)}$$

$$= \frac{0{\cdot}23}{i} v_0 \sqrt{k/m}\; e^{1{\cdot}83i\sqrt{k/m}\,t},$$

$$\text{Res}\,(-\,1{\cdot}83i\sqrt{k/m}) = \lim_{p \to -1{\cdot}83i\sqrt{k/m}} \frac{m v_0(2mp^2 + 4k)e^{pt}}{\dfrac{d}{dp}(2m^2 p^4 + 10mkp^2 + 11k^2)}$$

$$= -\,\frac{0{\cdot}23}{i} v_0 \sqrt{k/m}\; e^{-1{\cdot}83i\sqrt{k/m}\,t}.$$

Therefore

$$q_1(t) = \frac{0 \cdot 082}{i} v_0 \sqrt{m/k} (e^{1 \cdot 28 i \sqrt{k/m}\, t} - e^{-1 \cdot 28 i \sqrt{k/m}\, t})$$

$$+ \frac{0 \cdot 23}{i} v_0 \sqrt{k/m} (e^{1 \cdot 83\, i \sqrt{k/m}\, t} - e^{-1 \cdot 83 i \sqrt{k/m}\, t}),$$

or

$$q_1(t) = v_0 \sqrt{m/k} [0 \cdot 164 \sin 1 \cdot 28 \sqrt{k/m}\ t + 0 \cdot 46 \sin 1 \cdot 83 \sqrt{k/m}\ t].$$

Similarly, for the residues of the function appearing in (5.6.9) we have

$$\text{Res}\ (1 \cdot 28 i \sqrt{k/m}) = \lim_{p \to 1 \cdot 28 i \sqrt{k/m}} \frac{m k v_0 e^{pt}}{\dfrac{d}{dp} (2m^2 p^4 + 10 m k p^2 + 11 k^2)}$$

$$= \frac{0 \cdot 114}{i} v_0 \sqrt{m/k}\ e^{1 \cdot 28 i \sqrt{k/m}\, t},$$

$$\text{Res}\ (-1 \cdot 28 i \sqrt{k/m}) = -\frac{0 \cdot 114}{i} v_0 \sqrt{m/k}\ e^{-1 \cdot 28 i \sqrt{k/m}\, t},$$

$$\text{Res}\ (1 \cdot 83 i \sqrt{k/m}) = -\frac{0 \cdot 079}{i} v_0 \sqrt{m/k}\ e^{1 \cdot 83 i \sqrt{k/m}\, t},$$

$$\text{Res}\ (-1 \cdot 83 i\ k/m) = \frac{0 \cdot 079}{i} v_0 \sqrt{m/k}\ e^{-1 \cdot 83 i \sqrt{k/m}\, t}.$$

Consequently

$$q_2(t) = v_0 \sqrt{m/k} [0 \cdot 288 \sin 1 \cdot 28 \sqrt{k/m}\ t - 0 \cdot 158 \sin 1 \cdot 83 \sqrt{k/m}\ t].$$

Exercise. Determine the kinetic and potential energies of the system shown in Fig. 5.6.2 and determine the equations of motion. Solve them if $k_1 = 2k$, $k_2 = k$, $m_1 = 3m$, $m_2 = 4m$, $q_1(0) = d$ and $q_2(0) = -2d$.

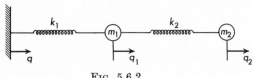

FIG. 5.6.2

5.7 Systems Involving Resistances

Frictional forces are always present in physical systems. In many cases, however, they are so small that they may be neglected and the system treated as a conservative one. In that case, as we have seen in the previous section, the equations of motion are determined from a knowledge of only the kinetic and potential energies of the system.

Suppose, now, that viscous damping is present in a system and is so large that it cannot be neglected. Furthermore, let it be assumed that the frictional forces are *linear* functions of the generalized velocities $\dot{q}_k$. If such a force is denoted by $-\partial F/\partial \dot{q}_k$, where

(5.7.1) $$F = \tfrac{1}{2} \sum_{i=1}^{n} \sum_{j=1}^{n} b_{ij} \dot{q}_i \dot{q}_j,$$

with $b_{ij} = b_{ji}$, then Lagrange's equations become

(5.7.2.) $$\frac{d}{dt}\left(\frac{\partial T}{\partial \dot{q}_k}\right) - \frac{\partial T}{\partial q_k} + \frac{\partial U}{\partial q_k} = -\frac{\partial F}{\partial \dot{q}_k} \quad (k = 1, 2, \cdots, n).$$

The expression $-\partial F/\partial \dot{q}_k$ is called a *dissipative force* and F the *dissipation function*. The b_{ij}'s are often referred to as *damping* coefficients.

In this instance the matrix equation of motion is

(5.7.3) $$\mathbf{A}\ddot{\mathbf{Q}}(t) + \mathbf{B}\dot{\mathbf{Q}}(t) + \mathbf{C}\mathbf{Q}(t) = 0,$$

where $\mathbf{A} = [a_{ij}]$, $\mathbf{B} = [b_{ij}]$ and $\mathbf{C} = [c_{ij}]$.

If the initial-value matrices are

$$\mathbf{Q}(0) = \begin{bmatrix} q_1(0) \\ \vdots \\ q_n(0) \end{bmatrix} \quad \text{and} \quad \dot{\mathbf{Q}}(0) = \begin{bmatrix} q_1(0) \\ \vdots \\ q_n(0) \end{bmatrix},$$

then the solution of (5.7.3) is readily seen to be
(5.7.4)
$$\mathbf{Q}(t) = L^{-1}\{(\mathbf{A}p^2 + \mathbf{B}p + \mathbf{C})^{-1}[(\mathbf{A}p + \mathbf{B})\mathbf{Q}(0) + \mathbf{A}\dot{\mathbf{Q}}(0)]\}.$$

If in addition to frictional forces each particle m_k of the system is acted upon by a total force $P_k(t)$, then the matrix equation is

(5.7.5) $$\mathbf{A}\ddot{\mathbf{Q}}(t) + \mathbf{B}\dot{\mathbf{Q}}(t) + \mathbf{C}\mathbf{Q}(t) = \mathbf{P}(t),$$

where $$\mathbf{P}(t) = \begin{bmatrix} P_1(t) \\ \vdots \\ P_n(t) \end{bmatrix}.$$

Example. A taut string is loaded with two masses m_1 and m_2 at distances l_1 and l_3 from two fixed ends, while the distance between them is l_2. The system is immersed in a viscous medium and the masses m_1 and m_2 are given transverse displacements d_1 and d_2, respectively. At $t = 0$ they are released from rest. Determine the subsequent motion.

Let Fig. 5.7.1 represent the configuration at time $t > 0$. The kinetic energy of the system is

$$T = \tfrac{1}{2}(m_1 \dot{q}_1{}^2 + m_2 \dot{q}_2{}^2).$$

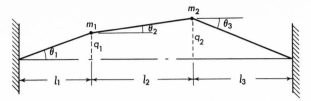

FIG. 5.7.1

If we assume that the tension in the string is k, then for small displacements the potential energy is k times the increase in length of the string due to the displacements of the masses m_1 and m_2. The increase in length of any segment is

$$l_i(\sec \theta_i - 1) \sim l_i \frac{\theta_i^2}{2}, \quad i = 1, 2, 3.$$

since θ_i is considered small. Furthermore, $\theta_1 \sim q_1/l_1$, $\theta_2 \sim (q_2 - q_1)/l_2$ and $\theta_3 \sim q_2/l_3$. Therefore the potential energy is

$$U = \frac{k}{2}\left[\frac{q_1^2}{l_1} + \frac{(q_2 - q_1)^2}{l_2} + \frac{q_2^2}{l_3}\right]$$

Suppose, now, that $F = \frac{1}{2}[k_1\dot{q}_1^2 + k_2\dot{q}_2^2]$ so that $-\partial F/\partial \dot{q}_1 = -k_1\dot{q}_1$ and $-\partial F/\partial \dot{q}_2 = -k_2\dot{q}_2$. Then from (5.7.2) we have the equations

$$m_1\ddot{q}_1 + k_1\dot{q}_1 + k\left(\frac{1}{l_1} + \frac{1}{l_2}\right)q_1 - \frac{k}{l_2}q_2 = 0,$$

$$m_2\ddot{q}_2 + k_2\dot{q}_2 - \frac{k}{l_2}q_1 + k\left(\frac{1}{l_2} + \frac{1}{l_3}\right)q_2 = 0.$$

Thus

$$\mathbf{A} = \begin{bmatrix} m_1 & 0 \\ 0 & m_2 \end{bmatrix}, \qquad \mathbf{B} = \begin{bmatrix} k_1 & 0 \\ 0 & k_2 \end{bmatrix}$$

$$\mathbf{C} = \begin{bmatrix} k\left(\frac{1}{l_1} + \frac{1}{l_2}\right) & -\frac{k}{l_2} \\ -\frac{k}{l_2} & k\left(\frac{1}{l_2} + \frac{1}{l_3}\right) \end{bmatrix},$$

and the initial-value matrices are

$$\mathbf{Q}(0) = \begin{bmatrix} d_1 \\ d_2 \end{bmatrix}, \qquad \dot{\mathbf{Q}}(0) = \begin{bmatrix} 0 \\ 0 \end{bmatrix}.$$

Let us consider the particular case when $m_1 = 1$, $m_2 = 2$, $k_1 = 1$, $k_2 = 4$, $k = 1$, $l_1 = l_2 = l_3 = l$, $d_2 = 2d$, $d_1 = d$.   Then

$$\mathbf{A} = \begin{bmatrix} 1 & 0 \\ 0 & 2 \end{bmatrix}, \qquad \mathbf{B} = \begin{bmatrix} 1 & 0 \\ 0 & 4 \end{bmatrix}, \qquad \mathbf{C} = \begin{bmatrix} 2 & -1 \\ -1 & 2 \end{bmatrix},$$

$$\mathbf{Q}(0) = \begin{bmatrix} 2d \\ d \end{bmatrix}, \qquad \dot{\mathbf{Q}}(0) = \begin{bmatrix} 0 \\ 0 \end{bmatrix},$$

and

$$\mathbf{A}p + \mathbf{B} = \begin{bmatrix} p+1 & 0 \\ 0 & 2p+4 \end{bmatrix}, \qquad (\mathbf{A}p + \mathbf{B})\mathbf{Q}(0) = \begin{bmatrix} 2(p+1)d \\ 2(p+2)d \end{bmatrix},$$

$$(\mathbf{A}p + \mathbf{B})\mathbf{Q}(0) + \mathbf{A}\dot{\mathbf{Q}}(0) = \begin{bmatrix} p+1 \\ p+2 \end{bmatrix} 2d.$$

Also

$$\mathbf{A}p^2 + \mathbf{B}p + \mathbf{C} = \begin{bmatrix} p^2 + p + 2 & -1 \\ -1 & 2p^2 + 4p + 2 \end{bmatrix}$$

and $$(\mathbf{A}p^2 + \mathbf{B}p + \mathbf{C})^{-1} = \frac{\begin{bmatrix} 2p^2 + 4p + 2 & 1 \\ 1 & p^2 + p + 2 \end{bmatrix}}{2p^4 + 6p^3 + 10p^2 + 10p + 3}$$

so that

$$(\mathbf{A}p^2 + \mathbf{B}p + \mathbf{C})^{-1}[(\mathbf{A}p + \mathbf{B})\mathbf{Q}(0) + \mathbf{A}\dot{\mathbf{Q}}(0)]$$

$$= \frac{d \begin{bmatrix} 2p^3 + 6p^2 + 7p + 4 \\ p^3 + 3p^2 + 5p + 5 \end{bmatrix}}{p^4 + 3p^3 + 5p^2 + 5p + 1 \cdot 5}.$$

The roots of $p^4 + 3p^3 + 5p^2 + 5p + 1 \cdot 5 = 0$ are $p = -0 \cdot 49$, $-1 \cdot 43$, and $-0 \cdot 54 \pm 1 \cdot 39i$.   Therefore

$$L^{-1} \left\{ \frac{2p^3 + 6p^2 + 7p + 4}{p^4 + 3p^3 + 5p^2 + 5p + 1 \cdot 5} \right\} = \sum \text{Res} \frac{(2p^3 + 6p^2 + 7p + 4)e^{pt}}{p^4 + 3p^3 + 5p^2 + 5p + 1 \cdot 5}$$

at the poles $-0 \cdot 49$, $-1 \cdot 43$, and $-0 \cdot 54 \pm 1 \cdot 39i$.

We have

$$\text{Res}\,(-\,0{\cdot}49) = \lim_{p\to-0{\cdot}49} \frac{(2p^3 + 6p^2 + 7p + 4)e^{pt}}{\dfrac{d}{dp}(p^4 + 3p^3 + 5p^2 + 5p + 1{\cdot}5)}$$

$$= e^{-0{\cdot}49t},$$

$$\text{Res}\,(-\,1{\cdot}43) = \lim_{p\to-1{\cdot}43} \frac{(2p^3 + 6p^2 + 7p + 4)e^{pt}}{\dfrac{d}{dp}(p^4 + 3p^3 + 5p^2 + 5p + 1{\cdot}5)}$$

$$= -\,0{\cdot}16e^{-1{\cdot}43t}$$

$$\text{Res}\,(-\,0{\cdot}54 + 1{\cdot}39i) = \lim_{p\to-0{\cdot}54+1{\cdot}39i} \frac{(2p^3 + 6p^2 + 7p + 4)e^{pt}}{\dfrac{d}{dp}(p^4 + 3p^3 + 5p^2 + 5p + 1{\cdot}5)}$$

$$= \frac{23{\cdot}98 - 12{\cdot}85i}{40{\cdot}69}e^{(-0{\cdot}54+1{\cdot}39i)t},$$

$$\text{Res}\,(-\,0{\cdot}54 - 1{\cdot}39i) = \lim_{p\to-0{\cdot}54-1{\cdot}39i} \frac{(2p^3 + 6p^2 + 7p + 4)e^{pt}}{\dfrac{d}{dp}(p^4 + 3p^3 + 5p^2 + 5p + 1{\cdot}5)}$$

$$= \frac{23{\cdot}98 + 12{\cdot}85i}{40{\cdot}69}e^{(-0{\cdot}54-1{\cdot}39i)t},$$

Hence

$$q_1(t) = e^{-0{\cdot}49t} - 0{\cdot}16e^{-1{\cdot}43t} + e^{-0{\cdot}54t}[1{\cdot}16 \cos 1{\cdot}39t + 0{\cdot}63 \sin 1{\cdot}39t].$$

In a similar manner we find that

$$q_2(t) = 1{\cdot}75e^{-0{\cdot}49t} - 0{\cdot}41e^{-1{\cdot}43t} + e^{-0{\cdot}54t}[-\,0{\cdot}34 \cos 1{\cdot}39t \\ -\,0{\cdot}06 \sin 1{\cdot}39t].$$

Exercise. Solve the problem of the preceding example if $m_1 = 1$, $m_2 = 2$, $k_1 = 3$, $k_2 = 2$, $k = 1$, $l_1 = l_2 = l_3 = l$ and

$$\mathbf{Q}(0) = \begin{bmatrix} 0 \\ 0 \end{bmatrix}, \qquad \dot{\mathbf{Q}}(0) = \begin{bmatrix} v_0 \\ -\,3v_0 \end{bmatrix}$$

5.8 Matric Equations Arising in the Mathematical Theory of Aircraft Flutter

When an airplane travels at high speeds it is subjected to vibrations. Aeronautical engineers have observed that under certain conditions and speeds these vibrations become so violent that control over the airplane is lost or some part of the aircraft structure (such as the wing, aileron, or tail) fails.   This phenomenon is referred to as "flutter" and is the subject of intense investigation by aeronautical engineers.   One of the objects of these investigations is to determine the critical speed at which flutter occurs for a particular type of aircraft structure. Another is to improve its design so as to enable the airplane to travel at maximum operating speed without attaining this critical speed.

It is not possible to enter here into the mathematical theories of flutter.   The reader interested in this matter will find pertinent material in the *NACA Rept. 685, 1940*, by T. Theodorsen and I. E. Garrick.   We shall only indicate the system of differential equations that arises and illustrate how it may be solved by the Laplace transformation with the help of matrix methods.

In dealing with a physical problem of any complexity it is necessary to idealize it in order to facilitate its solution.   Our simplified model will be an elastic airplane wing attached to the body as a rigid base and placed at a small angle of incidence in an airstream.   We shall assume that our system is one consisting of only *three* degrees of freedom, namely, the bending and twisting of the wing, and the relative deflection of the aileron.   On the basis of these assumptions it is found that the differential equations of motion for small oscillations are three in number

$$a_{11} U_1''(t) + a_{12} U_2''(t) + a_{13} U_3''(t) + b_{11} U_1'(t) + b_{12} U_2'(t)$$
$$+ b_{13} U_3'(t) + c_{11} U_1(t) + c_{12} U_2(t) + c_{13} U_3(t) = 0,$$
$$a_{21} U_1''(t) + a_{22} U_2''(t) + a_{23} U_3''(t) + b_{21} U_1'(t) + b_{22} U_2'(t)$$
$$+ b_{23} U_3'(t) + c_{21} U_1(t) + c_{22} U_2(t) + c_{23} U_3(t) = 0,$$
$$a_{31} U_1''(t) + a_{32} U_2''(t) + a_{33} U_3''(t) + b_{31} U_1'(t) + b_{32} U_2'(t)$$
$$+ b_{33} U_3'(t) + c_{31} U_1(t) + c_{32} U_2(t) + c_{33} U_3(t) = 0,$$

where the a_{ij}'s, b_{ij}'s, and c_{ij}'s are constants determined from an analysis of the aircraft structure.   These equations can be written in the condensed form

$$\sum_{j=1}^{3} a_{ij} U_j''(t) + b_{ij} U_j'(t) + c_{ij} U_j(t) = 0, \quad i = 1, 2, 3.$$

If we now define $\mathbf{A} = [a_{ij}]$, $\mathbf{B} = [b_{ij}]$, $\mathbf{C} = [c_{ij}]$ and

$$\mathbf{U}(t) = \begin{bmatrix} U_1(t) \\ U_2(t) \\ U_3(t) \end{bmatrix},$$

then the preceding equations of flutter may be written as the single matric equation

(5.8.1) $$\mathbf{A}U''(t) + \mathbf{B}U'(t) + \mathbf{C}U(t) = 0,$$

which is a type we have already considered.

Let $\mathbf{U}(0) = \begin{bmatrix} U_1(0) \\ U_2(0) \\ U_3(0) \end{bmatrix}$ and $\mathbf{U}'(0) = \begin{bmatrix} U_1'(0) \\ U_2'(0) \\ U_3'(0) \end{bmatrix}$ be given. Then,

taking the Laplace transform of (5.8.1), we have

$$(\mathbf{A}p^2 + \mathbf{B}p + \mathbf{C})\mathbf{u}(p) = (p\mathbf{A} + \mathbf{B})\mathbf{U}(0) + \mathbf{A}\mathbf{U}'(0)$$

from which

$$\mathbf{u}(p) = (\mathbf{A}p^2 + \mathbf{B}p + \mathbf{C})^{-1}[(p\mathbf{A} + \mathbf{B})\mathbf{U}(0) + \mathbf{A}\mathbf{U}'(0)],$$

and hence

$$\mathbf{U}(t) = L^{-1}\{(\mathbf{A}p^2 + \mathbf{B}p + \mathbf{C})^{-1}[(p\mathbf{A} + \mathbf{B})\mathbf{U}(0) + \mathbf{A}\mathbf{U}'(0)]\},$$

provided that the matrix $\mathbf{A}p^2 + \mathbf{B}p + \mathbf{C}$ is non-singular.

Example. For the sake of reducing the arithmetic and algebra that arise in the solution of a system of three equations in three unknowns, let us assume in this illustrative example that the aerodynamic constants of an airplane are such that

$$\mathbf{A} = \begin{bmatrix} 1 & 0 & -1 \\ 0 & 1 & 0 \\ 1 & 0 & 1 \end{bmatrix}, \quad \mathbf{B} = \begin{bmatrix} 1 & 1 & 0 \\ 1 & 1 & 0 \\ 0 & 0 & 1 \end{bmatrix}, \quad \mathbf{C} = \begin{bmatrix} 1 & 0 & 1 \\ 0 & 1 & 0 \\ -1 & 0 & 1 \end{bmatrix}.$$

Furthermore, let the initial conditions be

$$\mathbf{U}(0) = \begin{bmatrix} 1 \\ 2 \\ 3 \end{bmatrix}, \quad \mathbf{U}'(0) = \begin{bmatrix} 3 \\ 2 \\ 1 \end{bmatrix}.$$

Then the following results can easily be verified, namely, that

$$(p\mathbf{A} + \mathbf{B})\mathbf{U}(0) + \mathbf{A}\mathbf{U}'(0) = \begin{bmatrix} -2p + 5 \\ 2p + 5 \\ 4p + 7 \end{bmatrix},$$

$$\mathbf{A}p^2 + \mathbf{B}p + \mathbf{C} = \begin{bmatrix} p^2 + p + 1 & p & -p^2 + 1 \\ p & p^2 + p + 1 & 0 \\ p^2 - 1 & 0 & p^2 + p + 1 \end{bmatrix},$$

and

$$(\mathbf{A}p^2 + \mathbf{B}p + \mathbf{C})^{-1} = \frac{\begin{bmatrix} (p^2 + p + 1)^2 & -p(p^2 + p + 1) \\ -p(p^2 + p + 1) & 2p^4 + 2p^3 + p^2 + 2p + 1 \\ (p^2 - 1)(p^2 + p + 1) & -p(p^2 - 1) \end{bmatrix}}{\begin{vmatrix} p^2 + p + 1 & p & -p^2 + 1 \\ p & p^2 + p + 1 & 0 \\ p^2 - 1 & 0 & p^2 + p + 1 \end{vmatrix}}$$

$$\begin{matrix} -(p^2 - 1)(p^2 + p + 1) \\ p(p^2 - 1) \\ p^4 + 2p^3 + 2p^2 + 2p + 1 \end{matrix}$$

From this

$$\mathbf{u}(p) = \frac{\begin{bmatrix} (p^2 + p + 1)^2 & -p(p^2 + p + 1) & -(p^2-1)(p^2+p+1) \\ -p(p^2 + p + 1) & 2p^4 + 2p^3 + p^2 + 2p + 1 & -p(p^2-1) \\ -(p^2 - 1)(p^2 + p + 1) & p(p^2 - 1) & p^4 + 2p^3 + 2p^2 + 2p + 1 \end{bmatrix} \begin{bmatrix} -2p + 5 \\ 2p + 5 \\ 4p + 7 \end{bmatrix}}{2(p + 1)^2(p^2 - p + 1)(p^2 + p + 1)}$$

$$= \frac{\begin{bmatrix} (2p^3 + 8p^2 - 6p - 2)(p^2 + p + 1) \\ 4p^5 + 12p^4 + 2p^3 + 8p^2 + 14p + 5 \\ 2(p + 1)(3p^4 + 4p^3 + 7p^2 + 2p + 6) \end{bmatrix}}{2(p + 1)^2(p^2 - p + 1)(p^2 + p + 1)}$$

and

$$\mathbf{U}(t) = \begin{bmatrix} L^{-1}\left\{\dfrac{2p^3 + 8p^2 - 6p - 2}{2(p + 1)^2(p^2 - p + 1)}\right\} \\[2em] L^{-1}\left\{\dfrac{4p^5 + 12p^4 + 2p^3 + 8p^2 + 14p + 5}{2(p + 1)^2(p^2 - p + 1)(p^2 + p + 1)}\right\} \\[2em] L^{-1}\left\{\dfrac{3p^4 + 4p^3 + 7p^2 + 2p + 6}{(p + 1)(p^2 - p + 1)(p^2 + p + 1)}\right\} \end{bmatrix}.$$

The roots of the equation $(p + 1)^2(p^2 - p + 1)(p^2 + p + 1) = 0$ are the double root $- 1$ and the roots $\frac{1}{2}(1 \pm i\sqrt{3})$ and $\frac{1}{2}(- 1 \pm i\sqrt{3})$. Therefore

$$L^{-1}\left\{\frac{2p^3 + 8p^2 - 6p - 2}{2(p + 1)^2(p^2 - p + 1)}\right\} = \sum \text{Res} \frac{(2p^3 + 8p^2 - 6p - 2)e^{pt}}{2(p + 1)^2(p^2 - p + 1)}$$

at the double pole $p = - 1$ and the simple poles $p = \frac{1}{2}(1 \pm i\sqrt{3})$.

Computing the residues, we have

$$\text{Res}\,(- 1) = \lim_{p \to -1} \frac{d}{dp}\left[\frac{(2p^3 + 8p^2 - 6p - 2)e^{pt}}{2(p^2 - p + 1)}\right] = \frac{15t - 9}{9}e^{-t},$$

$$\text{Res}\left(\frac{1 + i\sqrt{3}}{2}\right) = \lim_{p \to \frac{1+i\sqrt{3}}{2}} \frac{(2p^3 + 8p^2 - 6p - 2)e^{pt}}{2(p + 1)^2\left(p - \dfrac{1 - i\sqrt{3}}{2}\right)}$$

$$= \frac{1}{3\sqrt{3}}(3\sqrt{3} + 2i)e^{(1+i\sqrt{3}/2)t},$$

$$\text{Res}\left(\frac{1 - i\sqrt{3}}{2}\right) = \lim_{p \to \frac{1-i\sqrt{3}}{2}} \frac{(2p^3 + 8p^2 - 6p - 2)e^{pt}}{2(p + 1)^2\left(p - \dfrac{1 + i\sqrt{3}}{2}\right)}$$

$$= \frac{1}{3\sqrt{3}}(3\sqrt{3} - 2i)e^{(1-i\sqrt{3}/2)t}.$$

The sum of these residues gives

$$U_1(t) = \frac{15t - 9}{9}e^{-t} + 2e^{t/2}\left(\cos\frac{\sqrt{3}}{2}t - \frac{2}{3\sqrt{3}}\sin\frac{\sqrt{3}}{2}t\right).$$

To determine $U_2(t)$ we evaluate

$$\sum \text{Res} \frac{(4p^5 + 12p^4 + 2p^3 + 8p^2 + 14p + 5)e^{pt}}{2(p + 1)^2(p^2 - p + 1)(p^2 + p + 1)}$$

at the double pole -1 and the simple poles $\frac{1}{2}(1 \pm i\sqrt{3})$ and $\frac{1}{2}(-1 \pm i\sqrt{3})$. The results are

$$\text{Res}\,(-1) = \lim_{p \to -1} \frac{d}{dp}\left[\frac{(4p^5 + 12p^4 + 2p^3 + 8p^2 + 14p + 5)e^{pt}}{2(p^4 + p^2 + 1)}\right]$$

$$= \frac{5t - 14}{6}e^{-t},$$

$$\text{Res}\left(\frac{1 + i\sqrt{3}}{2}\right) = \lim_{p \to \frac{1+i\sqrt{3}}{2}} \frac{(4p^5 + 12p^4 + 2p^3 + 8p^2 + 14p + 5)e^{pt}}{2(p + 1)^2\left(p - \dfrac{1 - i\sqrt{3}}{2}\right)(p^2 + p + 1)}$$

$$= -\frac{5\sqrt{3} + 7i}{24}e^{(1+i\sqrt{3})t/2},$$

$$\text{Res}\left(\frac{1 - i\sqrt{3}}{2}\right) = \overline{\text{Res}\left(\frac{1 + i\sqrt{3}}{2}\right)} = -\frac{5\sqrt{3} - 7i}{24}e^{(1-i\sqrt{3})t/2},$$

$$\text{Res}\left(\frac{-1 + i\sqrt{3}}{2}\right) = \lim_{p \to \frac{-1+i\sqrt{3}}{2}} \frac{(4p^5 + 12p^4 + 2p^3 + 8p^2 + 14p + 5)e^{pt}}{2(p + 1)^2(p^2 - p + 1)\left(p + \dfrac{1 + i\sqrt{3}}{2}\right)}$$

$$= \frac{19\sqrt{3} - 9i}{8\sqrt{3}}e^{(-1+i\sqrt{3})t/2},$$

$$\text{Res}\left(\frac{-1 - i\sqrt{3}}{2}\right) = \overline{\text{Res}\left(\frac{-1 + i\sqrt{3}}{2}\right)} = \frac{19\sqrt{3} + 9i}{8\sqrt{3}}e^{(-1-i\sqrt{3})t/2}.$$

Thus

$$U_2(t) = \frac{5t - 14}{6}e^{-t} - e^{t/2}\left(\frac{5}{12}\cos\frac{\sqrt{3}}{2}t - \frac{7}{12\sqrt{3}}\sin\frac{\sqrt{3}}{2}t\right)$$

$$+ e^{-t/2}\left(\frac{19}{4}\cos\frac{\sqrt{3}}{2}t + \frac{9}{4\sqrt{3}}\sin\frac{\sqrt{3}}{2}t\right).$$

For $U_3(t)$ we compute

$$\sum \text{Res}\,\frac{(3p^4 + 4p^3 + 7p^2 + 2p + 6)e^{pt}}{(p + 1)(p^2 - p + 1)(p^2 + p + 1)}$$

at the simple pole $p = -1$ and the simple poles $\frac{1}{2}(1 \pm i\sqrt{3})$ and $\frac{1}{2}(-1 \pm i\sqrt{3})$.

Proceeding as before, we obtain

$$\text{Res}\,(-1) = \lim_{p \to -1} \frac{(3p^4 + 4p^3 + 7p^2 + 2p + 6)e^{pt}}{(p^2 - p + 1)(p^2 + p + 1)} = \frac{10}{3}e^{-t},$$

$$\text{Res}\left(\frac{1+i\sqrt{3}}{2}\right) = \lim_{p \to \frac{1+i\sqrt{3}}{2}} \frac{(3p^4 + 4p^3 + 7p^2 + 2p + 6)e^{pt}}{(p+1)\left(p - \frac{1-i\sqrt{3}}{2}\right)(p^2 + p + 1)}$$

$$= \frac{2 - 3i\sqrt{3}}{6} e^{(1+i\sqrt{3})t/2},$$

$$\text{Res}\left(\frac{1-i\sqrt{3}}{2}\right) = \overline{\text{Res}\left(\frac{1+i\sqrt{3}}{2}\right)} = \frac{2 + 3i\sqrt{3}}{6} e^{(1-i\sqrt{3})t/2},$$

$$\text{Res}\left(\frac{-1+i\sqrt{3}}{2}\right) = \lim_{p \to \frac{-1+i\sqrt{3}}{2}} \frac{(3p^4 + 4p^3 + 7p^2 + 2p + 6)e^{pt}}{(p+1)(p^2 - p + 1)\left(p + \frac{1+i\sqrt{3}}{2}\right)}$$

$$= -\frac{\sqrt{3} + 4i}{2\sqrt{3}} e^{(-1+i\sqrt{3})t/2},$$

$$\text{Res}\left(\frac{-1-i\sqrt{3}}{2}\right) = \overline{\text{Res}\left(\frac{-1+i\sqrt{3}}{2}\right)} = -\frac{\sqrt{3} - 4i}{2\sqrt{3}} e^{(-1-i\sqrt{3})t/2}.$$

Consequently

$$U_3(t) = \frac{10}{3}e^{-t} + e^{t/2}\left(\frac{2}{3}\cos\frac{\sqrt{3}}{2}t + \sin\frac{\sqrt{3}}{2}t\right)$$

$$- e^{-t/2}\left(\cos\frac{\sqrt{3}}{2}t - \frac{4}{\sqrt{3}}\sin\frac{\sqrt{3}}{2}t\right).$$

5.9 Stable and Unstable Systems

We shall say that a system is *stable* if the amplitudes of oscillation are *bounded* or are *damped out* as $t \to \infty$. On the other hand, if the amplitudes of oscillation become *infinite* as $t \to \infty$, then the system will be termed *unstable*.

According to this definition the aircraft whose aerodynamic constants are those of the preceding example is *unstable*. This is due to the fact that $e^{t/2}$ occurs in each of the functions $U_1(t)$, $U_2(t)$, and $U_3(t)$ so that as $t \to \infty$ the amplitudes of oscillation become infinite. Since the poles $p = \frac{1}{2}(1 \pm i\sqrt{3})$ gave rise to the terms involving $e^{t/2}$ it is clear that the *stability* or *instability* of the motion could have been predicted simply by examining the roots of the equation

$$(5.9.1) \qquad\qquad |\mathbf{A}p^2 + \mathbf{B}p + \mathbf{C}| = 0.$$

A study of the preceding example as well as those previously solved should make the following remarks plausible.

Corresponding to a *real root* $\gamma \neq 0$, there is a term in the solution of the form $A_0 e^{\gamma t}$ which becomes infinite or tends to zero as $t \to \infty$, depending on whether γ is *positive* or *negative*. If $\gamma = 0$, we have the constant amplitude A_0.

When γ is an m-fold ($m > 1$) *real root* of (5.9.1) then terms of the form

$$e^{\gamma t}(A_0 + A_1 t + \cdots + A_{m-1} t^{m-1})$$

will appear. Here again the amplitude of the oscillation *increases* or *decreases* (numerically) when $t \to \infty$ according as $\gamma \geqslant 0$ or $\gamma < 0$.

Suppose, now, that (5.9.1) has the *complex conjugate numbers* $p = \alpha \pm i\beta (\alpha \neq 0)$ as roots. Then the corresponding term in the solution will be

(5.9.2) $e^{\alpha t}(A_0 \cos \beta t + B_0 \sin \beta t),$

where A_0 and B_0 are constants. If $\alpha > 0$ the term (5.9.2) becomes

Table 5.9.1

Roots of $\|\mathbf{A}p^2 + \mathbf{B}p + \mathbf{C}\| = 0$	Behavior of Corresponding Terms in the Solution as $t \to \infty$	Type of System if It Contains Terms Corresponding to the Roots Indicated
(Simple, real, positive)	Infinite	Unstable (no matter how the other terms behave as $t \to \infty$)
(Multiple, real, $\geqslant 0$)	Infinite	Unstable (no matter how the other terms behave as $t \to \infty$)
(Simple complex conjugate, $\mathrm{Re}(p) > 0$)	Infinite	Unstable (no matter how the other terms behave as $t \to \infty$)
(Multiple complex conjugate, $\mathrm{Re}(p) > 0$)	Infinite	Unstable (no matter how the other terms behave as $t \to \infty$)
(Simple, 0)	Bounded	Stable (provided other terms are bounded or tend to zero as $t \to \infty$)
(Multiple, real, < 0)	Tends to zero	Stable (provided other terms are bounded or tend to zero as $t \to \infty$)
(Pure imaginary)	Bounded	Stable (provided other terms are bounded or tend to zero as $t \to \infty$)
(Multiple complex conjugate, $\mathrm{Re}(p) < 0$)	Tends to zero	Stable (provided other terms are bounded or tend to zero as $t \to \infty$)

infinite as $t \to \infty$. If $\alpha = 0$ the amplitude of the oscillation is clearly finite, and if $\alpha < 0$ the term (5.9.2) tends to zero as $t \to \infty$.

In case $p = \alpha \pm i\beta$ is an m-fold ($m > 1$) pair of complex roots, the corresponding terms appearing in the general solution are of the form

$$(5.9.3) \quad e^{\alpha t}[(A_0 + A_1 t + \cdots + A_{m-1}t^{m-1}) \cos \beta t \\ + (B_0 + B_1 t + \cdots + B_{m-1}t^{m-1}) \sin \beta t].$$

It is clear that if $\alpha \geqslant 0$ then (5.9.3) becomes infinite as $t \to \infty$ and if $\alpha < 0$ then (5.9.3) tends to zero as $t \to \infty$.

For a system to be stable, therefore, the solution must contain terms each of which tends to zero or is bounded as $t \to \infty$. Instability is ensured whenever at least one of the terms in the solution becomes infinite as $t \to \infty$. Table 5.9.1 summarizes the preceding discussion.

PROBLEMS

For the determination of the roots of some of the algebraic equations that arise in the solution of systems of differential equations Graeffe's method* can be used advantageously.

Solve the following systems of equations:

1. $Y_1'(t) + a Y_1(t) + b Y_2(t) = t, \quad Y_2'(t) + b Y_1(t) + a Y_2(t) = e^t,$
$$Y_1(0) = 1, \quad Y_2(0) = -1.$$

2: $2Y_1'(t) - Y_2'(t) + Y_1(t) = te^t, \quad Y_1'(t) - 2Y_2'(t) + Y_2(t) = t^2,$
$$Y_1(0) = Y_2(0) = 0.$$

3. $Y_1'(t) - 4Y_2'(t) + Y_1(t) - 2Y_2(t) = \sin t,$
$$4Y_1'(t) + Y_2'(t) + 3Y_1(t) + Y_2(t) = \cos t,$$
$$Y_1(0) = Y_2(0) = 0.$$

4. $Y_1'(t) = Y_3(t), \quad Y_2'(t) = Y_1(t), \quad Y_3'(t) = Y_2(t),$
$$Y_1(0) = Y_2(0) = Y_3(0) = a.$$

5. $Y_2'(t) - Y_3(t) = 3,$
$Y_3'(t) - Y_2(t) - Y_1(t) = 1 - t,$
$Y_3(t) - 4Y_1(t) = -2,$
$$Y_1(0) = Y_2(0) = Y_3(0) = b.$$

6. $Y_1''(t) + a^2 Y_1(t) = b Y_2(t), \quad Y_2''(t) + a^2 Y_2(t) = -c Y_1(t),$
$$Y_1(0) = Y_2(0) = 1, \quad Y_1'(0) = Y_2'(0) = 2.$$

7. $Y_1''(t) + a Y_1'(t) - b Y_2'(t) - c Y_2(t) = 0,$

$$Y_2''(t) - m Y_2'(t) - n Y_2(t) + \frac{na}{c} Y_1'(t) = 0,$$

$$Y_1(0) = c_1, \quad Y_2(0) = c_2, \quad Y_1'(0) = c_3, \quad Y_2'(0) = c_4.$$

* See M. B. Reed and G. B. Reed, *Mathematical Methods in Electrical Engineering*, Harper & Brothers, 1951, Chap. 4.

8. $2Y_1''(t) - Y_1'(t) - Y_2''(t) + 3Y_2(t) = 0,$
   $2Y_1''(t) + 5Y_1'(t) + Y_2''(t) + Y_2(t) = 0,$
   $\qquad Y_1(0) = Y_2(0) = 0, \quad Y_1'(0) = Y_2'(0) = 1.$

9. $Y_1''(t) + 4Y_1(t) + Y_2''(t) - Y_2(t) = 0,$
   $Y_1''(t) + Y_1'(t) + 2Y_2''(t) = 0,$
   $\qquad Y_1(0) = 1, \quad Y_2(0) = -1, \quad Y_1'(0) = 2, \quad Y_2'(0) = -2.$

   In the following network problems it is assumed that each network is dead initially.

10. In the network of Fig. 5.9.1, $R_1 = 10$ ohms, $R_2 = 15$ ohms, $R_3 = 20$ ohms, $L_1 = 5$ henrys, and $L_2 = 10$ henrys. Find the branch currents I_1, I_2, and I_3 for $t > 0$ if

    (a) $E_1(t) = 110$ volts, $E_2(t) = E_0[1(t - t_0) - 1(t - t_1)]$ volts, $t_0 < t_1$;
    (b) $E_1(t) = E_0, \quad 0 < t < T/2, \quad E_2(t) = 0.$
    $\qquad\quad = -E_0, \quad T/2 < t < T,$
  $E(t + T) = E(t).$

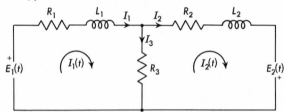

FIG. 5.9.1

11. In the network of Fig. 5.9.2, $R_1 = R_2 = 15$ ohms and $L_3 = 15$ henrys. Find the branch currents I_1, I_2, and I_3 for $t > 0$ if $E_1(t) = 110$ volts, $E_2(t) = \sin nt$ volts.

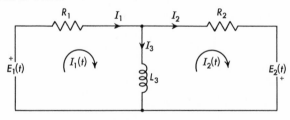

FIG. 5.9.2

12. In the network of Fig. 5.9.3, $R_1 = 100$ ohms, $R_2 = 200$ ohms and $C_3 = 10^{-6}$ farad. Find the branch currents I_1, I_2, and I_3 for $t > 0$ if $E_1(t) = \cos 2t$ volts and $E_2(t) = E_0[1(t - t_0) - 1(t - t_1)]$ volts, $t_0 < t_1$.

13. In the network of Fig. 5.9.4, $R_1 = R_2 = R_3 = 100$ ohms, $L_1 = 10$ henrys, $L_2 = 20$ henrys, $L_3 = 30$ henrys, $C_1 = C_2 = C_3 = 10^{-5}$ farad. Find the branch currents I_1, I_2, and I_3 for $t > 0$ if $E_1(t) = \sin t$ volts and $E_2(t) = \cos 3t$ volts.

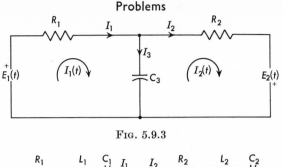

Fig. 5.9.3

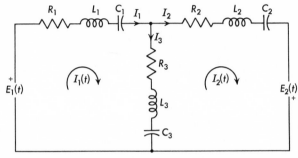

Fig. 5.9.4

14. The integro-differential equations for the network of Fig. 5.9.5 are

$$L_1 I_1'(t) + R_1 I_1(t) + \frac{1}{C_1} \int_0^t I_1(\tau)\, d\tau + L_{12} I_2'(t) = E_1(t),$$

$$L_{12} I_1'(t) + L_2 I_2'(t) + R_2 I_2'(t) + \frac{1}{C_2} \int_0^t I_2(\tau)\, d\tau = E_2(t).$$

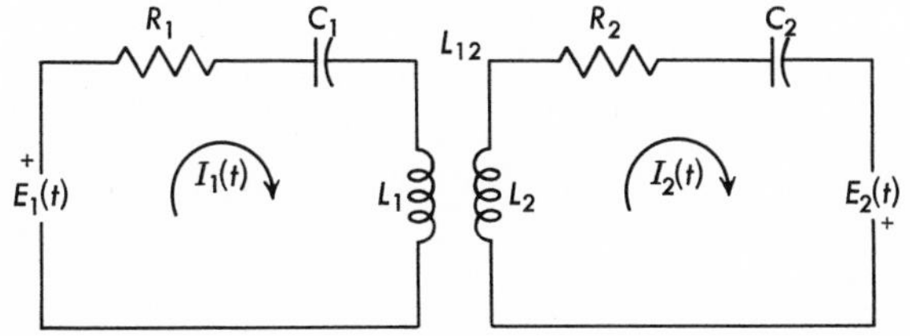

Fig. 5.9.5

Solve this system for I_1 and I_2 if

(a) $R_1 = 50$ ohms, $R_2 = 30$ ohms, $C_1 = C_2 = 10^{-5}$ farad, $L_1 = 20$ henrys, $L_{12} = -20$ henrys, $E_1(t) = 110$ volts, $E_2(t) = 220$ volts.

(b) $R_1 = R_2 = 10$ ohms, $C_1 = C_2 = 10^{-6}$ farad, $L_1 = L_2 = 15$ henrys, $L_{12} = 10$ henrys, $E_1(t) = \cos 5t$ volts, $E_2(t) = E_0[1(t - t_0) - 1(t - t_1)]$ volts, $t_0 < t_1$.

The oscillations in the following problems are assumed to be small.

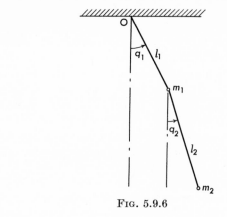

Fig. 5.9.6

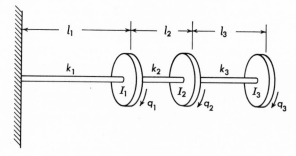

Fig. 5.9.7

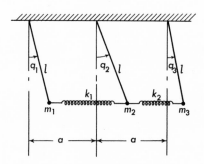

Fig. 5.9.8

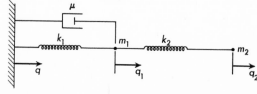

Fig. 5.9.9

15. Determine the expressions for the kinetic and potential energies of the system shown in Fig. 5.9.6.   Write the matric equation of motion and solve it for $l_1 = l$, $l_2 = 2l$, $m_1 = 2m$, $m_2 = 3m$, $q_1(0) = \frac{1}{2}$, $q_2(0) = -1$, $\dot{q}_1(0) = \dot{q}_2(0) = 0$.

16. Find the expressions for the kinetic and potential energies of the system shown in Fig. 5.9.7.   Write the matric equation of motion and solve it for $l_1 = l_2 = l_3 = l$, $I_1 = I$, $I_2 = I$, $I_3 = 2I$, $k_1 = k_2 = k_3 = k$, $q_1(0) = 1$, $q_2(0) = 0$, $q_3(0) = -1$, $\dot{q}_1(0) = \dot{q}_2(0) = \dot{q}_3(0) = 0$.

17. Determine the expressions for the kinetic and potential energies of the system shown in Fig. 5.9.8.   Write the matric equation of motion and solve it for $l = 2$, $m_1 = 1$, $m_2 = 2$, $m_3 = 3$, $q_1(0) = 2$, $q_2(0) = -1$, $q_3(0) = 1$, $\dot{q}_1(0) = \dot{q}_2(0) = \dot{q}_3(0) = 0$.

18. Write the matric equation of motion for the problem of Fig. 5.9.9 and solve it for $F = \frac{1}{2}\mu\dot{q}_1^2$ and the following values: $k_1 = 2k$, $k_2 = 3k$, $m_1 = m$, $m_2 = 3m$, $\mu = 1$, $q_1(0) = \frac{1}{2}$, $q_2(0) = 0$, $\dot{q}_1(0) = 0$, $\dot{q}_2(0) = -\frac{1}{2}$.

19. The coefficients of the matric differential equation of flutter (5.8.1) have the values:

$$
A = \begin{bmatrix} 5\cdot32 & 1\cdot70 & 0\cdot45 \\ 0\cdot24 & 0\cdot01 & 0\cdot18 \\ 1\cdot08 & 0\cdot13 & 0\cdot84 \end{bmatrix}, \qquad
B = \begin{bmatrix} 75\cdot02 & 8\cdot31 & 12\cdot50 \\ 3\cdot75 & 2\cdot51 & 1\cdot92 \\ 9\cdot62 & 1\cdot37 & 11\cdot11 \end{bmatrix}
$$

$$
C = \begin{bmatrix} 8\cdot88 & 1\cdot08 & 3\cdot23 \\ 0\cdot28 & 0 & 0\cdot01 \\ 0\cdot75 & 0\cdot15 & 0\cdot39 \end{bmatrix}.
$$

Determine $U_1(t)$, $U_2(t)$, and $U_3(t)$ if

$$
U(0) = \begin{bmatrix} 1\cdot00 \\ 0\cdot75 \\ 2\cdot15 \end{bmatrix}, \qquad
U'(0) = \begin{bmatrix} 0\cdot85 \\ 1\cdot30 \\ 0\cdot10 \end{bmatrix}.
$$

CHAPTER VI

Linear Difference Equations with Constant Coefficients

When certain problems arising in probability, statistics, mechanics, theory of structures, theory of networks, etc., are analyzed, it is found that they lead to difference equations. The problems that give rise to these equations are characterized by the fact that the variables undergo finite changes. Such is the case, for example, when one studies certain problems in probability theory, the disintegration of radioactive elements, structures, and electrical or mechanical systems having many identical component parts. In view of their increasing importance in the solution of engineering problems, we shall devote this chapter to the study of certain types of difference equations.

6.1 Linear Difference Equations with Constant Coefficients

A *differential equation* is one which involves an independent variable t, a dependent variable Y and one or more *derivatives* dY/dt, d^2Y/dt^2, etc. A *difference equation*, on the other hand, is one which involves an independent variable t, a dependent variable Y and one or more *differences* ΔY_t, $\Delta^2 Y_t$, etc., where

$$(6.1.1) \qquad \begin{aligned} \Delta Y_t &= Y_{t+1} - Y_t, \\ \Delta^2 Y_t &= \Delta(\Delta Y_t) = Y_{t+2} - 2Y_{t+1} + Y_t, \end{aligned}$$

$$\cdot \quad \cdot \quad \cdot \quad \cdot \quad \cdot \quad \cdot \quad \cdot \quad \cdot \quad \cdot \quad \cdot$$

$$\Delta^n Y_t = \Delta(\Delta^{n-1} Y_t) = \sum_{r=0}^{n} (-1)^r \frac{n!}{r!(n-r)!} Y_{t+n-r}.$$

The symbols ΔY_t, $\Delta^2 Y_t$, $\cdots$, $\Delta^n Y_t$ are called the first, second, $\cdots$, and nth differences, respectively.

The problem of solving difference equations, in general, is beset with many difficulties. We shall be content here with the solution of certain difference equations which arise in the applications. To be specific, we shall restrict ourselves to the *linear difference equation of order n* with constant coefficients:

(6.1.2) $b_n \Delta^n Y_t + b_{n-1} \Delta^{n-1} Y_t + \cdots + b_1 \Delta Y_t + b_0 Y_t = F_t,$

$$t = 0, 1, 2, \cdots$$

where $b_n, b_{n-1}, \cdots, b_1, b_0$ are constants, $F_0, F_1, F_2, \cdots$ is a *given sequence* and $Y_0, Y_1, Y_2, \cdots$ is the *unknown sequence*.

By making use of relations (6.1.1), equation (6.1.2) can be replaced by

(6.1.3) $a_n Y_{t+n} + a_{n-1} Y_{t+n-1} + \cdots + a_1 Y_{t+1} + a_0 Y_t = F_t,$

where the constants a_i can be expressed in terms of the constants b_i. In the analysis of physical problems equations of both forms arise. However, since (6.1.2) can always be transformed into (6.1.3), we may deal with (6.1.3) exclusively.

As in the case of differential equations, we desire a solution of the difference equation (6.1.2) or (6.1.3) subject to certain initial or boundary conditions which we shall stipulate later on. Before embarking on a detailed discussion, let us consider an example which will serve to indicate the method to be followed in the general treatment.

Example. Solve $Y_{t+1} = 2Y_t$, subject to the initial condition $Y_0 = \frac{1}{2}$. If we treat the problem numerically, we obtain:

$$Y_1 = 2Y_0 = 1, \quad Y_2 = 2Y_1 = 2, \quad Y_3 = 2Y_2 = 4, \quad Y_4 = 2Y_3 = 8,$$

$$\cdots Y_t = 2^{t-1}, \cdots.$$

This sequence of values is plotted in Fig. 6.1.1 and constitutes a numerical solution of our problem.

If we are to use the Laplace transformation to solve difference equations, it is apparent that we must deal with functions defined over sets other than those consisting of discrete points. This can be done by constructing step functions. To do this, let us introduce a convenient symbol which will serve to facilitate the representation of step functions.

If x is a number, the symbol $[x]$, read the *greatest integer in x*, is the integer such that

$$[x] \leqslant x < [x] + 1.$$

For example, $[\frac{3}{4}] = 0$, $[-2\frac{1}{2}] = -3$, $[3] = 3$, and $[\sqrt{3}] = 1$. From the above inequality it follows immediately that

$$x - 1 < [x] \leqslant x.$$

In terms of the notation just introduced, we can now construct the step function

(6.1.4) $$Y(t) = 2^{[t]-1}, \quad (t \geqslant 0),$$

shown in Fig. 6.1.2, corresponding to the sequence

(6.1.5) $$Y_t = 2^{t-1}, \quad t = 0, 1, 2, \cdots.$$

From the graph we see that the left end points of the steps constitute the sequence of points (6.1.5) which is the solution of the given difference equation.

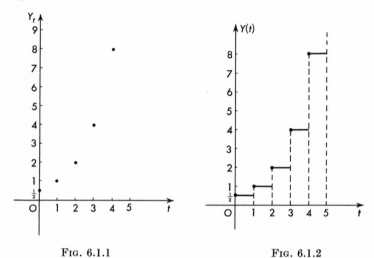

FIG. 6.1.1   FIG. 6.1.2

This suggests the general procedure. We replace the difference equation (6.1.3), whose solution is a sequence, by a difference equation, whose solution is a step function, and recover the sequence from the step function by taking the left end points of the steps. Thus, let $Y(t) = Y_{[t]}$ and $F(t) = F_{[t]}$ represent step functions. Then equation (6.1.3) is replaced by the corresponding difference equation

(6.1.6) $$a_n Y(t + n) + a_{n-1} Y(t + n - 1) + \cdots + a_1 Y(t + 1) + a_0 Y(t) = F(t),$$

whose solution, being a step function, includes the solution of (6.1.3), which is a sequence, as a special case.

As in the solution of differential equations, the Laplace transform is most advantageously employed to solve *initial value problems*, which for (6.1.6) would mean that initially a step function is prescribed, i.e.,

$$Y(t) = Y_{[t]}, \quad 0 \leqslant t < n.$$

However, the Laplace transform can also be used to solve *boundary value* problems, some of which will be considered later on.

6.2 Transforms of $Y(t+1)$, $Y(t+2)$, $\cdots$, $Y(t+n)$

Since the first step in solving a difference equation is that of taking the Laplace transform of both sides, it is necessary to know what $L\{Y(t+1)\}$, $L\{Y(t+2)\}$, etc., are.

For the transform of $Y(t+1)$ we have

$$L\{Y(t+1)\} = \int_0^\infty e^{-pt} Y(t+1)\, dt.$$

Making the substitution $t + 1 = \tau$, $dt = d\tau$, in the preceding integral, we get

$$\int_0^\infty e^{-pt} Y(t+1)\, dt = e^p \int_1^\infty e^{-p\tau} Y(\tau)\, d\tau$$

$$= e^p \int_0^\infty e^{-p\tau} Y(\tau)\, d\tau. - e^p \int_0^1 e^{-p\tau} Y(\tau)\, d\tau$$

If we stipulate that $Y(t)$ have the constant value Y_0 for $0 \leqslant t < 1$, then

$$(6.2.1) \qquad L\{Y(t+1)\} = e^p L\{Y(t)\} + \frac{1-e^p}{p} Y_0.$$

Similarly, for the $L\{Y(t+2)\}$ we have

$$(6.2.2) \qquad \int_0^\infty e^{-pt} Y(t+2)\, dt = e^p \int_1^\infty e^{-p\tau} Y(\tau+1)\, d\tau.$$

An analogous substitution $\tau + 1 = T$ yields

$$\int_1^\infty e^{-p\tau} Y(\tau+1)\, d\tau = e^p \int_2^\infty e^{-pT} Y(T)\, dT$$

$$= e^p \left[\int_0^\infty e^{-pT} Y(T)\, dT - \int_0^2 e^{-pT} Y(T)\, dT \right]$$

$$= e^p \left[L\{Y(t)\} - Y_0 \int_0^1 e^{-pT}\, dT - Y_1 \int_1^2 e^{-pT}\, dT \right]$$

$$= e^p \left[L\{Y(t)\} + Y_0 \left(\frac{e^{-p}-1}{p} \right) + Y_1 e^{-p} \left(\frac{e^{-p}-1}{p} \right) \right],$$

where we have stipulated that $Y(t) = Y_1$, for $1 \leqslant t < 2$. Upon substituting the above result in the right member of (6.2.2), we get

$$(6.2.3) \qquad L\{Y(t+2)\} = e^{2p} L\{Y(t)\} + \frac{1-e^p}{p} (Y_0 e^p + Y_1).$$

By induction we obtain

$$(6.2.4) \quad L\{Y(t+n)\} = e^{np} L\{Y(t)\} + \frac{1-e^p}{p} [Y_0 e^{(n-1)p} + Y_1 e^{(n-2)p}$$

$$+ \cdots + Y_{n-2} e^p + Y_{n-1}],$$

where initially
$$Y(t) = Y_0, \quad 0 \leqslant t < 1,$$
$$= Y_1, \quad 1 \leqslant t < 2,$$
$$\cdot \quad \cdot \quad \cdot \quad \cdot \quad \cdot \quad \cdot$$
$$= Y_{n-1}, \quad (n-1) \leqslant t < n.$$

Let us return to the difference equation

(6.2.5)
$$Y_{t+1} = 2Y_t, \quad Y_0 = \tfrac{1}{2}.$$

In order to solve it by the Laplace transform method we first replace it by the difference equation

(6.2.6)
$$Y(t+1) = 2Y(t), \text{ with } Y(t) = \tfrac{1}{2}, \quad 0 \leqslant t < 1.$$

Then, upon taking transforms of both sides, we get

$$e^p L\{Y(t)\} + \frac{1}{2}\frac{1-e^p}{p} = 2L\{Y(t)\},$$

whence
$$L\{Y(t)\} = \frac{1}{2}\frac{e^p-1}{p(e^p-2)},$$

and

(6.2.7)
$$Y(t) = L^{-1}\left\{\frac{1}{2}\frac{e^p-1}{p(e^p-2)}\right\}.$$

The problem now is that of determining the inverse transform of the expression within the braces of (6.2.7). This can be done (a) by building a table of the Laplace transforms of step functions frequently arising in the solution of linear difference equations, resolving the inverse transform into partial fractions and then reading off the transform from the table, or (b) by expanding the inverse transform in powers of e^{-p} and using Translation Theorem I. We shall favor the first method because the solution is expressed in a more convenient form and illustrate the second method by means of an example.

The determination of the transforms of some common step functions will be left to the reader as an exercise later on. To illustrate the procedure that can be used we shall obtain the Laplace transform of the step function $a^{[t]}$, where a is a real number.

We have

$$\int_0^\infty e^{-pt} a^{[t]} dt = \sum_{n=0}^\infty a^n \int_n^{n+1} e^{-pt} dt$$
$$= \sum_{n=0}^\infty -a^n e^{-pt}/p \Big]_n^{n+1}$$
$$= \sum_{n=0}^\infty a^n \cdot \frac{e^{-np}-e^{-(n+1)p}}{p}$$
$$= \frac{(e^p-1)e^{-p}}{p} \sum_{n=0}^\infty a^n e^{-np}.$$

The expression $\sum\limits_{n=0}^{\infty} a^n e^{-np}$ is a geometric series with common ratio equal to ae^{-p}. If p is taken so that $|ae^{-p}| < 1$, i.e., $\text{Re}(p) > \ln|a|$, then the series will converge to $1/(1 - ae^{-p})$. Thus

(6.2.8)
$$L\{a^{[t]}\} = \frac{e^p - 1}{p(e^p - a)}.$$

We are now in the position to solve equation (6.2.6), since from (6.2.7) and (6.2.8) we obtain

(6.2.9)
$$Y(t) = \frac{1}{2} L^{-1}\left\{\frac{e^p - 1}{p(e^p - 2)}\right\} = \frac{1}{2} \cdot 2^{[t]} = 2^{[t]-1},$$

which can easily be shown to satisfy (6.2.6).

Let us solve the same difference equation

$$Y(t + 1) = 2Y(t), \qquad Y(t) = \tfrac{1}{2}, \quad 0 \leqslant t < 1$$

by the second method mentioned above. From (6.2.7) we have

$$Y(t) = \frac{1}{2} L^{-1}\left\{\frac{e^p - 1}{p(e^p - 2)}\right\} = \frac{1}{2} L^{-1}\left\{\frac{1}{p}\left(1 + \frac{1}{e^p - 2}\right)\right\}.$$

By taking $\text{Re}(p) > \ln 2$ it follows that $2|e^{-p}| < 1$, and hence

$$\frac{1}{e^p - 2} = \sum_{k=1}^{\infty} 2^{k-1} e^{-kp}.$$

Consequently

$$Y(t) = \frac{1}{2} L^{-1}\left\{\frac{1}{p}\right\} + \frac{1}{2} L^{-1}\left\{\sum_{k=1}^{\infty} 2^{k-1} \frac{e^{-kp}}{p}\right\}.$$

Assuming that the order of the operators L^{-1} and $\sum\limits_{k=1}^{\infty}$ can be interchanged, we obtain

$$Y(t) = \frac{1}{2} L^{-1}\left\{\frac{1}{p}\right\} + \sum_{k=1}^{\infty} 2^{k-2} L^{-1}\left\{\frac{e^{-kp}}{p}\right\}.$$

From the tables $L^{-1}\{1/p\} = 1$, and by Translation Theorem I

$$L^{-1}\left\{\frac{e^{-kp}}{p}\right\} = 1(t - k).$$

Therefore,

(6.2.10)
$$Y(t) = \tfrac{1}{2} + \tfrac{1}{2} \sum_{k=1}^{\infty} 2^{k-1} 1(t - k).$$

To verify that (6.2.10) is the solution of our equation we note that

$$Y(t+1) = \tfrac{1}{2} + \tfrac{1}{2}\sum_{k=1}^{\infty} 2^{k-1}1(t+1-k)$$

$$= \tfrac{1}{2} + \tfrac{1}{2}\sum_{k=0}^{\infty} 2^{k}1(t-k)$$

$$= \tfrac{1}{2} + \tfrac{1}{2} + \sum_{k=1}^{\infty} 2^{k-1}1(t-k)$$

$$= 1 + \sum_{k=1}^{\infty} 2^{k-1}1(t-k).$$

But this is $2Y(t)$ and hence the verification is complete.

Example. Solve $Y(t+2) - 5Y(t+1) - 14Y(t) = 0$, subject to initial conditions $Y(t) = Y_0,\quad 0 \leqslant t < 1,$
$$= Y_1,\quad 1 \leqslant t < 2.$$

Taking the Laplace transform of both sides and making use of formulas (6.2.1) and (6.2.2), we have

$$(e^{2p} - 5e^p - 14)L\{Y(t)\} = \frac{e^p - 1}{p}(Y_0 e^p + Y_1 - 5Y_0),$$

whence

$$Y(t) = L^{-1}\left\{\frac{e^p - 1}{p} \cdot \frac{Y_0 e^p + Y_1 - 5Y_0}{(e^p - 7)(e^p + 2)}\right\}.$$

The second factor when decomposed into partial fractions yields

$$\frac{Y_0 e^p + Y_1 - 5Y_0}{(e^p - 7)(e^p + 2)} \equiv \frac{Y_1 + 2Y_0}{9}\frac{1}{e^p - 7} - \frac{Y_1 - 7Y_0}{9}\frac{1}{e^p + 2},$$

and therefore

$$Y(t) = \frac{Y_1 + 2Y_0}{9}L^{-1}\left\{\frac{e^p - 1}{p(e^p - 7)}\right\} + \frac{7Y_0 - Y_1}{9}L^{-1}\left\{\frac{e^p - 1}{p(e^p - 2)}\right\}.$$

Consequently by (6.2.8),

$$Y(t) = \frac{Y_1 + 2Y_0}{9}(7)^{[t]} + \frac{7Y_0 - Y_1}{9}(-2)^{[t]}.$$

The corresponding difference equation

$$Y_{t+2} - 5Y_{t+1} - 14Y_t = 0$$

has the solution

$$Y_t = \frac{Y_1 + 2Y_0}{9}(7)^t + \frac{7Y_0 - Y_1}{9}(-2)^t, \quad t = 0, 1, 2, \cdots.$$

6.3 The Laplace Transform of [t] $a^{[t]}$

Another step function whose Laplace transform is desirable to have is the step function

$$Y(t) = [t]a^{[t]},$$

where a is a real number.   A graph of this function for a equal to 2 is shown in Fig. 6.3.1.   For its Laplace transform we have

$$\int_0^\infty e^{-pt}[t]a^{[t]}\,dt$$

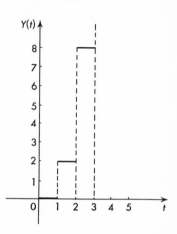

$$= \sum_{n=0}^{\infty} na^n \int_n^{n+1} e^{-pt}\,dt$$

$$= \sum_{n=0}^{\infty} -\frac{na^n e^{-pt}}{p}\Bigg]_n^{n+1}$$

$$= \sum_{n=0}^{\infty} na^n \frac{e^{-np} - e^{-(n+1)p}}{p}$$

$$= \frac{e^p - 1}{p} \sum_{n=0}^{\infty} na^n e^{-(n+1)p}$$

$$= \frac{(e^p - 1)e^{-p}}{p} \sum_{n=0}^{\infty} na^n e^{-np}.$$

FIG. 6.3.1

Now

$$\sum_{n=0}^{\infty} na^n e^{-np} = \sum_{n=0}^{\infty} \frac{d}{dp}(-a^n e^{-np})$$

$$= \frac{d}{dp} \sum_{n=0}^{\infty} (-a^n e^{-np}) = \frac{d}{dp}[-1/(1 - ae^{-p})]$$

$$= \frac{ae^p}{(e^p - a)^2} \quad \text{for } \operatorname{Re}(p) = x > \ln|a|.$$

The interchange of the operators $\displaystyle\sum_{n=0}^{\infty}$ and $\dfrac{d}{dp}$ is justifiable because all

the functions $u_n(p) = -a^n e^{-np}$ are analytic and $\displaystyle\sum_{n=0}^{\infty}(-a^n e^{-np})$ converges

uniformly to $1/(ae^{-p} - 1)$ for $\operatorname{Re}(p) = x > \ln|a|.$*   Thus

(6.3.1) $$L\{[t]a^{[t]}\} = \frac{a(e^p - 1)}{p(e^p - a)^2}.$$

Example.   Solve the difference equation

$$Y(t + 2) + 2Y(t + 1) + Y(t) = 2^{[t]}, \quad Y(t) = 0, \quad 0 \leqslant t < 2.$$

---

* See e.g., K. Knopp, *Theory of Functions*, Part 1, Dover Publications, Inc., p. 74.

The Laplace transform of both sides yields

$$(e^{2p} + 2e^p + 1)L\{Y(t)\} = \frac{e^p - 1}{p(e^p - 2)},$$

whence

$$Y(t) = L^{-1}\left\{\frac{e^p - 1}{p} \cdot \frac{1}{(e^p - 2)(e^p + 1)^2}\right\}.$$

Retaining the first factor within the braces and resolving the second factor into its partial fractions, we obtain

$$\frac{1}{(e^p - 2)(e^p + 1)^2} \equiv -\frac{1}{3}\frac{1}{(e^p + 1)^2} - \frac{1}{9}\frac{1}{e^p + 1} + \frac{1}{9}\frac{1}{e^p - 2},$$

and therefore

$$Y(t) = -\frac{1}{3}L^{-1}\left\{\frac{e^p - 1}{p(e^p + 1)^2}\right\} - \frac{1}{9}L^{-1}\left\{\frac{e^p - 1}{p(e^p + 1)}\right\} + \frac{1}{9}L^{-1}\left\{\frac{e^p - 1}{p(e^p - 2)}\right\}.$$

Using formulas (6.2.8) and (6.3.1), we get

$$Y(t) = \tfrac{1}{3}[t](- 1)^{[t]} - \tfrac{1}{9}(- 1)^{[t]} + \tfrac{1}{9}(2)^{[t]}.$$

The solution of

$$Y_{t+2} + 2Y_{t+1} + Y_t = 2^t, \quad Y_0 = Y_1 = 0$$

is clearly

$$Y_t = \tfrac{1}{3}t(- 1)^t - \tfrac{1}{9}(- 1)^t + \tfrac{1}{9}(2)^t, \quad t = 0, 1, 2, \cdots.$$

Remark. It will have been noticed that the factor $(e^p - 1)/p$ has been retained and the remaining factor resolved into partial fractions. This was done to facilitate the evaluation of the inverses, since, as an examination of Tables 6.4.1 and 6.4.2 shows, this factor appears as a multiplier of many of the inverses. Retaining it and decomposing the remaining rational function into partial fractions will be especially helpful when solving homogeneous difference equations, i.e., those for which $F(t) \equiv 0$ in equation 6.1.6. In the non-homogeneous case ($F(t) \not\equiv 0$), Table 6.4.2 will be found useful.

6.4 The Laplace Transform of $[t]^2$

Let us next determine the transform of the step function

$$Y(t) = [t]^2$$

shown in Fig. 6.4.1. As before,

$$\int_0^\infty e^{-pt}[t]^2\,dt = \sum_{n=0}^\infty n^2 \int_n^{n+1} e^{-pt}\,dt = -\sum_{n=0}^\infty \frac{n^2 e^{-pt}}{p}\Big]_n^{n+1}$$

$$= e^{-p}\frac{e^p - 1}{p}\sum_{n=0}^\infty n^2 e^{-np} = \frac{(e^p - 1)e^{-p}}{p}\sum_{n=0}^\infty \frac{d^2}{dp^2}(e^{-np}).$$

Here again the operations $\sum\limits_{n=0}^{\infty}$ and d^2/dp^2 in the preceding expression can be interchanged and therefore

$$\int_0^\infty e^{-pt}[t]^2\,dt$$

$$= \frac{(e^p - 1)e^{-p}}{p}\frac{d^2}{dp^2}\sum_{n=0}^{\infty} e^{-np}$$

$$= \frac{(e^p - 1)e^{-p}}{p}\frac{d^2}{dp^2}\frac{1}{1 - e^{-p}}$$

for $\mathrm{Re}(p) = x > 0.$

Performing the indicated differentiation and simplifying, we obtain

$$L\{[t]^2\} = \frac{e^p + 1}{p(e^p-1)^2}, \quad t > 0.$$

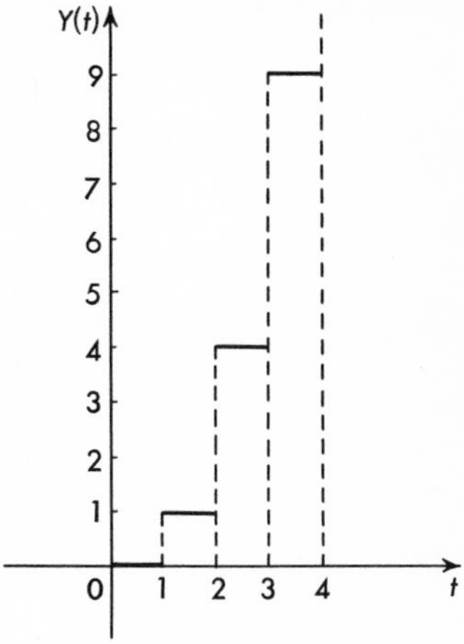

FIG. 6.4.1

To facilitate the solution of difference equations we give the Tables 6.4.1 and 6.4.2 of the transforms of some step functions and certain of their combinations.

Table 6.4.1. Transforms of Common Step Functions

	$L^{-1}\{F(t)\} = f(p)$	$F(t)$
	$m, b,$ and a are real numbers	
1.	$1/p$	1
2.	$\dfrac{1}{p(e^p - 1)}$	$[t]$
3.	$\dfrac{e^p + 1}{p(e^p - 1)^2}$	$[t]^2$
4.	$\dfrac{(e^p - 1)e^{-p}}{p}(-1)^k\dfrac{d^k}{dp^k}(1 - e^{-p})^{-1}$	$[t]^k, \quad k = 0, 1, 2, \cdots$
5.	$\dfrac{e^p - 1}{p(e^p - a)}$	$a^{[t]}$
6.	$\dfrac{a(e^p - 1)}{p(e^p - a)^2}$	$[t]a^{[t]}$

Table 6.4.1—*continued*

$L^{-1}\{F(t)\} = f(p)$	$F(t)$
m, *b*, and *a* are real numbers	
7. $\dfrac{(e^p - 1)e^{-p}}{p}(-1)^k \dfrac{d^k}{dp^k}(1 - ae^{-p})^{-1}$	$[t]^k a^{[t]}, \quad k = 0, 1, 2, \cdots$
8. $\dfrac{e^p - 1}{p} \cdot \dfrac{1}{e^{2p} - 2ae^p \cos m + a^2}$	$\dfrac{a^{[t]-1} \sin m[t]}{\sin m}$
9. $\dfrac{e^p - 1}{p} \cdot \dfrac{e^p - a \cos m}{e^{2p} - 2ae^p \cos m + a^2}$	$a^{[t]} \cos m[t]$
10. $\dfrac{e^p - 1}{p} \cdot \dfrac{1}{e^{2p} - 2e^p \cos m + 1}$	$\dfrac{\sin m[t]}{\sin m}$
11. $\dfrac{e^p - 1}{p} \cdot \dfrac{e^p - \cos m}{e^{2p} - 2e^p \cos m + 1}$	$\cos m[t]$
12. $\dfrac{e^p - 1}{p} \cdot \dfrac{1}{(e^p - a)(e^p - b)}, \quad (b \neq a)$	$\dfrac{b^{[t]} - a^{[t]}}{b - a}$

Exercise.   Verify the transforms of the step functions 4 and 7.

Table 6.4.2.   Transforms of Combinations of Step Functions

$L^{-1}\{F(t)\} = f(p)$	$F(t)$
m, *a*, *b*, A_0, A_1, A_2 are real numbers	
13. $\dfrac{A_0 e^p + (A_1 - A_0)}{p(e^p - 1)}$	$A_1[t] + A_0$
14. $\dfrac{A_0 e^{2p} + (A_2 + A_1 - 2A_0)e^p + (A_2 - A_1 + A_0)}{p(e^p - 1)^2}$	$A_2[t]^2 + A_1[t] + A_0$
15. $\dfrac{(A_1 + A_0)e^p - (A_1 + aA_0)}{p(e^p - a)}$	$A_1 a^{[t]} + A_0$
16. $\dfrac{[(A_0 + A_1)e^{2p} + \{aA_2 - (a + 1)A_1 - 2aA_2\}e^p + a(aA_0 + A_1 - A_2)]}{p(e^p - a)^2}$	$A_2[t]a^{[t]} + A_1 a^{[t]} + A_0$

Table 6.4.2—*continued*

$L^{-1}\{F(t)\} = f(p)$	$F(t)$
$m,\ a,\ b,\ A_0,\ A_1,\ A_2,$ are real numbers	
17. $\dfrac{[(A_0 + A_1)e^{2p} + \{A_2 - 2A_1 - (1 + a)A_0\}e^p + (A_1 + aA_0 - aA_2)]}{p(e^p - 1)(e^p - a)}$	$A_2[t] + A_1a^{[t]} + A_0$
18. $\dfrac{[(A_1 + A_0)e^{3p} + \{A_3 - 3A_1 + A_2 - (2 + a)A_0\}e^{2p} + \{(1 - a)A_3 - (1 + a)A_2 + 3A_1 + A_0(2a + 1)\}e^p - (A_1 - aA_2 + aA_3 + aA_0)]}{p(e^p - 1)^2(e^p - a)}$	$A_3[t]^2 + A_2[t] + A_1a^{[t]} + A_0$
19. $\dfrac{e^p - 1}{p} \cdot \dfrac{(A_1 + A_0)e^p - (A_1b + A_0a)}{(e^p - a)(e^p - b)}$ $(b \ne a)$	$A_1a^{[t]} + A_0b^{[t]}$
20. $\dfrac{[(A_0 + A_1 + A_2)e^{2p} - \{A_0(a + b) + A_1(1 + b) + A_2(1 + a)\}e^p + (A_0ab + A_1b + A_2a)]}{p(e^p - a)(e^p - b)}$	$A_2b^{[t]} + A_1a^{[t]} + A_0$
21. $\dfrac{e^p - 1}{p} \cdot \dfrac{A_0e^p + (A_1 \sin m - A_0 \cos m)}{e^{2p} - 2e^p \cos m + 1}$	$A_1 \sin m[t] + A_0 \cos m[t]$
22. $\dfrac{e^p - 1}{p} \cdot \dfrac{A_0e^p + a(A_1 \sin m - A_0 \cos m)}{e^{2p} - 2ae^p \cos m + a^2}$	$a^{[t]}(A_1 \sin m[t] + A_0 \cos m[t])$
23. $\dfrac{[(A_1 + A_0)e^{2p} + \{a(A_2 \sin m - A_1 \cos m - 2A_0 \cos m) - A_1\}e^p - a(A_2 \sin m - A_1 \cos m - aA_0)]}{p(e^{2p} - 2ae^p \cos m + a^2)}$	$a^{[t]}(A_2 \sin m[t] + A_1 \cos m[t]) + A_0$
24. $\dfrac{e^p - 1}{p} \cdot \dfrac{A_0e^p + a(A_1 - A_0)}{(e^p - a)^2}$	$A_1[t]a^{[t]} + A_0a^{[t]}$
25. $\dfrac{e^p - 1}{p} \cdot \dfrac{[(A_2 + A_1 + A_0)e^{2p} - \{bA_2 + aA_1 + c(A_2 + A_1) + (a + b)A_0\}e^p + c(bA_2 + aA_1) + abA_0]}{(e^p - a)(e^p - b)(e^p - c)},\ (a \ne b \ne c)$	$A_2a^{[t]} + A_1b^{[t]} + A_0c^{[t]}$

Table 6.4.2—*continued*

	$L^{-1}\{F(t)\} = f(p)$	$F(t)$
	m, a, b, A_0, A_1, A_2, are real numbers	
26.	$\dfrac{e^p - 1}{p} \cdot \dfrac{\begin{aligned}&[(A_0 + A_2 + A_3)e^{3p}\\&+\{A_1 \sin m - A_0 \cos m\\&\quad - (a+b)A_0 - (bA_2 + aA_3)\\&\quad - 2(A_2 + A_3)\cos m\}e^{2p}\\&+\{2(bA_2 + aA_3)\cos m\\&\quad + (A_2 + A_3)\\&\quad - (a+b)(A_1 \sin m\\&\quad - A_0 \cos m) + A_0 ab\}e^p\\&\quad - (bA_2 + aA_3)]\end{aligned}}{\begin{aligned}&(e^p - a)(e^p - b)(e^{2p}\\&\quad - 2e^p \cos m + 1)\end{aligned}}, (b \neq a)$	$\begin{aligned}&A_3 b^{[t]} + A_2 a^{[t]}\\&\quad + A_1 \sin m[t]\\&\quad + A_0 \cos m[t]\end{aligned}$
27.	$\dfrac{e^p - 1}{p} \cdot \dfrac{\begin{aligned}&[(A_0 + A_2)e^{2p}\\&+ (A_1 \sin m - A_0 \cos m\\&\quad - 2A_2 \cos m - A_0)e^p\\&\quad + A_2 - a(A_1 \sin m\\&\quad - A_0 \cos m)]\end{aligned}}{(e^p - a)(e^{2p} - 2e^p \cos m + 1)}$	$\begin{aligned}&A_2 a^{[t]} + A_1 \sin m[t]\\&\quad + A_0 \cos m[t]\end{aligned}$
28.	$\dfrac{e^p - 1}{p} \cdot \dfrac{\begin{aligned}&(A_1 \sin m + A_0 \cos m)e^{2p}\\&\quad - 2aA_0 e^p + a^2(A_0 \cos m\\&\quad - A_1 \sin m)\end{aligned}}{(e^{2p} - 2ae^p \cos m + a^2)^2}$	$\begin{aligned}&[t]a^{[t]-1}(A_1 \sin m[t]\\&\quad + A_0 \cos m[t])\end{aligned}$
29.	$\dfrac{e^p - 1}{p} \cdot \dfrac{\begin{aligned}&[A_2 e^{3p} + \{(A_1 + aA_3)\sin m\\&\quad + (A_0 - 3aA_2)\cos m\}e^{2p}\\&\quad + a\{(aA_2 - 2A_0)\\&\quad - 2a \cos m\,(A_3 \sin m\\&\quad - A_2 \cos m)\}e^p\\&\quad + a^2\{(A_0 \cos m - A_1 \sin m)\\&\quad + a(A_3 \sin m - A_2 \cos m)\}]\end{aligned}}{(e^{2p} - 2ae^p \cos m + a^2)^2}$	$\begin{aligned}&a^{[t]}(A_3 \sin m[t]\\&\quad + A_2 \cos m[t])\\&+[t]a^{[t]-1}(A_1 \sin m[t]\\&\quad + A_0 \cos m[t])\end{aligned}$

In order to illustrate the use of the tables we shall solve the following difference equation

$$(6.4.1) \qquad\qquad Y_{t+1} - 2Y_t = t^2 - 1, \quad Y_0 = 0.$$

Transforming this equation into one involving step functions, we obtain

(6.4.2) $Y(t+1) - 2Y(t) = [t]^2 - 1, \quad Y(t) = 0, \quad 0 \leqslant t < 1.$

The transform of both sides yields

$$(e^p - 2)L\{Y(t)\} = \frac{e^p + 1}{p(e^p - 1)^2} - \frac{1}{p}$$

and consequently

(6.4.3) $Y(t) = L^{-1}\left\{\dfrac{e^p + 1}{p(e^p - 1)^2(e^p - 2)}\right\} - L^{-1}\left\{\dfrac{1}{p(e^p - 2)}\right\}.$

The inverse transform of the first expression on the right can be obtained from formula 18, Table 6.4.2. In this case $a = 2$. Comparing coefficients in the numerators of each fraction, the following simultaneous equations are obtained

$$A_1 + A_0 = 0,$$
$$A_3 - 3A_1 + A_2 - 4A_0 = 0,$$
$$-A_3 - 3A_2 + 3A_1 + 5A_0 = 1,$$
$$-A_1 + 2A_2 - 2A_3 - 2A_0 = 1.$$

As the solution of this system, we get: $A_0 = -3$, $A_1 = 3$, $A_2 = -2$, and $A_3 = -1$. Therefore

$$L^{-1}\left\{\frac{e^p + 1}{p(e^p - 1)^2(e^p - 2)}\right\} = -[t]^2 - 2[t] + 3 \cdot 2^{[t]} - 3.$$

Similarly, making use of formula (15), Table 6.4.2, we get for the inverse of the second term on the right of equation (6.4.3)

$$A_1 + A_0 = 0$$
$$-(A_1 + 2A_0) = 1,$$

from which we obtain: $A_1 = 1$, $A_0 = -1$. Hence

$$L^{-1}\left\{\frac{1}{p(e^p - 2)}\right\} = 2^{[t]} - 1.$$

Substituting these values in (6.4.3) and simplifying gives

$$Y(t) = 2^{[t]+1} - [t]^2 - 2[t] - 2$$

as the solution of (6.4.2).

Equation (6.4.1) therefore has the solution

$$Y_t = 2^{t+1} - t^2 - 2t - 2.$$

6.5 The Laplace Transform of $a^{[t]} e^{im[t]}$

The transforms of the step functions $a^{[t]} \sin m[t]$ and $a^{[t]} \sin m[t]$, namely, formulas 8 and 9 given in Table 6.4.1 can be obtained simultaneously by determining the transform of $a^{[t]} e^{im[t]}$ and equating real and imaginary parts. Here a and m are real numbers.

As before

$$(6.5.1) \qquad \int_0^\infty e^{-pt} a^{[t]} e^{im[t]}\, dt = \sum_{n=0}^\infty e^{nmi}\; a^n \int_n^{n+1} e^{-pt}\, dt$$

$$= \sum_{n=0}^\infty a^n e^{nmi} \cdot \frac{e^{-np}(1 - e^{-p})}{p}$$

$$= \frac{1 - e^{-p}}{p} \sum_{n=0}^\infty a^n e^{n(mi-p)}.$$

Now $\sum_{n=0}^\infty a^n e^{n(mi-p)}$ is a geometric series with common ratio ae^{mi-p}.
Therefore, if $|ae^{mi-p}| < 1$, i.e., $\mathrm{Re}(p) > \ln|a|$, the series will converge and we shall have

$$\sum_{n=0}^\infty a^n e^{n(mi-p)} = \frac{1}{1 - ae^{mi-p}} = \frac{e^p}{(e^p - a\cos m) - ia\sin m}$$

$$= \frac{e^p[(e^p - a\cos m) + ia\sin m]}{e^{2p} - 2ae^p\cos m + a^2}.$$

Since $a^{[t]} e^{im[t]} = a^{[t]} \cos m[t] + ia^{[t]} \sin m[t]$, from (6.5.1) we obtain

$$\int_0^\infty e^{-pt} a^{[t]} \cos m[t]\, dt + i \int_0^\infty e^{-pt} a^{[t]} \sin m[t]\, dt$$

$$= \frac{e^p - 1}{p} \cdot \frac{[(e^p - a\cos m) + ia\sin m]}{e^{2p} - 2ae^p\cos m + a^2}.$$

By equating the real and imaginary parts of both sides it follows that

$$(6.5.2) \qquad L\{a^{[t]} \cos m[t]\} = \frac{e^p - 1}{p} \cdot \frac{e^p - a\cos m}{e^{2p} - 2ae^p\cos m + a^2},$$

and

$$(6.5.3) \qquad L\{a^{[t]} \sin m[t]\} = \frac{e^p - 1}{p} \cdot \frac{a\sin m}{e^{2p} - 2ae^p\cos m + a^2}.$$

In taking the transform of both sides of a difference equation, for example, such as

$$(6.5.4) \qquad a_2 Y(t+2) + a_1 Y(t+1) + a_0 Y(t) = F(t),$$

where a_2, a_1, and a_0 are constants, the left side is always a polynomial in e^p multiplying $L\{Y(t)\}$, and the right side is a function of p, say $\phi(p)$. Thus, in the case of equation (6.5.4), we have

$$(6.5.5) \qquad (a_2 e^{2p} + a_1 e^p + a_0) \cdot L\{Y(t)\} = \phi(p),$$

where $\qquad \phi(p) = L\{F(t)\} + \frac{e^p - 1}{p}(Y_0 e^p + Y_1) + \frac{e^p - 1}{p} Y_0.$

The polynomial in e^p multiplying $L\{Y(t)\}$, when set equal to zero, is called the *characteristic equation* of the homogeneous difference equation

$$(6.5.6) \qquad a_2 Y(t+2) + a_1 Y(t+1) + a_0 Y(t) = 0.$$

The roots of the characteristic equations of the problems treated so far have all been real. Formulas (6.5.2) and (6.5.3) were developed to take care of the case when the characteristic equation has a pair of complex roots. We illustrate their use by means of two examples.

Example I. Solve $4Y(t+2) + Y(t) = 0$, $Y(t) = 0$, $0 \leqslant t < 1$; $Y(t) = 1$, $1 \leqslant t < 2$. The transform of the difference equation gives

$$(4e^{2t} + 1) \cdot L\{Y(t)\} = \frac{e^p - 1}{p},$$

and hence

$$(6.5.7) \qquad Y(t) = \tfrac{1}{4} L^{-1} \left\{ \frac{e^p - 1}{p} \cdot \frac{1}{e^{2p} + 1/4} \right\}.$$

Comparing the denominator of the fraction in formula (6.5.3) with that of the second factor of equality (6.5.7), we have

$$e^{2p} - 2ae^p \cos m + a^2 \equiv e^{2p} + \tfrac{1}{4},$$

whence $\cos m = 0$, $a^2 = \tfrac{1}{4}$. From this $m = \pm k\pi/2$, $k = 1, 3, 5, \cdots$, and $a = \pm \tfrac{1}{2}$. Thus, making use of (6.5.3), we obtain from (6.5.7)

$$Y(t) = \frac{(\pm \tfrac{1}{2})^{[t]-1} \sin \dfrac{k\pi}{2}[t]}{4 \sin \dfrac{k\pi}{2}}, \qquad k = 1, 3, 5, \cdots \ (t \geqslant 0).$$

By substituting $a = 1$ in formulas (6.5.2) and (6.5.3) the following two important special cases are obtained

$$(6.5.8) \qquad L\{\cos m[t]\} = \frac{e^p - 1}{p} \cdot \frac{e^p - \cos m}{e^{2p} - 2e^p \cos m + 1},$$

and

$$(6.5.9) \qquad L\{\sin m[t]\} = \frac{e^p - 1}{p} \cdot \frac{\sin m}{e^{2p} - 2e^p \cos m + 1}.$$

Example 2. Solve: $Y(t+1) + Y(t) = \sin m[t]$, $Y(t) = 0$, $0 \leqslant t < 1$. The transform of both sides of the difference equation yields

$$(e^p + 1)L\{Y(t)\} = \frac{e^p - 1}{p} \cdot \frac{\sin m}{e^{2p} - 2e^p \cos m + 1},$$

whence

$$(6.5.10) \qquad Y(t) = L^{-1} \left\{ \frac{e^p - 1}{p} \cdot \frac{\sin m}{(e^p + 1)(e^{2p} - 2e^p \cos m + 1)} \right\}.$$

Making use of the theorem on the decomposition into partial fractions, we have

$$(6.5.11) \quad \frac{1}{(e^p + 1)(e^{2p} - 2e^p \cos m + 1)} \equiv -\frac{e^p + 2 \cos m - 1}{e^{2p} - 2e^p \cos m + 1} + \frac{1}{e^p + 1}.$$

In order to make use of formulas (6.5.8) and (6.5.9) we alter the first fraction on the right by subtracting and adding cos m in the numerator and write

$$\frac{e^p + 2 \cos m - 1}{e^{2p} - 2e^p \cos m + 1} \equiv \frac{e^p - \cos m}{e^{2p} - 2e^p \cos m + 1} + \frac{3 \cos m - 1}{e^{2p} - 2e^p \cos m + 1}.$$

Substituting this in (6.5.11) and the result in (6.5.10), we get

$$Y(t) = -\sin m L^{-1}\left\{\frac{e^p - 1}{p} \cdot \frac{e^p - \cos m}{e^{2p} - 2e^p \cos m + 1}\right\}$$
$$- (3 \cos m - 1)L^{-1}\left\{\frac{e^p - 1}{p} \cdot \frac{\sin m}{e^{2p} - 2e^p \cos m + 1}\right\} + L^{-1}\left\{\frac{e^p - 1}{p(e^p + 1)}\right\}.$$

Making use of formulas (6.5.8), (6.5.9), and formula (5), we finally get
$$Y(t) = -(\sin m) \cos m[t] - (3 \cos m - 1) \sin m[t] + (-1)^{[t]}.$$

Exercise.   By considering the $L\{[t]^k a^{[t]} e^{im[t]}\}$ verify that

$$(6.5.12) \quad L\{[t]^k a^{[t]} \cos m[t]\} =$$

$$\frac{1 - e^{-p}}{p}(-1)^k \frac{d^k}{dp^k}\left[\frac{e^p(e^p - a \cos m)}{e^{2p} - 2ae^p \cos m + a^2}\right],$$

and

$$(6.5.13) \quad L\{[t]^k a^{[t]} \sin m[t]\} =$$

$$\frac{1 - e^{-p}}{p}(-1)^k \frac{d^k}{dp^k}\left[\frac{ae^p \sin m}{e^{2p} - 2ae^p \cos m + a^2}\right],$$

where a and m are real numbers and $k = 0, 1, 2, \cdots$.   These formulas are useful when the characteristic equation has multiple complex roots.

6.6 Systems of Difference Equations

The theory of systems of difference equations parallels somewhat the theory of systems of ordinary differential equations.   Here again matrix methods can be applied to good advantage especially in more complicated systems.   We shall confine ourselves to linear systems of the first and second order.   The extension to systems of higher order will then be evident.

Consider the system of difference equations

(6.6.1)
$$a_{11}Y_1(t+1) + a_{12}Y_2(t+1) + \cdots + a_{1n}Y_n(t+1) + \cdots$$
$$+ b_{11}Y_1(t) + b_{12}Y_2(t) + \cdots + b_{1n}Y_n(t) = F_1(t),$$
$$a_{21}Y_1(t+1) + a_{22}Y_2(t+1) + \cdots + a_{2n}Y_n(t+1) + \cdots$$
$$+ b_{21}Y_1(t) + b_{22}Y_2(t) + \cdots + b_{2n}Y_n(t) = F_2(t),$$
$$\cdot \quad \cdot \quad \cdot \quad \cdot \quad \cdot \quad \cdot \quad \cdot \quad \cdot \quad \cdot$$
$$a_{n1}Y_1(t+1) + a_{n2}Y_2(t+1) + \cdots + a_{nn}Y_n(t+1) + \cdots$$
$$+ b_{n1}Y_1(t) + b_{n2}Y(t) + \cdots + b_{nn}Y_n(t) = F_n(t),$$

where the a_{ij}'s are constants and $Y_i(t)$, $F_i(t)$ are step functions. System (6.6.1) is to be solved subject to the initial conditions

$$Y_1(t) = Y_{10},\ 0 \leqslant t < 1;\ Y_2(t) = Y_{20},\ 0 \leqslant t < 1; \cdots;\ Y_n(t) = Y_{n0},$$
$$0 \leqslant t < 1.$$

As in the case for differential equations, let

$$\mathbf{A} = \begin{bmatrix} a_{11} & a_{12} \cdots a_{1n} \\ a_{21} & a_{22} \cdots a_{2n} \\ \cdot & \cdot \quad \cdot \quad \cdot \\ a_{n1} & a_{n2} \cdots a_{nn} \end{bmatrix}, \quad \mathbf{B} = \begin{bmatrix} b_{11} & b_{12} \cdots b_{1n} \\ b_{21} & b_{22} \cdots b_{2n} \\ \cdot & \cdot \quad \cdot \quad \cdot \\ b_{n1} & b_{n2} \cdots b_{nn} \end{bmatrix},$$

$$\mathbf{Y}(t) = \begin{bmatrix} Y_1(t) \\ Y_2(t) \\ \vdots \\ Y_n(t) \end{bmatrix}, \quad \mathbf{F}(t) = \begin{bmatrix} F_1(t) \\ F_2(t) \\ \vdots \\ F_n(t) \end{bmatrix}, \quad \mathbf{\bar{Y}} = \begin{bmatrix} Y_{10} \\ Y_{20} \\ \vdots \\ Y_{n0} \end{bmatrix}.$$

With these definitions (6.6.1) can be written compactly as the single *matric difference equation*

(6.6.2) $$\mathbf{A}\mathbf{Y}(t+1) + \mathbf{B}\mathbf{Y}(t) = \mathbf{F}(t).$$

Furthermore, let

$$L\{\mathbf{Y}(t)\} = \begin{bmatrix} L\{Y_1(t)\} \\ L\{Y_2(t)\} \\ \vdots \\ L\{Y_n(t)\} \end{bmatrix} = \begin{bmatrix} y_1(p) \\ y_2(p) \\ \vdots \\ y_n(p) \end{bmatrix} = \mathbf{y}(p),$$

$$L\{\mathbf{F}(t)\} = \begin{bmatrix} L\{F_1(t)\} \\ L\{F_2(t)\} \\ \vdots \\ L\{F_n(t)\} \end{bmatrix} = \begin{bmatrix} f_1(p) \\ f_2(p) \\ \vdots \\ f_n(p) \end{bmatrix} = \mathbf{f}(p).$$

Then, upon taking the Laplace transform of both sides of (6.6.2), we obtain

$$(\mathbf{A}e^p + \mathbf{B}) \cdot \mathbf{y}(p) = \mathbf{f}(p) - \frac{1 - e^p}{p}\mathbf{A}\overline{\mathbf{Y}},$$

whence

$$\mathbf{y}(p) = (\mathbf{A}e^p + \mathbf{B})^{-1}\left[\mathbf{f}(p) - \frac{1 - e^p}{p}\mathbf{A}\overline{\mathbf{Y}}\right]$$

and

(6.6.3) $$\mathbf{Y}(t) = L^{-1}\left\{(\mathbf{A}e^p + \mathbf{B})^{-1}\left[\mathbf{f}(p) - \frac{1 - e^p}{p}\mathbf{A}\overline{\mathbf{Y}}\right]\right\}.$$

Example I.   Find the step functions $Y_1(t)$ and $Y_2(t)$ that satisfy the following system of difference equations

$$Y_2(t + 1) - Y_1(t) = 0,$$
$$Y_1(t + 1) - 4Y_2(t) = 1,$$
$$Y_1(t) = 1, \quad 0 \leqslant t < 1; \quad Y_2(t) = 0, \quad 0 \leqslant t < 1.$$

We have

$$\mathbf{A} = \begin{bmatrix} 0 & 1 \\ 1 & 0 \end{bmatrix}, \qquad \mathbf{B} = \begin{bmatrix} -1 & 0 \\ 0 & -4 \end{bmatrix},$$

whence

$$\mathbf{A}e^p + \mathbf{B} = \begin{bmatrix} 0 & e^p \\ e^p & 0 \end{bmatrix} + \begin{bmatrix} -1 & 0 \\ 0 & -4 \end{bmatrix} = \begin{bmatrix} -1 & e^p \\ e^p & -4 \end{bmatrix}$$

and

$$(\mathbf{A}e^p + \mathbf{B})^{-1} = \frac{\begin{bmatrix} -4 & -e^p \\ -e^p & -1 \end{bmatrix}'}{4 - e^{2p}} = \frac{\begin{bmatrix} -4 & -e^p \\ -e^p & -1 \end{bmatrix}}{4 - e^{2p}}.$$

Since

$$\mathbf{f}(p) = \begin{bmatrix} 0 \\ \dfrac{1}{p} \end{bmatrix} \quad \text{and} \quad \overline{\mathbf{Y}} = \begin{bmatrix} 1 \\ 0 \end{bmatrix},$$

then

$$\mathbf{f}(p) - \frac{1 - e^p}{p}\mathbf{A}\overline{\mathbf{Y}} = \begin{bmatrix} 0 \\ \dfrac{1}{p} \end{bmatrix} - \begin{bmatrix} 0 & 1 \\ 1 & 0 \end{bmatrix}\begin{bmatrix} \dfrac{1 - e^p}{p} \\ 0 \end{bmatrix} = \begin{bmatrix} 0 \\ \dfrac{e^p}{p} \end{bmatrix}$$

and

$$\mathbf{y}(p) = \frac{\begin{bmatrix} -4 & -e^p \\ \\ -e^p & -1 \end{bmatrix}\begin{bmatrix} 0 \\ \\ \dfrac{e^p}{p} \end{bmatrix}}{4 - e^{2p}} = \frac{\begin{bmatrix} -\dfrac{e^{2p}}{p} \\ \\ -\dfrac{e^p}{p} \end{bmatrix}}{4 - e^{2p}}.$$

Therefore

$$\mathbf{Y}(t) = \begin{bmatrix} L^{-1}\left\{\dfrac{e^{2p}}{p(e^p - 2)(e^p + 2)}\right\} \\ \\ L^{-1}\left\{\dfrac{e^p}{p(e^p - 2)(e^p + 2)}\right\} \end{bmatrix} = \begin{bmatrix} Y_1(t) \\ \\ Y_2(t) \end{bmatrix}.$$

Making use of formula 20, Table 6.4.2, we readily find that

$$Y_1(t) = (2)^{[t]} + \tfrac{1}{3}(-2)^{[t]} - \tfrac{1}{3}, \quad Y_2(t) = (2)^{[t]-1} - \tfrac{1}{6}(-2)^{[t]} - \tfrac{1}{3},$$

which can be shown to satisfy the given system of difference equations.

We next treat the system of second order difference equations

(6.6.4)

$$a_{11}Y_1(t + 2) + \cdots + a_{1n}Y_n(t + 2) + b_{11}Y_1(t + 1) + \cdots$$
$$+ b_{1n}Y_n(t + 1) + c_{11}Y_1(t) + \cdots + c_{1n}Y_n(t) = F_1(t),$$
$$a_{21}Y_1(t + 2) + \cdots + a_{2n}Y_n(t + 2) + b_{21}Y_1(t + 1) + \cdots$$
$$+ b_{2n}Y_n(t + 1) + c_{21}Y_1(t) + \cdots + c_{2n}Y_n(t) = F_2(t),$$

$$\cdot \quad \cdot \quad \cdot \quad \cdot \quad \cdot \quad \cdot \quad \cdot \quad \cdot \quad \cdot \quad \cdot$$

$$a_{n1}Y_1(t + 2) + \cdots a_{nn}Y_n(t + 2) + b_{n1}Y_1(t + 1) + \cdots$$
$$+ b_{nn}Y_n(t + 1) + c_{n1}Y_1(t) + \cdots + c_{nn}Y_n(t) = F_n(t),$$

where the a_{ij}'s are constants and $Y_i(t)$, $F_i(t)$ are step functions. We shall solve system (6.6.4) subject to the following initial conditions

$$Y_1(t) = Y_{10}, \quad Y_2(t) = Y_{20}, \cdots, Y_n(t) = Y_{n0}, \quad 0 \leqslant t < 1;$$
$$Y_1(t) = Y_{11}, \quad Y_2(t) = Y_{21}, \cdots, Y_n(t) = Y_{n1}, \quad 1 \leqslant t < 2.$$

Letting $\mathbf{A} = [a_{ij}]$, $\mathbf{B} = [b_{ij}]$, and $\mathbf{C} = [c_{ij}]$,

$$\mathbf{Y}(t) = \begin{bmatrix} Y_1(t) \\ Y_2(t) \\ \vdots \\ Y_n(t) \end{bmatrix} \quad \text{and} \quad \mathbf{F}(t) = \begin{bmatrix} F_1(t) \\ F_2(t) \\ \vdots \\ F_n(t) \end{bmatrix},$$

system (6.6.4) can be written as the single *matric difference equation*

(6.6.5) $\quad \mathbf{AY}(t + 2) + \mathbf{BY}(t + 1) + \mathbf{CY}(t) = \mathbf{F}(t).$

As before, let $L\{\mathbf{Y}(t)\} = \mathbf{y}(p)$, $L\{\mathbf{F}(t)\} = \mathbf{f}(p)$,

$$\overline{\mathbf{Y}} = \begin{bmatrix} Y_{10} \\ \vdots \\ Y_{n0} \end{bmatrix} \quad \text{and} \quad \overline{\overline{\mathbf{Y}}} = \begin{bmatrix} Y_{11} \\ \vdots \\ Y_{n1} \end{bmatrix}$$

Then, taking the Laplace transform of (6.6.5), we find that

$$\mathbf{A}\left[e^{2p}\mathbf{y}(p) + \frac{1 - e^p}{p}(\overline{\mathbf{Y}}e^p + \overline{\overline{\mathbf{Y}}})\right] + \mathbf{B}\left[e^p\mathbf{y}(p) + \frac{1 - e^p}{p}\overline{\mathbf{Y}}\right] + \mathbf{C}\mathbf{y}(p) = \mathbf{f}(p),$$

from which

$$(\mathbf{A}e^{2p} + \mathbf{B}e^p + \mathbf{C})\mathbf{y}(p) = \mathbf{f}(p) - \frac{1 - e^p}{p}[\mathbf{A}(\overline{\mathbf{Y}}e^p + \overline{\overline{\mathbf{Y}}}) + \mathbf{B}\overline{\mathbf{Y}}],$$

and finally

$$\mathbf{Y}(t) = L^{-1}\left\{(\mathbf{A}e^{2p} + \mathbf{B}e^p + \mathbf{C})^{-1}\left[\mathbf{f}(p) - \frac{1 - e^p}{p}\left\{\mathbf{A}(\overline{\mathbf{Y}}e^p + \overline{\overline{\mathbf{Y}}}) + \mathbf{B}\overline{\mathbf{Y}}\right\}\right]\right\}.$$

Exercise. Solve the system
$$Y_1(t + 2) + 9Y_2(t) = 1,$$
$$Y_2(t + 2) + 4Y_1(t) = 2.$$
$Y_1(t) = Y_2(t) = 0$, $0 \leqslant t < 1$; $Y_1(t) = 1$, $Y_2(t) = 2$, $1 \leqslant t < 2$.
[*Hint:* Show that

$$Y_1(t) = L^{-1}\left\{\frac{e^p(e^{2p} - 18)}{p(e^{2p} + 6)(e^{2p} - 6)}\right\}$$

$$Y_2(t) = L^{-1}\left\{\frac{2e^p(e^{2p} - 2)}{p(e^{2p} + 6)(e^{2p} - 6)}\right\}$$

By resolving $\dfrac{e^p(e^{2p} - 18)}{(e^{2p} + 6)(e^{2p} - 6)}$ and $\dfrac{e^p(e^{2p} - 2)}{(e^{2p} + 6)(e^{2p} - 6)}$ into partial fractions and using formulas (20) and (23), Table 6.4.2, obtain the results

$$Y_1(t) = \frac{2}{7}\left\{(\pm \sqrt{6})^{[t]-1}\frac{\sin \frac{k\pi}{2}[t]}{\sin \frac{k\pi}{2}} - (\pm \sqrt{6})\cos \frac{k\pi}{2}[t] + 1\right\}$$

$$- \frac{1}{10}\left\{(1 + \sqrt{6})(\sqrt{6})^{[t]} + (1 - \sqrt{6})(-\sqrt{6})^{[t]} - 2\right\}, \quad k = 1, 3, 5, \cdots,$$

$$Y_2(t) = \frac{4}{21}\left\{(\pm \sqrt{6})^{[t]-1}\frac{\sin \frac{k\pi}{2}[t]}{\sin \frac{k\pi}{2}} - (\pm \sqrt{6})^{[t]}\cos \frac{k\pi}{2}[t] + 1\right\}$$

$$+ \frac{1}{15}\left\{(1 + \sqrt{6})(\sqrt{6})^{[t]} + (1 - \sqrt{6})(-\sqrt{6})^{[t]} - 2\right\}, \quad k = 1, 3, 5, \cdots].$$

6.7 Sequences of Numbers

A problem that can at times be solved is that of determining the nth term of a sequence if its terms are so related that they give rise to a difference equation. One of the simplest of such sequences is the arithmetic progression of the *first order*, i.e., one in which the differences of successive terms are constant. For instance, the following sequence

$$1, 5, 9, 13, 17, \cdots$$

is an arithmetic sequence of the first order because the successive differences

$$4, 4, 4, 4, \cdots$$

are constant. A sequence is called an arithmetic progression of the *second order* if the differences of successive terms form an arithmetic progression of the *first order*. For example, the sequence

$$1, 3, 7, 13, 21, \cdots$$

is an arithmetic progression of the second order because the differences of successive terms, namely,

$$2, 4, 6, 8, \cdots$$

obviously form an arithmetic progression of first order.

In general, a sequence is called an arithmetic progression of the kth *order* if the differences of successive terms form an arithmetic progression of order $(k-1)$.

Now, suppose that

$$Y_0, Y_1, Y_2, Y_3, \cdots, Y_t, \cdots$$

represents an arithmetic progression of second order. This implies that

$$\Delta^2 Y_t = c,$$

where c is a constant, or equivalently that

(6.7.1) $$Y_{t+2} - 2Y_{t+1} + Y_t = c.$$

If the latter equation is changed into one involving step functions, then

(6.7.2) $$Y(t+2) - 2Y(t+1) + Y(t) = c,$$

which we shall solve subject to the initial conditions $Y(t) = Y_0$, $0 \leqslant t < 1$ and $Y(t) = Y_1$, $1 \leqslant t < 2$.

Taking the transform of both sides of (6.7.2) gives

$$
\begin{aligned}
(e^p - 1)^2 L\{Y(t)\} &= \frac{e^p - 1}{p}(Y_0 e^p + Y_1) - 2\frac{e^p - 1}{p}Y_0 + \frac{c}{p} \\
&= \frac{Y_0 e^{2p} + (Y_1 - 3Y_0)e^p + (2Y_0 - Y_1 + c)}{p},
\end{aligned}
$$

whence

(6.7.3) $$Y(t) = L^{-1}\left\{\frac{Y_0 e^{2p} + (Y_1 - 3Y_0)e^p + (2Y_0 - Y_1 + c)}{p(e^p - 1)^2}\right\}.$$

By comparing (6.7.3) with formula (14), we obtain the following simultaneous equations

$$A_0 = Y_0,$$
$$A_2 + A_1 - 2A_0 = Y_1 - 3Y_0,$$
$$A_2 - A_1 + A_0 = 2Y_0 - Y_1 + c,$$

which when solved give: $A_0 = Y_0$, $A_1 = Y_1 - Y_0 - c/2$ and $A_2 = c/2$.

Therefore

$$Y(t) = (c/2)[t]^2 + (Y_1 - Y_0 - c/2)[t] + Y_0$$

is the solution of equation (6.7.2) and

$$Y_t = (c/2)t^2 + (Y_1 - Y_0 - c/2)t + Y_0, \quad t = 0, 1, 2 \cdots$$

the solution of equation (6.7.1).

6.8 Compound Interest

Actuarial theory and the mathematics of finance make use of certain difference equations. We shall consider a simple equation connected with compound interest.

Suppose that Y_0 represents the principal, Y_t the amount to which Y_0 will accumulate at the end of the tth interest period, and $r > 0$ the rate of interest for one period. Then, by definition of compound interest, the amount Y_{t+1} accumulated at the end of the $(t+1)$ period is equal to the amount at the end of the tth period plus the interest on this amount for the $(t+1)$ period. Therefore

$$Y_{t+1} = Y_t + rY_t.$$

To find the amount at the end of the tth period we solve the corresponding difference equation

$$Y(t + 1) - (1 + r)Y(t) = 0, \quad Y(t) = Y_0, \quad 0 \leqslant t < 1.$$

The transformed equation is

$$[e^p - (1 + r)]L\{Y(t)\} = \frac{e^p - 1}{p}Y_0,$$

whence

$$Y(t) = L^{-1}\left\{\frac{Y_0(e^p - 1)}{p[e^p - (1 + p)]}\right\}.$$

From Table 6.4.1 we therefore get

$$Y(t) = Y_0(1 + r)^{[t]}$$

or

$$Y_t = Y_0(1 + r)^t,$$

which is the familiar formula obtained in mathematics of finance.

6.9 Continuous Beams

An important engineering problem that can be solved by using difference equations is that of finding the moments at the $n + 1$ supports of a continuous beam subjected to certain loadings. In such problems the so-called equation of *three moments*[*] is used to determine the unknown moments $Y_1, Y_2, \cdots, Y_{n-1}$ when the moments at each end Y_0 and Y_n are given.

If the beam is of uniform cross section, the left end is free, a moment

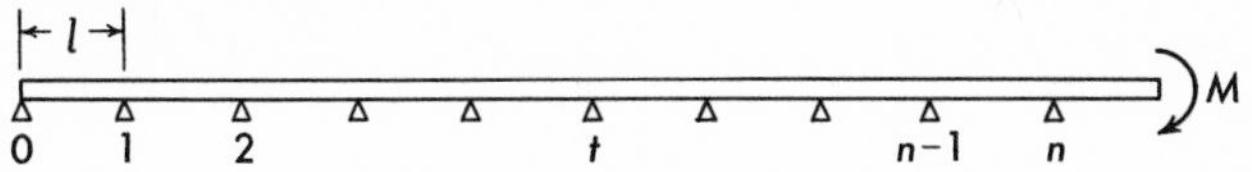

FIG. 6.9.1

of value M is applied at the right end, the supports are equally spaced, and no loads act between them (Fig. 6.9.1), then the three moments equation becomes[†]

$$Y_t + 4Y_{t+1} + Y_{t+2} = 0,$$

with the additional conditions $Y_0 = 0$, $Y_n = M$. In terms of step functions, this equation corresponds to

(6.9.1) $$Y(t) + 4Y(t + 1) + Y(t + 2) = 0,$$

with $Y(t) = 0$, $0 \leqslant t < 1$; $Y(t) = M$, $n \leqslant t < n + 1$. This is an example of a *two-point boundary* value problem since conditions are specified at the two ends of the beam. The other problems involving difference equations were *initial value* problems.

The transform of equation (6.9.1) is

(6.9.2) $$(e^{2p} + 4e^p + 1)L\{Y(t)\} = Y_1 \frac{e^p - 1}{p},$$

where Y_1 is still to be determined. The coefficient of $L\{Y(t)\}$ factors into

$$(e^p + 2 - \sqrt{3})(e^p + 2 + \sqrt{3}) = (e^p + 0 \cdot 268)(e^p + 3 \cdot 732).$$

Hence

(6.9.3) $$Y(t) = Y_1 L^{-1}\left\{\frac{e^p - 1}{p(e^p + 0 \cdot 268)(e^p + 3 \cdot 732)}\right\}.$$

We may now proceed by using formula 19, Table 6.4.2. Comparing coefficients, we find that

$$A_1 + A_0 = 0,$$
$$3 \cdot 732A_1 + 0 \cdot 268A_0 = 1,$$

from which

$$A_1 = 0 \cdot 288, \quad A_0 = -0 \cdot 288.$$

---

[*] See S. Timoshenko and D. H. Young, *Theory of Structures*, p. 342.
[†] *Loc. cit.*

Thus

$$L^{-1}\left\{\frac{e^p - 1}{p(e^p + 0\cdot268)(e^p + 3\cdot732)}\right\} = 0\cdot288[(-0\cdot268)^{[t]} - (-3\cdot732)^{[t]}],$$

and from (6.9.3) it follows that

$$Y(t) = 0\cdot288\,Y_1[(-0\cdot268)^{[t]} - (-3\cdot732)^{[t]}].$$

The value of Y_1 is determined from the condition given for the right end of the beam, namely,

$$M = 0\cdot288\,Y_1[(-0\cdot268)^n - (-3\cdot732)^n].$$

We next consider the case of a continuous beam of n equal spans

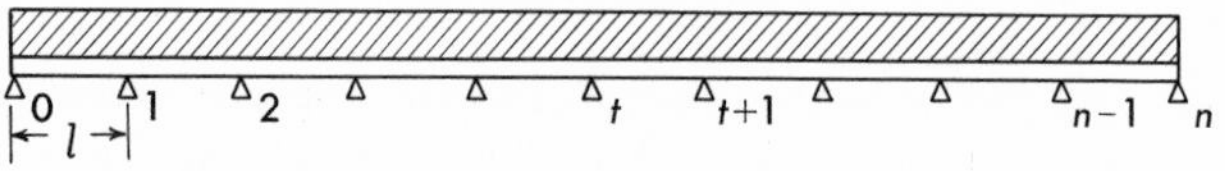

FIG. 6.9.2

with a uniformly distributed load of $w$lb/ft (Fig. 6.9.2). The three moment equation in this case becomes

$$(6.9.4) \qquad\qquad Y_{t+2} + 4Y_{t+1} + Y_t = - wl^2/2,$$

and the boundary conditions, since both ends are free, $Y_0 = Y_n = 0$. Hence the corresponding problem for step functions is

$$Y(t + 2) + 4Y(t + 1) + Y(t) = - wl^2/2,$$
$$Y(t) = 0, \quad 0 \leqslant t < 1; \quad Y(t) = 0, \quad n \leqslant t < n + 1.$$

Proceeding as usual, we have

$$(e^{2p} + 4e^p + 1)\, L\{Y(t)\} = Y_1\frac{e^p - 1}{p} - \frac{wl^2}{2p},$$

and

$$(6.9.5) \quad Y(t) = Y_1 L^{-1}\left\{\frac{e^p - 1}{p(e^p + 0\cdot268)(e^p + 3\cdot732)}\right\}$$
$$- \frac{wl^2}{2}\, L^{-1}\left\{\frac{1}{p(e^p + 0\cdot268)(e^p + 3\cdot732)}\right\}.$$

The inverse transform of the first expression on the right was obtained above and that of the second expression is found from formula (20), Table 6.4.2. We are led to the following equations

$$A_0 + A_1 + A_2 = 0,$$
$$- 4A_0 - 2\cdot732A_1 - 0\cdot732A_2 = 0,$$
$$A_0 - 3\cdot732A_1 - 0\cdot268A_2 = 1,$$

which when solved give: $A_0 = 0 \cdot 144$, $A_1 = -0 \cdot 236$, and $A_2 = 0 \cdot 092$. Hence, from (6.9.5) and Table 6.4.2, it follows that

$$Y(t) = 0 \cdot 288 Y_1[(-0 \cdot 268)^{[t]} - (-3 \cdot 732)^{[t]}]$$

$$- \frac{wl^2}{2}[0 \cdot 092(-3 \cdot 732)^{[t]} - 0 \cdot 236(-0 \cdot 268)^{[t]} + 0 \cdot 144].$$

The value of Y_1 is determined from the equation

$$0 = 0 \cdot 288 Y_1[(-0 \cdot 268)^n - (-3 \cdot 732)^n] - \frac{wl^2}{2}[0 \cdot 092(-3 \cdot 732)^n$$

$$- 0 \cdot 236(-0 \cdot 268)^n + 0 \cdot 144].$$

6.10 Horizontal Vibrations of Equal Masses on an Infinite Elastic String

A simple, but important, example of an iterated structure which lends itself to analysis by means of a difference equation is that shown in Fig. 6.10.1.   Here, particles of equal mass m are attached by helical

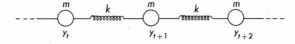

FIG. 6.10.1

springs of stiffness k.   If y_{t+1} represents the displacement of the $(t + 1)$ mass particle, and we neglect the masses of the springs as being small in comparison with those of the mass particles, then the equation of motion of this mass is clearly

(6.10.1) $$m\frac{d^2 y_{t+1}}{dt^2} = k(y_{t+2} - y_{t+1}) - k(y_{t+1} - y_t).$$

This equation, which has both ordinary derivatives and differences, is called a *difference-differential* equation.

We shall not consider the general solution of equation (6.10.1), instead, we shall investigate the so-called normal modes of vibration, i.e., those modes for which the motion of y_{t+1} is harmonic, so that $y_{t+1} = Y_{t+1} \sin \omega t$, where Y_{t+1} is the displacement and ω is the frequency of vibration.   Substituting this value in (6.10.1), we obtain a pure difference equation of the form

(6.10.2) $$- m\omega^2 Y_{t+1} = k(Y_{t+2} - 2Y_{t+1} + Y_t),$$

or, if we let $(m\omega^2)/k = \mu^2$,

(6.10.3) $$Y_{t+2} + (\mu^2 - 2)Y_{t+1} + Y_t = 0.$$

In terms of step functions this equation becomes

(6.10.4) $$Y(t + 2) + (\mu^2 - 2)Y(t + 1) + Y(t) = 0.$$

The transform of the preceding equation yields

$$[e^{2p} + (\mu^2 - 2)e^p + 1]L\{Y(t)\}$$
$$= \frac{e^p - 1}{p}(Y_0 e^p + Y_1) + Y_0 \frac{e^p - 1}{p}(\mu^2 - 2),$$

from which

(6.10.5) $$Y(t) = L^{-1}\left\{\frac{e^p - 1}{p} \cdot \frac{Y_0 e^p + (\mu^2 - 2)Y_0 + Y_1}{e^{2p} + (\mu^2 - 2)e^p + 1}\right\}.$$

It is clear that the nature of the inverse transform depends on the roots of the characteristic equation

(6.10.6) $$e^{2p} + (\mu^2 - 2)e^p + 1 = 0.$$

Three cases can be distinguished depending on whether the discriminant $[(\mu^2 - 2)^2 - 4] < 0, > 0$ or $= 0$, and these are equivalent to the cases $0 < |\mu| < 2, |\mu| > 2$ and $|\mu| = 2$ or 0.

   Case I. $0 < |\mu| < 2$.   In this instance the roots of equation (6.10.6) are imaginary and the solution of equation (6.10.4) will be of the form (formula 21, Table 6.4.2)

(6.10.7) $$Y(t) = A_1 \sin m[t] + A_0 \cos m[t],$$

where $m = \text{arc cos}(1 - \mu^2/2)$ and

$$A_0 = Y_0,$$

(6.10.8) $$A_1 \sin m - A_0 \cos m = (\mu^2 - 2)Y_0 + Y_1.$$

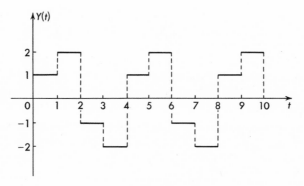

FIG. 6.10.2

   Let us consider the particular case $\mu = \sqrt{2}$, $Y_0 = 1$, $Y_1 = 2$. Then $\cos m = 0$, $m = k\pi/2$, $k = \pm 1, \pm 3, \cdots$ Choosing the value $k = 1$ (other values of k lead to the same result), we find from the system of equations (6.10.8) that $A_0 = 1$ and $A_1 = 2$.   Hence for a string extending from $t = 0$ to $t = \infty$, the displacements are found from the equation

(6.10.9) $$Y(t) = 2 \sin \frac{\pi}{2}[t] + \cos \frac{\pi}{2}[t].$$

The graph of this equation is shown in Fig. 6.10.2.

Case II. $|\mu| > 2$. The roots of equation (6.10.6) in this case are real and the solution is of the form (formula 19, Table 6.4.2)

(6.10.10) $$Y(t) = A_1 a^{[t]} + A_0 b^{[t]},$$

where
$$a = [-(\mu^2 - 2) + \sqrt{(\mu^2 - 2)^2 - 4}]/2,$$
$$b = [-(\mu^2 - 2) - \sqrt{(\mu^2 - 2)^2 - 4}]/2,$$

and A_1, A_2 are connected by the following system of equations

(6.10.11) $$A_1 + A_0 = Y_0,$$
$$-(A_1 b + A_0 a) = (\mu^2 - 2)Y_0 + Y_1.$$

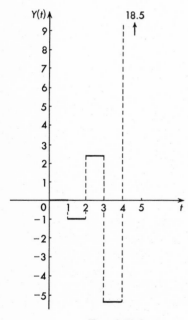

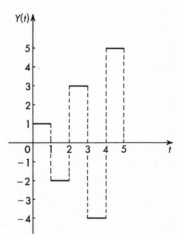

FIG. 6.10.3   FIG. 6.10.4

As a particular case let us take $\mu = \sqrt{5}$, $Y_0 = 0$, and $Y_1 = -1$. We easily find that $a = (-3 + \sqrt{5})/2 = -0 \cdot 38$, $b = (-3 - \sqrt{5})/2 = -2 \cdot 62$, $A_0 = 1/\sqrt{5}$, and $A_1 = -1/\sqrt{5}$. Hence from (6.10.10)
$$Y(t) = [(-2 \cdot 62)^{[t]} - (-0 \cdot 38)^{[t]}]/\sqrt{5},$$
whose graph is shown in Fig. 6.10.3.

Case III. $|\mu| = 2$, or 0.   The roots of equation (6.10.6) are equal here and from formula 24, Table II, we have

(6.10.12) $$Y(t) = A_1[t]a^{[t]} + A_0 a^{[t]},$$

where $a = -1$ and

$$A_0 = Y_0,$$
$$A_0 - A_1 = Y_1 - 2Y_0.$$

Solving this system and substituting in (6.10.12), we find that

$$Y(t) = -(Y_0 + Y_1)[t](-1)^{[t]} + Y_0(-1)^{[t]}.$$

For the initial conditions $Y_0 = 1$, $Y_1 = -2$ the preceding equation becomes

$$Y(t) = (-1)^{[t]} + (-1)^{[t]}[t],$$

and its graph is displayed in Fig. 6.10.4.

6.11 Electrical Filters

Periodic structures occur frequently in electrical engineering in circuit analysis.   One such structure is a network consisting of elements* arranged in an iterated manner and commonly called an

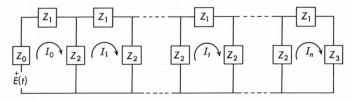

Fig. 6.11.1

electrical filter because it passes certain frequencies and stops others. Several arrangements are possible, but since the frequency characteristics are in general the same for all these arrangements, we shall consider the so-called ladder filter (Fig. 6.11.1).   In the drawing Z_0, Z_1, Z_2, and Z_3 are the impedances,† and we are assuming that the applied voltage $E(t) = E_0 e^{i\omega t}$ and the current in each mesh $I_k(t) = I_k e^{i\omega t}$. As is also seen, all the meshes have identical components except the first and last, which terminate in Z_0 and Z_3, respectively.

---

* Resistors, capacitors, and inductors.

† In the case we are treating, each total impedance is of the form

$$Z = i\omega L + R + \frac{1}{Ci\omega},$$

where $i\omega L$ is the impedance of the inductor, R the impedance of the resistor, and $\frac{1}{Ci\omega}$ the impedance of the capacitor.

Let us derive the equations for each mesh on the assumption that the network was dead initially. Applying Kirchhoff's voltage law to each successive mesh, we have (after some slight rearrangement of terms)

(6.11.1)
$$(Z_0 + Z_1 + Z_2)I_0 - Z_2I_1 = E_0,$$
$$- Z_2I_2 + (Z_1 + 2Z_2)I_1 - Z_2I_0 = 0,$$
. . . .
$$- Z_2I_{t+2} + (Z_1 + 2Z_2)I_1 - Z_2I_0 = 0,$$
. . . .
$$(Z_1 + Z_2 + Z_3)I_n - Z_2I_{n-1} = 0.$$

The difference equation

(6.11.2) $\quad I_{t+2} - (2 + Z_1/Z_2)I_{t+1} + I_t = 0, \quad t = 0, 1, 2, \cdots, n.$

governs the currents in each mesh except the first and last. In terms of step functions, equation (6.11.2) is of the form

(6.11.3) $\quad I(t + 2) - (2 + Z_1/Z_2)I(t + 1) + I(t) = 0,$
$$t = 0, 1, 2, \cdots, n.$$

We now make the assumption that the resistance R of the filter is so small that it can be neglected, so that the complex impedance is of the form

(6.11.4)
$$Z = i\omega L - \frac{i}{\omega C}.$$

Then the ratio $Z_1/Z_2 = (\omega L_1 - 1/\omega C_1)/(\omega L_2 - 1/\omega C_2)$ is a real number and the characteristic equation corresponding to (6.11.3), namely,

(6.11.5) $\qquad e^{2p} - (2 + Z_1/Z_2)e^p + 1 = 0$

has real coefficients. Since we have assumed that the current is sinusoidal (i.e., a wave) equation (6.11.5) must have imaginary roots. This will occur when
$$(2 + Z_1/Z_2)^2 - 4 < 0,$$
or when
(6.11.6) $\qquad - 4 < Z_1/Z_2 < 0.$

We shall now discuss the following important special cases:

(i) *Filter consisting of inductors and capacitors arranged as shown in Fig. 6.11.2.* In this case $Z_1 = i\omega L_1$, $Z_2 = 1/(i\omega C_2)$ and $Z_1/Z_2 = -\omega^2 L_1 C_2$. Therefore from inequality (6.11.6) we have

$$0 < \omega^2 < \frac{4}{L_1 C_2}.$$

The preceding result implies that the filter of Fig. 6.11.2 passes only those currents (i.e., waves) whose frequencies are less than $2/\sqrt{L_1C_2}$. This device is called a *low-pass filter*.

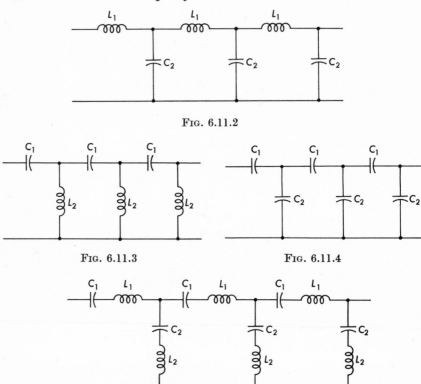

FIG. 6.11.2

FIG. 6.11.3

FIG. 6.11.4

FIG. 6.11.5

(ii) *Filter shown in Fig. 6.11.3.* Here $Z_1 = 1/(i\omega C_1)$, $Z_2 = i\omega L_2$ and inequality (6.11.6) becomes (after some obvious manipulations)

$$0 > \omega^2 > \frac{1}{4L_2C_1}.$$

Therefore this device passes only waves whose frequencies are greater than $1/(2\sqrt{L_2C_1})$; it is called a *high-pass* filter.

(iii) *Filter shown in Fig. 6.11.4.* This device is called a *wave-trap* because it prevents waves from passing through the system. This can be seen as follows. Since $Z_1 = 1/(i\omega C_1)$, $Z_2 = 1/(i\omega C_2)$ and $Z_1/Z_2 = C_2/C_1$, we have from inequality (6.11.6)

$$-4 < C_2/C_1 < 0,$$

which is impossible to satisfy because C_2 and C_1 are positive numbers. In other words, for this case the characteristic equation cannot have imaginary roots.

Exercise. Discuss the filter shown in Fig. 6.11.5 (page 192).

PROBLEMS

Solve the following difference equations:

1. $2Y_{t+2} - 5Y_{t+1} + 2Y_t = t$, $Y_0 = C_0$, $Y_1 = C_1$.
   Ans. $Y_t = 1 - t + \frac{2}{3}(2C_0 - C_1 - 2)(\frac{1}{2})^t + \frac{1}{3}(2C_1 - C_0 + 1)(2)^t$.

2. $Y(t + 2) - 5Y(t + 1) + 6Y(t) = a^{[t]}$, $(a \neq 2$ or $3)$, $Y(t) = Y_0$, $0 \leqslant t < 1$; $Y(t) = Y_1$, $1 \leqslant t < 2$. Discuss the cases: $a = 2$, $a = 3$.

   Ans. $Y(t) = \left(Y_1 - 2Y_0 - \dfrac{1}{a-3}\right)(3)^{[t]} + \left(3Y_0 - Y_1 + \dfrac{1}{a-2}\right)(2)^{[t]}$
   $$+ \frac{a^{[t]}}{(a-2)(a-3)}, \ (a \neq 2 \text{ or } 3).$$

3. $Y_{t+2} + 6Y_{t+1} + 9Y_t = k$, $Y_0 = C_0$, $Y_1 = C_1$.

   Ans. $Y_t = \left[\dfrac{5(C_1 - 9C_0)}{21}t + \dfrac{C_1 - 2C_0}{7} + \dfrac{k}{4}\right](-3)^t + \dfrac{5C_0 - C_1}{7} - \dfrac{k}{4}$.

4. $\Delta^2 Y_t + \Delta Y_t = \cos mt$, $Y_0 = C_0$, $Y_1 = C_1$.
   [*Hint*: Use Formula 23 with $a = 1$.]

   Ans. $Y_t = C_0 + \left\{(C_1 - C_0) + \dfrac{1}{2}\dfrac{1 + \cos m}{\sin m}\sin m(t - 1)\right.$
   $$\left. - \tfrac{1}{2}\cos m(t - 1) + \tfrac{1}{2}\right\} \cdot 1(t - 1).$$

5. $Y(t + 3) - 2Y(t + 2) - Y(t + 1) + 2Y(t) = 0$, $Y(t) = 0$, $0 \leqslant t < 1$; $Y(t) = -2$, $1 \leqslant t < 2$; $Y(t) = 1$, $2 \leqslant t < 3$.
   Ans. $Y(t) = \frac{1}{3}(2)^{[t]} + \frac{7}{6}(-1)^{[t]} - \frac{3}{2}$.

6. $Y_{t+2} - n^2 Y_t = \sin mt$, $Y_0 = C_0$, $Y_1 = C_1$, $(n \neq 0)$.
   Ans. $Y_t = \frac{1}{2}(C_0 + C_1/n)(n)^t + \frac{1}{2}(C_0 - C_1/n)(-n)^t$
   $$+ \left(\frac{\sin 2m}{2(n^2 + 1)} - \frac{\sin m}{2n}\right)(-n)^t + \left(\frac{\sin 2m}{2(n^2 + 1)} + \frac{\sin m}{2n}\right)(n)^t$$
   $$+ \frac{(\cos 2m - n^2)}{n^2 + 1}\sin mt - \frac{\sin 2m}{n^2 + 1}\cos mt.$$

   Discuss the case $n = 0$.

   Ans. $Y_t = C_0 + (C_1 - C_0) \cdot 1(t - 1) - C_1 \cdot 1(t - 2)$
   $$+ \sin m(t - 2) \cdot 1(t - 2), \ t = 0, 1, 2, \cdots.$$

7. $\Delta^3 Y_t - 5\Delta Y_t + 2Y_t = 2^t$, $Y_0 = 0$, $Y_1 = Y_2 = 1$.
   [*Hint*: Use Formula 25.]

$$Ans. \quad Y_t = \frac{24\sqrt{2}-21}{158}(\sqrt{2})^t - \frac{29+12\sqrt{2}}{158}(-\sqrt{2})^t + \frac{25-6\sqrt{2}}{79}(3)^t.$$

8. $Y(t+2) + 2Y(t+1) + 4Y(t) = \cos\frac{\pi}{2}[t]$, $Y(t) = 0$, $0 \leqslant t < 1$;

   $Y(t) = 5$, $1 \leqslant t < 2$.
   [*Hint*: Separate into partial fractions and use Formulas 21 and 22.]

$$Ans. \quad Y(t) = \frac{1}{13}(2\sin\frac{\pi}{2}[t] + 3\cos\frac{\pi}{2}[t]) + \frac{\sqrt{3}}{13}(2)^{[t]}(20\sin\frac{2}{3}\pi[t]$$
$$- \sqrt{3}\cos\frac{2}{3}\pi[t]).$$

9. $Y(t+2) + 4Y(t) = [t]([t]-1)$, $Y(t) = -1$, $0 \leqslant t < 1$;
   $Y(t) = 1$, $1 \leqslant t < 2$.

$$Ans. \quad Y(t) = \frac{1}{25}\Big\{5[t]^2 - 9[t] - 0{\cdot}4 + 2^{[t]}(14{\cdot}7\sin\frac{\pi}{2}[t]$$
$$- 24{\cdot}6\cos\frac{\pi}{2}[t])\Big\}.$$

10. $Y(t+4) + 2Y(t+2) + Y(t) = 0$, $Y(t) = 0$, $0 \leqslant t < 1$, $Y(t) = 0$,
    $1 \leqslant t < 2$, $Y(t) = 5$, $2 \leqslant t < 3$, $Y(t) = -1$, $3 \leqslant t < 4$.

$$Ans. \quad Y(t) = \frac{1}{2}\Big\{([t]-1)\sin\frac{\pi}{2}[t] - 5[t]\cos\frac{\pi}{2}[t]\Big\}.$$

Solve the following systems of difference equations:

11. $Y_1(t+1) - Y_2(t) = [t]$, $Y_2(t+1) - Y_1(t) = -([t]+1)$.
    $Y_1(t) = 2$, $0 \leqslant t < 1$; $Y_2(t) = -1$, $0 \leqslant t < 1$.
    Ans. $Y_1(t) = \frac{3}{2}(-1)^{[t]} + \frac{1}{2}$, $Y_2(t) = -[t] - \frac{3}{2}(-1)^{[t]} + \frac{1}{2}$.

12. $Y_1(t+1) + 2Y_2(t) = 0$, $Y_2(t+1) + Y_1(t) = a$.
    $Y_1(t) = 1$, $0 \leqslant t < 1$; $Y_2(t) = 0$, $1 \leqslant t < 2$.
    Ans. $Y_1(t) = [1 - a\sqrt{2}(1 + \sqrt{2})](\sqrt{2})^{[t]-2}$
    $$+ [1 + a\sqrt{2}(1 - \sqrt{2})](-\sqrt{2})^{[t]-2} + 2a,$$
    $Y_2(t) = [a(1 + \sqrt{2}) - 2^{-\frac{1}{2}}](\sqrt{2})^{[t]-2}$
    $$+ [a(1 - \sqrt{2}) + 2^{-\frac{1}{2}}](-\sqrt{2})^{[t]-2} - a.$$

13. $Y_1(t+2) - Y_2(t+1) = a^{[t]}$, $Y_2(t+2) - Y_1(t+1) = a^{-[t]}$,
    $$(a \neq 1 \text{ or } -1)$$
    $Y_1(t) = Y_2(t) = 0$, $0 \leqslant t < 1$; $Y_1(t) = Y_2(t) = 0$, $1 \leqslant t < 2$.

$$Ans. \quad Y_1(t) = \frac{1}{2(a+1)}(-1)^{[t]} + \frac{1}{a^2-1}a^{[t]} - \frac{1}{2(a-1)}$$
$$+ \Big\{\frac{a}{2(a+1)}(-1)^{[t]-1} + \frac{a^{-[t]+3}}{1-a^2} - \frac{a}{2(1-a)}\Big\}1(t-1),$$

$$Y_2(t) = \frac{a}{2(1+a)}(-1)^{[t]} + \frac{a^{-[t]+2}}{1-a^2} - \frac{a}{2(1-a)}$$

$$+ \left\{ \frac{1}{2(a+1)}(-1)^{[t]-1} + \frac{1}{a^2-1}a^{[t]-1} - \frac{1}{2(a-1)} \right\} 1(t-1).$$

14. $Y_1(t+2) + Y_2(t) = a$, $Y_2(t+1) + Y_1(t) = 0$.
   $Y_1(t) = Y_2(t) = 0$, $0 \leqslant t < 1$; $Y_1(t) = Y_2(t) = 0$, $1 \leqslant t < 2$.

   Ans. $Y_1(t) = \dfrac{a}{3}\left\{ [t] - \dfrac{2}{\sqrt{3}}\sin\dfrac{2\pi}{3}[t] \right\}$,

   $Y_2(t) = \dfrac{a}{3}\left\{ 1 - [t] - \dfrac{1}{\sqrt{3}}\sin\dfrac{2\pi}{3}[t] - \cos\dfrac{2\pi}{3}[t] \right\}$.

15. Find the nth term Y_n of the arithmetic sequence $Y_0,\ Y_1,\ Y_2, \cdots$, $Y_t, \cdots$ of order 3 if $Y_0,\ Y_1,\ Y_2$ are known.

16. The sequence of numbers $0, 1, 1, 2, 3, 5, 8, 13, 21, \cdots$ is called *Fibonacci's* sequence. Find the difference equation satisfied by the elements of this sequence and solve it for the xth term.

   Ans. $Y_x = \dfrac{\sqrt{5}}{5}\left[\left(\dfrac{1+\sqrt{5}}{2}\right)^x - \left(\dfrac{1-\sqrt{5}}{2}\right)^x \right]$.

17. A seed is planted. When it is one year old it produces tenfold, and when two years old and upwards eighteenfold. Every seed is planted as soon as produced. Find the number of grains at the end of the xth year.

   Ans. $Y_x = \dfrac{1}{3\sqrt{17}}\left[\left(\dfrac{11+3\sqrt{17}}{2}\right)^x - \left(\dfrac{11-3\sqrt{17}}{2}\right)^x \right]$.

18. An annuity fund is formed by depositing equal periodic payments P and allowing them to accumulate at compound interest r. Express this statement in the form of a difference equation and solve it to find the amount of the annuity at the end of t years.

19. In a problem from probability theory concerning simple chains of dependent trials, the following difference equation arises

   $$Y_{t+1} + (a-b)Y_t = a, \quad (a \neq b \text{ or } b-1)$$

   where Y_t is the probability of the occurrence of an event in the tth trial and a as well as b are certain known constants. Solve this equation if the initial probability is Y_0.

   Ans. $Y_t = \left(Y_0 + \dfrac{a}{b-a-1} \right)(b-a)^t + \dfrac{a}{1+a-b}$.

20. A certain problem from probability when analyzed yields the following difference equation:

   $$Y_{t+2} - Y_{t+1} + aY = a, \quad a < 1.$$

   Solve this equation subject to the initial conditions $Y_0 = Y_1 = 0$.

21. A continuous beam supported at $n + 1$ equidistant points is acted upon by n equal concentrated loads P situated at the midpoints of the successive spans of length l (Fig. 6.11.6). If the difference equation for this case is

$$Y_{t+2} + 4Y_{t+1} + Y_t = -\tfrac{3}{4}Pl,$$

find the moments $Y_t,\ t = 1, 2, \cdots, n - 1$.

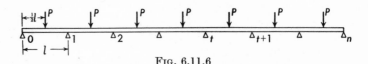

FIG. 6.11.6

22. An infinitely extended string, under a tension T, carries equidistant masses m and is immersed in a viscous fluid. Discuss the nature of the wave propagation if one of the masses is subjected to a harmonic transversal motion.

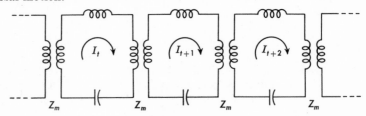

FIG. 6.11.7

23. Figure 6.11.7 represents a chain of coupled electric circuits. If Z_m represents the mutual impedance between the adjacent meshes, Z the self-impedance of a mesh, and I_t the current in the tth mesh, obtain the difference equation connecting these quantities and discuss the solution.

CHAPTER VII

Linear Partial Differential Equations

A great number of problems that arise in the physical sciences require the solution of partial differential equations subject to certain prescribed conditions. Although many of these equations are non-linear and hence not suitable for treatment by transform methods, still, a large number of these problems lead to the important linear second order partial differential equation with constant coefficients

$$(7.0) \quad AU_{xx}(x,t) + BU_{xt}(x,t) + CU_{tt}(x,t) + DU_x(x,t) + EU_t(x,t) \\ + FU(x,t) = G(x,t),$$

which is amenable to transform methods.

The solutions of (7.0) are known to possess markedly different properties depending on whether the expression $B^2 - 4AC$ is (i) *greater than zero*, (ii) *less than zero*, or (iii) *equal to zero*. In the first case (7.0) is said to be of *hyperbolic* type, in the second, of *elliptic* type, and in the third, of *parabolic* type. The Laplace transform is quite effective when applied to equation (7.0) if it is of *hyperbolic* or *parabolic* type, but rather ineffective for an *elliptic* type. In the latter case, the Fourier sine or cosine transforms (to be introduced later) can be used if conditions on *rectangular* boundaries are prescribed. If the boundaries are more complicated, *analytic* functions can be used in many cases to transform these boundaries into rectangular ones and thus reduce the problem to the preceding one. In what follows we shall be concerned primarily with a linear partial differential equation such as (7.0) of hyperbolic or parabolic type.

7.1 The Diffusion Equation

Let us suppose that two substances are dissolved in a liquid and that the concentration of one substance is greater than that of the other. If we imagine that the substances were placed in two different regions separated by a permeable membrane, then it is well known that there is a transport of the dissolved substance from the region of higher concentration to that of lower concentration. This transport, we note, takes place in the direction of *decreasing concentration* and continues until a state of equilibrium is reached.

An empirical law of diffusion (serving well as a first approximation) states that *the rate of diffusion of a dissolved substance across a unit area of a surface in the direction of the normal to that surface is proportional to the rate of change of the concentration with respect to the distance along that normal.* Stated symbolically

$$(7.1.1) \qquad\qquad P = -D\frac{\partial C}{\partial n},$$

where C is the concentration of the dissolved substance (expressed in gm/cm^3), D is the "coefficient of diffusion" (which we shall here assume to be constant), n is the distance measured along a directed normal to the surface, and P the time rate of transport of substance across a unit area of this surface. The minus sign indicates the fact that the diffusion takes place in the direction of decreasing concentration.

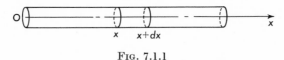

Fig. 7.1.1

Now, let diffusion of a substance take place in the positive x-direction of a cylinder of unit cross section (Fig. 7.1.1) and let $C(x,t)$ represent the concentration at a distance x from a fixed point O of the cylinder at time t. According to (7.1.1) the time rate of transport of dissolved substance across the section at x (assumed normal to the x-axis) is

$$-D\frac{\partial C(x,t)}{\partial x},$$

and that across the section $x + dx$,

$$-D\frac{\partial C(x + dx,t)}{\partial x}.$$

Hence the net rate of accumulation of dissolved substance in the cylinder of length dx is

$$(7.1.2) \qquad\qquad -D\left[\frac{\partial C(x,t)}{\partial x} - \frac{\partial C(x + dx,t)}{\partial x}\right].$$

If squares and higher powers of differentials are neglected, then by Taylor's theorem we have approximately

$$C(x + dx,t) = C(x,t) + \frac{\partial C(x,t)}{\partial x}\,dx.$$

Therefore (7.1.2) becomes

(7.1.2)
$$D\frac{\partial^2 C(x,t)}{\partial x^2}\,dx.$$

On the other hand, the net rate of accumulation of substance within this cylinder is also equal to

(7.1.3)
$$\frac{\partial C(x,t)}{\partial t}\,dx.$$

Hence, equating (7.1.2) and (7.1.3), we obtain

(7.1.4)
$$\frac{\partial C}{\partial t} = D\frac{\partial^2 C}{\partial x^2},$$

which is termed the *one-dimensional diffusion equation*.

By proceeding in an analogous manner the following *two-* and *three-dimensional diffusion equations* can be derived:

(7.1.5)
$$\frac{\partial C}{\partial t} = D\left[\frac{\partial^2 C}{\partial x^2} + \frac{\partial^2 C}{\partial y^2}\right],$$

and

(7.1.6)
$$\frac{\partial C}{\partial t} = D\left[\frac{\partial^2 C}{\partial x^2} + \frac{\partial^2 C}{\partial y^2} + \frac{\partial^2 C}{\partial z^2}\right].$$

In deriving these equations it is assumed that the medium is isotropic and the dissolved substance is not being produced in the solution by some chemical reaction.

Equation (7.1.6) is also known as the *heat equation* since it is satisfied by the temperature $T(x,t)$ within a solid in the absence of heat sources.

We observe that the one-dimensional diffusion equation (7.1.4) is a special case of equation (7.0) and of hyperbolic type. The following examples illustrate the use of the Laplace transformation in solving boundary value problems in connection with this equation.

Example 1. A salt solution is confined to region I (Fig. 7.1.2) lying between two impermeable boundaries $x = -l$ and $x = 0$. At $t = 0$ the boundary $x = 0$ is replaced by a permeable membrane (offering no resistance to transport) and the solute diffuses across the membrane into region II containing another salt solution which extends to ∞ and whose concentration is initially C_1. If the solution in region I is

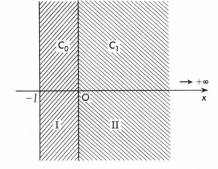

Fig. 7.1.2

maintained at the constant concentration $C_0(> C_1)$, find the concentration in region II for $t > 0$.

Clearly, the *initial* condition is

$$(7.1.7) \qquad\qquad C(x,0) = C_1 \qquad\qquad (x > 0),$$

and the *boundary* conditions are

$$(7.1.8) \qquad C(0,t) = C_0, \qquad \lim_{x \to +\infty} C(x,t) = C_1 \qquad (t > 0).$$

For brevity, later on, we shall often include the initial condition with the boundary conditions. In addition, the concentration in region II must satisfy the differential equation

$$(7.1.9) \qquad\qquad C_t(x,t) = DC_{xx}(x,t) \qquad\qquad (x > 0,\ t > 0).$$

Let the Laplace transform of $C(x,t)$ with respect to t, i.e., $L_t\{C(x,t)\}$, be denoted by $c(x,p)$. Then

$$L_t\{C_t(x,t)\} = pc(x,p) - C_1,$$

and

$$L_t\{C_{xx}(x,t)\} = \int_0^\infty \frac{\partial^2}{\partial x^2}[e^{-pt}\, C(x,t)]\, dt.$$

If we assume that the function $e^{-pt}\, C(x,t)$ is such that the order of differentiation and integration can be interchanged, then

$$L_t\{C_{xx}(x,t)\} = \frac{\partial^2}{\partial x^2}\int_0^\infty e^{-pt}\, C(x,t)\, dt = c_{xx}(x,p),$$

and from (7.1.9), after taking the transform of both sides, we obtain

$$(7.1.10) \qquad\qquad Dc_{xx}(x,p) = pc(x,p) - C_1.$$

The transforms of the equalities (7.1.8) yield

$$(7.1.11) \qquad c(0,p) = C_0/p, \qquad \lim_{x \to +\infty} c(x,p) = C_1/p,$$

where in the last equality we assumed that interchanging the order of taking the limit as $x \to \infty$ and integrating with respect to t is a valid operation.

Since p is only a parameter in (7.1.10) and (7.1.11), ordinary rather than partial derivatives can be used and we may rewrite the original boundary value problem as

$$(7.1.12) \qquad\qquad \frac{d^2c}{dx^2} - \frac{p}{D}c = -\frac{C_1}{D},$$

$$(7.1.13) \qquad\qquad c(0,p) = C_0/p,$$

$$(7.1.14) \qquad\qquad \lim_{x \to \infty} c(x,p) = C_1/p.$$

The general solution of (7.1.12) can be written in the following two ways

$$(7.1.15) \qquad c(x,p) = c_1 e^{-\sqrt{p/D}\,x} + c_2 e^{\sqrt{p/D}\,x} + C_1/p,$$

and

$$(7.1.16) \qquad c(x,p) = c_1' \cosh \sqrt{p/D}\,x + c_2' \sinh \sqrt{p/D}\,x + C_1/p.$$

Of the two forms, the first is generally useful when the regions involved are infinite or semi-infinite (as in our case) and the second, when finite regions are involved. Using (7.1.15) and condition (7.1.14) it is clear that $c_2 = 0$. From (7.1.13) we find that $c_1 = (C_0 - C_1)/p$. Therefore

$$c(x,p) = \frac{C_0 - C_1}{p} e^{-\sqrt{p/D}\,x} + \frac{C_1}{p},$$

and upon taking inverse transforms of both sides, we obtain

$$(7.1.17) \qquad C(x,t) = C_1 + (C_0 - C_1)\,\mathrm{erfc}\left(\frac{x}{2\sqrt{Dt}}\right).$$

We view this solution, of course, as purely formal subject to verification. That is why the conditions for the validity of interchange of order of differentiation and integration, or the interchange of order of taking a limit and integrating need not be considered. The verification of the solution obtained by the Laplace transform method in the case of an nth order ordinary differential equation with constant coefficients and systems of such equations can be proved generally. However, this is not possible for partial differential equations, and each problem must be considered separately. We shall not attempt the task of verification for the variety of problems to be considered here. Instead, it will suffice to say that such a verification can be supplied for the problems that we shall deal with in this text, and the reader interested in the methods employed is referred to references 2 and 5 of Appendix A. Moreover, all the problems proposed here will have *unique* solutions.

In the problem under consideration, however, we shall show that (7.1.17) satisfies the boundary conditions as well as the differential equation. That condition (7.1.7) is satisfied follows immediately from (7.1.17) because $\mathrm{erfc}\,(\infty) = 0$. Furthermore, since $\mathrm{erfc}\,(0) = 1$ we also have from (7.1.17), $C(0,t) = C_0$. Clearly, $\lim_{x \to \infty} C(x,t) = C_1$.

Using the formula for differentiating an integral with respect to a parameter* we find that

$$\frac{\partial}{\partial t}\,\mathrm{erfc}\left(\frac{x}{2\sqrt{at}}\right) = \frac{x}{2\sqrt{\pi a}\,t^{3/2}}\,e^{-x^2/(4at)},$$

$$\frac{\partial^2}{\partial x^2}\,\mathrm{erfc}\left(\frac{x}{2\sqrt{at}}\right) = \frac{x}{2\sqrt{\pi}(at)^{3/2}}e^{-x^2/(4at)}.$$

---

* See R. Courant, *Differential and Integral Calculus,* Vol. II, p. 220.

Therefore,

$$C_t(x,t) = \frac{(C_0 - C_1)x}{2\sqrt{\pi a}\, t^{3/2}} e^{-x^2/(4at)}$$

and

$$C_{xx}(x,t) = \frac{(C_0 - C_1)x}{2\sqrt{\pi}(at)^{3/2}} e^{-x^2/(4at)}.$$

When these results are substituted in equation (7.1.9) they are seen to satisfy it identically. Thus, we have verified that (7.1.17) is the solution of our problem.

Exercise. Solve the problem of the preceding example for the following boundary conditions:

(i) $C(x,0) = C_1 x$, $(x > 0)$; $C(0,t) = C_0$, $\lim_{x \to +\infty} C(x,t) = C_1 x$, $(t > 0)$.

Ans. $C(x,t) = (C_0 - C_1 x)\, \mathrm{erfc}\left(\dfrac{x}{2\sqrt{Dt}}\right) + C_1 x.$

(ii) $C(x,0) = C_1$, $(x > 0)$; $C(0,t) = C_0 t^2/2$, $\lim_{x \to \infty} C(x,t) = C_1$, $(t > 0)$.

Ans. $C(x,t) = C_1\left[1 - \mathrm{erfc}\left(\dfrac{x}{2\sqrt{Dt}}\right)\right]$

$$+ C_0 \int_0^t \int_0^{t_1} \mathrm{erfc}\left(\frac{x}{2\sqrt{Dt_2}}\right) dt_2\, dt_1.$$

(iii) $C(x,0) = C_1 x$, $(x > 0)$; $C(0,t) = C_0 t^2/2$, $\lim_{x \to \infty} C(x,t) = C_1 x$, $(t > 0)$.

Ans. $C(x,t) = C_1 x\left[1 - \mathrm{erfc}\left(\dfrac{x}{2\sqrt{Dt}}\right)\right]$

$$+ C_0 \int_0^t \int_0^{t_1} \mathrm{erfc}\left(\frac{x}{2\sqrt{Dt_2}}\right) dt_2\, dt_1.$$

7.2 Diffusion in an Infinite Region

Two salt solutions having concentrations C_{00} and C_{11} ($C_{00} > C_{11}$) initially, are separated by a permeable membrane M offering no resistance * to transport from region I to region II, each of which is semi-infinite in extent (Fig. 7.2.1). If the diffusion coefficients of the salt

---

* For a case in which resistance to transport is considered see E. J. Scott, L. H. Tung, and H. G. Drickamer, " Diffusion through an Interface," *The Journal of Chemical Physics*, Vol. 19, No. 9, 1075–1078, September, 1951.

solutions in regions I and II are D_1 and D_2, respectively, let us determine formulas for the concentrations in these regions.

If $C(x,t)$ denotes the concentration, then it must satisfy the
equations

(7.2.1) $C_t(x,t) = D_1 C_{xx}(x,t)$
            $(x < 0, t > 0)$,

(7.2.2) $C_t(x,t) = D_2 C_{xx}(x,t)$
            $(x > 0, t > 0)$,

the initial conditions

(7.2.3)

$C(x,0) = C_{00}(-\infty < x < 0)$,
            $C(x,0) = C_{11}$
            $(0 < x < \infty)$,

and the boundary conditions

(7.2.4)

$\lim\limits_{x \to -\infty} C(x,t) = C_{00}$,

$\quad\lim\limits_{x \to \infty} C(x,t) = C_{11}$

$\qquad\qquad (t > 0)$

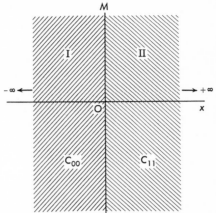

FIG. 7.2.1

(7.2.5) $C_1(0 -,t) = C_2(0 +,t)$, $- D_1 \dfrac{\partial C(0 -,t)}{\partial x} = - D_2 \dfrac{\partial C(0 +,t)}{\partial x}$

$\qquad\qquad\qquad\qquad\qquad\qquad\qquad\qquad (t > 0)$.

Conditions (7.2.3) are evident.   The first of the conditions (7.2.4)
states that the concentration at a point on the interface is the same as
this point is approached from either direction.   The second of these
conditions states that the amount of substance carried by diffusion in
region I to a unit area of the membrane per unit of time is the same as
the amount of substance carried from the membrane into region II per
unit of time per unit area.

Taking the transforms of the preceding conditions with respect to
t, we obtain

(7.2.6) $pc(x,p) - C_{00} = D_1 c_{xx}(x,p)$ $(x < 0)$,

(7.2.7) $pc(x,p) - C_{11} = D_2 c_{xx}(x,p)$ $(x > 0)$,

(7.2.8) $\lim\limits_{x \to -\infty} c(x,p) = C_{00}/p$, $\lim\limits_{x \to \infty} c(x,p) = C_{11}/p$,

(7.2.9) $c(0 -,p) = c(0 +,p)$, $- D_1 c_x(0 -,p) = - D_2 c_x(0 +,t)$.

The solution of (7.2.7) is

$\qquad c(x,p) = C_{00}/p + c_1 e^{\sqrt{p/D_1}\,x} + c_2 e^{-\sqrt{p/D_1}\,x}$ $(x < 0)$,

and in view of the first of the conditions (7.2.8) $c_2 = 0$.   Therefore

(7.2.10) $c(x,p) = C_{00}/p + c_1 e^{\sqrt{p/D_1}\,x}$ $(x < 0)$.

Similarly, the solution of (7.2.7) satisfying the second of the conditions (7.2.7) is

$$(7.2.11) \qquad c(x,p) = C_{11}/p + c_2' e^{-\sqrt{p/D_2}\,x} \qquad (x > 0).$$

The conditions (7.2.9) require that

$$c_1 + C_{00}/p = c_2' + C_{11}/p,$$

and

$$c_1 \sqrt{D_1} = -c_2' \sqrt{D_2},$$

from which

$$c_1 = \frac{\sqrt{D_2}(C_{11} - C_{00})}{p(\sqrt{D_1} + \sqrt{D_2})}, \qquad c_2' = \frac{\sqrt{D_1}(C_{00} - C_{11})}{p(\sqrt{D_1} + \sqrt{D_2})}.$$

Substituting these values in (7.2.10) and (7.2.11), we have

$$c(x,p) = \frac{C_{00}}{p} + \frac{\sqrt{D_2}(C_{11} - C_{00})}{p(\sqrt{D_1} + \sqrt{D_2})} \qquad (x < 0),$$

$$c(x,p) = \frac{C_{11}}{p} + \frac{\sqrt{D_1}(C_{00} - C_{11})}{p(\sqrt{D_1} + \sqrt{D_2})} \qquad (x > 0).$$

Whence, upon taking inverse transforms,

$$C(x,t) = C_{00} + \frac{\sqrt{D_2}(C_{11} - C_{00})}{\sqrt{D_1} + \sqrt{D_2}} \, \mathrm{erfc}\left(\frac{-x}{2\sqrt{D_1 t}}\right) \qquad (x < 0),$$

$$C(x,t) = C_{11} + \frac{\sqrt{D_1}(C_{00} - C_{11})}{\sqrt{D_1} + \sqrt{D_2}} \, \mathrm{erfc}\left(\frac{x}{2\sqrt{D_2 t}}\right) \qquad (x > 0).$$

Exercise. Solve the following boundary value problem:

$$C_t(x,t) = D_1 C_{xx}(x,t) \qquad (x < 0, t > 0),$$
$$C_t(x,t) = D_2 C_{xx}(x,t) \qquad (x > 0, t > 0),$$
$$C(x,0) = A e^{a^2 x}, \quad (-\infty < x < 0); \quad C(x,0) = B e^{-b^2 x}, \quad (0 < x < \infty),$$
$$\lim_{x \to -\infty} C(x,t) = 0, \qquad \lim_{x \to \infty} C(x,t) = 0 \qquad (t > 0),$$
$$C(0-,t) = C(0+,t), \qquad -D_1 C_x(0-,t) = -D_2 C_x(0+,t) \qquad (t > 0).$$

[*Hint:* Use the convolution theorem.]

Ans. $C(x,t) = A e^{a^2(x + a^2 D_1 t)}$

$$+ \frac{1}{\sqrt{\pi}(\sqrt{D_1} + \sqrt{D_2})} \int_0^t \left(\frac{a^2 A D_1}{\sqrt{\tau}} e^{a^4 D_1(t-\tau) - x^2/(4 D_1 \tau)}\right.$$
$$\left. - \frac{b^2 B D_2}{\sqrt{\tau}} e^{b^4 D_2(t-\tau) - x^2/(4 D_1 \tau)}\right) d\tau$$

$$+ \frac{x \sqrt{D_2}}{2\sqrt{\pi}(\sqrt{D_1} + \sqrt{D_2})} \int_0^t \left(\frac{A}{\sqrt{D_1}} \frac{e^{a^4 D_1(t-\tau) - x^2/(4 D_1 \tau)}}{\tau^{3/2}}\right.$$
$$\left. - \frac{B}{\sqrt{D_2}} \frac{e^{b^4 D_2(t-\tau) - x^2/(4 D_1 \tau)}}{\tau^{3/2}}\right) d\tau, \quad (x < 0, t > 0),$$

$$C(x,t) = Be^{-b^2(x-b^2D_2t)}$$

$$+ \frac{1}{\sqrt{\pi}(\sqrt{D_1} + \sqrt{D_2})} \int_0^t \left(\frac{a^2 A D_1}{\sqrt{\tau}} e^{a^4 D_1(t-\tau) - x^2/(4D_2\tau)} \right.$$

$$\left. - \frac{b^2 B D_2}{\sqrt{\tau}} e^{b^4 D_2(t-\tau) - x^2/(4D_2\tau)} \right) d\tau$$

$$- \frac{x\sqrt{D_1}}{2\sqrt{\pi}(\sqrt{D_1} + \sqrt{D_2})} \int_0^t \left(\frac{A}{\sqrt{D_1}} \frac{e^{a^4 D_1(t-\tau) - x^2/(4D_2\tau)}}{\tau^{3/2}} \right.$$

$$\left. - \frac{B}{\sqrt{D_2}} \frac{e^{b^4 D_2(t-\tau) - x^2/(4D_2\tau)}}{\tau^{3/2}} \right) d\tau, \quad (x > 0, t > 0).$$

7.3 Diffusion into a Slab

A solute diffuses from a solution into a dry porous infinite slab of thickness l immersed in this solution (Fig. 7.3.1).   If the concentration of the solution is made to remain constant at all time, an expression for the concentration $C(x,t)$ in the slab is required for $t > 0$.   Clearly, the following boundary value problem must be solved.

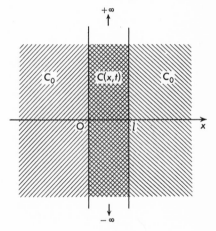

(7.3.1) $C_t(x,t) = DC_{xx}(x,t)$
$\qquad\qquad (0 < x < l, t > 0)$,

(7.3.2) $C(x,0) = 0$
$\qquad\qquad (0 < x < l)$,

(7.3.3)
$\quad C(0,t) = C_0, \qquad C(l,t) = C_0$
$\qquad\qquad (t > 0)$.

Application   of   the   Laplace transform with respect to t to each of the preceding expressions yields

Fig. 7.3.1

(7.3.4) $\qquad\qquad pc(x,p) - c(x,0) = Dc_{xx}(x,p) \qquad\qquad (0 < x < l)$,

(7.3.5) $\qquad\qquad\qquad\qquad c(x,0) = 0 \qquad\qquad\qquad (0 < x < l)$,

(7.3.6) $\qquad\qquad c(0,p) = C_0/p, \qquad c(l,p) = C_0/p$,

where as usual $L_t\{C(x,t)\} = c(x,p)$.

Because the thickness of the slab is finite, the solution of (7.3.4) most suitable for this problem is

(7.3.7) $\qquad\qquad c(x,p) = c_1 \cosh \sqrt{p/D}\, x + c_2 \sinh \sqrt{p/D}\, x$.

In view of conditions (7.3.6), we have

$$C_0/p = c_1, \qquad C_0/p = c_1 \cosh \sqrt{p/D}\, l + c_2 \sinh \sqrt{p/D}\, l,$$

and the values for c_1 and c_2 obtained from these equations when substituted in (7.3.7) yields the equation

$$c(x,p) = \frac{C_0}{p}\left[\frac{\cosh \sqrt{p/D}\, x \sinh \sqrt{p/D}\, l - \cosh \sqrt{p/D}\, l \sinh \sqrt{p/D}\, x}{\sinh \sqrt{p/D}\, l}\right.$$

$$\left. + \frac{\sinh \sqrt{p/D}\, x}{\sinh \sqrt{p/D}\, l}\right]$$

or

$$(7.3.8) \qquad c(x,p) = \frac{C_0}{p}\frac{\sinh (l - x)\sqrt{p/D}}{\sinh \sqrt{p/D}\, l} + \frac{C_0}{p}\frac{\sinh \sqrt{p/D}\, x}{\sinh \sqrt{p/D}\, l},$$

where the *principal value* of the *square root* is taken.

The function

$$(7.3.9) \qquad \frac{\sinh (l - x)\sqrt{p/D}}{p \sinh l\sqrt{p/D}} = \frac{l - x}{pl}\; \frac{1 + \dfrac{(l - x)^2}{3!}\dfrac{p}{D} + \cdots}{1 + \dfrac{l^2}{3!}\dfrac{p}{D} + \cdots},$$

since it involves integral powers of (p/D) is *single valued*. Furthermore, being the quotient of two convergent power series, it is analytic except at those values of p where the denominator vanishes, which occurs when $p = 0$ and $\sinh l\sqrt{p/D} = 0$, i.e., $l\sqrt{p/D} = in\pi$ or $p = - n^2\pi^2 D/l^2$, $n = 0, 1, 2, \cdots$. It appears as if $p = 0$ is a double pole. However, since

$$\lim_{p \to 0} \frac{\sinh (l - x)\sqrt{p/D}}{\sinh l\sqrt{p/D}} = \frac{l - x}{l} \neq 0,$$

$p = 0$ is a simple pole and the function (7.3.9) has only the simple poles $p = - n^2\pi^2 D/l^2$, $n = 0, 1, 2, \cdots$.

Similarly, the function

$$(7.3.10) \qquad \frac{\sinh x\sqrt{p/D}}{p \sinh l\sqrt{p/D}}$$

has the simple poles $p = - n^2\pi^2 D/l^2$, $n = 0, 1, 2, \cdots$.

To obtain the inverses of functions (7.3.9) and (7.3.10) we shall make use of the inversion integral, evaluating it by taking the radius of the semicircle in such a way that it will not pass through any pole of these functions. This will be so if we take, for example, $R_n = (n + \frac{1}{2})^2\pi^2 D/l^2$, where $n = 0, 1, 2, \cdots$. Now as $n \to \infty$, $R_n \to \infty$ and the functions can be shown to satisfy the conditions of Lemma III. Hence the integral along the contour $A_nB_nC_nD_nE_n$ of Fig. 2.9.2 tends to zero and the inverse transform will be the sum of the residues of the integrand at its infinite number of poles.

The residue of $\dfrac{e^{pt}\sinh(l-x)\sqrt{p/D}}{p\sinh l\sqrt{p/D}}$ at $p=0$ is most readily obtained by multiplying it by p, expanding the numerator and denominator in power series as in (7.3.9), and passing to the limit as $p \to 0$. We thus obtain the value $(l-x)/l$.

The residue at the pole $p = -n^2\pi^2 D/l^2$, $n = 1, 2, 3, \cdots$ is

$$\frac{e^{-n^2\pi^2 Dt/l^2}\sinh n\pi i(l-x)/l}{\left[p\dfrac{d}{dp}\sinh l\sqrt{p/D}\right]_{p=-n^2\pi^2 D/l^2}} = (-1)^n\frac{2}{n\pi}e^{-n^2\pi^2 Dt/l^2}\sin\frac{n\pi(l-x)}{l}.$$

In the same manner, the residue of the function (7.3.10) multiplied by e^{pt} at $p = 0$ is x/l and at $p = -n^2\pi^2 D/l^2$, $n = 1, 2, 3, \cdots$ it is

$$\frac{e^{-n^2\pi^2 Dt/l^2}\sinh n\pi i x/l}{\left[p\dfrac{d}{dp}\sinh l\sqrt{p/D}\right]_{p=-n^2\pi^2 D/l^2}} = (-1)^n\frac{2}{n\pi}e^{-n^2\pi^2 Dt/l^2}\sin\frac{n\pi x}{l}.$$

Adding these residues, we find that

$$C(x,t) = C_0\left[1 + \frac{2}{\pi}\sum_{n=1}^{\infty}(-1)^n\frac{1}{n}e^{-(n\pi/l)^2 Dt}(1-\cos n\pi)\sin\frac{n\pi}{l}x\right],$$

or finally

$$C(x,t) = C_0\left[1 - \frac{4}{\pi}\sum_{n=0}^{\infty}\frac{1}{2n+1}e^{-[(2n+1)\pi/l]^2 Dt}\sin\frac{2n+1}{l}\pi x\right].$$

We shall now give a useful alternative solution of the preceding problem in terms of the complementary error function. We have

$$\frac{\sinh(l-x)\sqrt{p/D}}{p\sinh l\sqrt{p/D}} = \frac{[e^{(l-x)\sqrt{p/D}} - e^{-(l-x)\sqrt{p/D}}]}{p(1 - e^{-2l\sqrt{p/D}})}e^{-l\sqrt{p/D}}$$

$$= \frac{[e^{(l-x)\sqrt{p/D}} - e^{-(l-x)\sqrt{p/D}}]}{p}\sum_{n=0}^{\infty}e^{-(2n+1)l\sqrt{p/D}}$$

$$= \frac{1}{p}\sum_{n=0}^{\infty}\left\{e^{-[2nl+x]\sqrt{p/D}} - e^{-[2(n+1)l-x]\sqrt{p/D}}\right\}.$$

Similarly,

$$\frac{\sinh x\sqrt{p/D}}{p\sinh l\sqrt{p/D}} = \frac{e^{-(l-x)\sqrt{p/D}} - e^{-(l+x)\sqrt{p/D}}}{p(1 - e^{-2l\sqrt{p/D}})}$$

$$= \frac{e^{-(l-x)\sqrt{p/D}} - e^{-(l+x)\sqrt{p/D}}}{p}\sum_{n=0}^{\infty}e^{-2nl\sqrt{p/D}}$$

$$= \frac{1}{p}\sum_{n=0}^{\infty}\left\{e^{-[(2n+1)l-x]\sqrt{p/D}} - e^{-[(2n+1)l+x]\sqrt{p/D}}\right\}.$$

Therefore, upon taking the inverse of both sides of (7.3.8) we obtain

$$C(x,t) = C_0 \sum_{n=0}^{\infty} \left\{ \operatorname{erfc}\left(\frac{2nl + x}{2\sqrt{Dt}}\right) - \operatorname{erfc}\left(\frac{2(n + 1)l - x}{2\sqrt{Dt}}\right) \right\}$$
$$+ C_0 \sum_{n=0}^{\infty} \left\{ \operatorname{erfc}\left(\frac{(2n + 1)l - x}{2\sqrt{Dt}}\right) - \operatorname{erfc}\left(\frac{(2n + 1)l + x}{2\sqrt{Dt}}\right) \right\}.$$

Exercise. In a certain problem of *diffusion out of a slab* the following boundary value problem must be solved:

$$\begin{aligned} C_t(x,t) &= DC_{xx}(x,t) & (0 < x < l, t > 0), \\ C(x,0) &= C_0 & (0 < x < l), \\ C(0,t) = 0, \quad C(l,t) &= 0 & (t > 0). \end{aligned}$$

Show that the concentration is given by the expression

$$C(x,t) = \frac{4C_0}{\pi} \sum_{n=0}^{\infty} \frac{1}{2n + 1} e^{-[(2n+1)\pi/l]^2 Dt} \sin \frac{2n + 1}{l} \pi x.$$

7.4 Diffusion from One Layer into Another

Two solutions having the same coefficient of diffusion D and in the forms of layers of thickness l each are in contact with each other (Fig. 7.4.1). If the initial concentration of one is C_0 and the other C_1, it is required to determine the concentration $C(x,t)$ for $t > 0$, if the concentrations at the faces $x = -l$ and $x = l$ are maintained at zero.

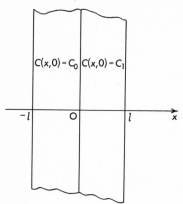

In this problem we seek a function $C(x,t)$ satisfying the equation

(7.4.1)
$$C_t(x,t) = DC_{xx}(x,t)$$
$$(-l < x < 0, 0 < x < l, t > 0)$$

and the boundary and initial conditions

(7.4.2) $\quad C(-l,t) = 0, \qquad C(l,t) = 0$
$$(t > 0),$$

Fig. 7.4.1

(7.4.3) $\quad C(0 -,t) = C(0 +,t), \qquad C_x(0 -,t) = C_x(0 +,t) \qquad (t > 0),$

(7.4.4) $\quad C(x,0) = C_0 \quad (-l < x < 0), \qquad C(x,0) = C_1$
$$(0 < x < l).$$

The first and second of the conditions (7.4.3) say that the concentration and flux of transport at the interface are the same as one approaches the interface from either direction, i.e., they are the continuity conditions across $x = 0$.

The transformed problem therefore becomes

$$(7.4.5) \qquad pc(x,p) - C_0 = Dc_{xx}(x,p) \qquad (-l < x < 0),$$

$$(7.4.6) \qquad pc(x,p) - C_1 = Dc_{xx}(x,p) \qquad (0 < x < l),$$

$$(7.4.7) \qquad c(-l,p) = 0, \qquad c(l,p) = 0,$$

$$(7.4.8) \qquad c(0-,p) = c(0+,p), \qquad c_x(0-,p) = c_x(0+,p).$$

Solving equation (7.4.5) and making use of the first of the conditions (7.4.7) yields the following two equations:

$$(7.4.9) \qquad c(x,p) = c_1 \cosh x\sqrt{p/D} + c_2 \sinh x\sqrt{p/D} + C_0/p$$
$$(-l < x < 0),$$

$$(7.4.10) \qquad 0 = c_1 \cosh l\sqrt{p/D} - c_2 \sinh l\sqrt{p/D} + C_0/p.$$

Similarly, solving equation (7.4.6) and making use of the second of the conditions (7.4.7) yields:

$$(7.4.11) \qquad c(x,p) = c_1' \cosh x\sqrt{p/D} + c_2' \sinh x\sqrt{p/D} + U_1/p$$
$$(0 < x < l),$$

$$(7.4.12) \qquad 0 = c_1' \cosh l\sqrt{p/D} + c_2' \sinh l\sqrt{p/D} + U_1/p.$$

Conditions (7.4.8) give

$$(7.4.13) \qquad c_1 + U_0/p = c_1' + U_1/p, \quad c_2 = c_2'.$$

Equations (7.4.10), (7.4.12), and (7.4.13) constitute a system of linear equations which when solved for the c's give

$$c_1 = \frac{C_1 - C_0}{2p} - \frac{C_1 + C_0}{2p \cosh l\sqrt{p/D}},$$

$$c_2 = c_2' = \frac{C_0 - C_1}{2p \sinh l\sqrt{p/D}} - \frac{(C_0 - C_1) \cosh l\sqrt{p/D}}{2p \sinh l\sqrt{p/D}},$$

$$c_1' = \frac{C_0 - C_1}{2p} - \frac{C_0 + C_1}{2p \cosh l\sqrt{p/D}}.$$

Substituting these values in (7.4.9) and (7.4.10) and simplifying finally yields

$$(7.4.14) \qquad c(x,p) = \frac{C_0}{p} - \frac{C_0 - C_1}{2p} \frac{\sinh (l+x)\sqrt{p/D}}{\sinh l\sqrt{p/D}}$$

$$- \frac{(C_0 + C_1) \cosh x\sqrt{p/D}}{2p \cosh l\sqrt{p/D}} + \frac{(C_0 - C_1) \sinh x\sqrt{p/D}}{2p \sinh l\sqrt{p/D}},$$
$$(-l < x < 0),$$

$$(7.4.15) \qquad c(x,p) = \frac{C_1}{p} + \frac{C_0 - C_1}{2p} \frac{\sinh (l-x)\sqrt{p/D}}{\sinh l\sqrt{p/D}}$$

$$- \frac{(C_0 + C_1) \cosh x\sqrt{p/D}}{2p \cosh l\sqrt{p/D}} + \frac{(C_0 - C_1) \sinh x\sqrt{p/D}}{2p \sinh l\sqrt{p/D}}$$
$$(0 < x < l).$$

The sum of the residues of $\dfrac{e^{pt} \sinh (l + x)\sqrt{p/D}}{2p \sinh l\sqrt{p/D}}$ at the poles $p = 0$

and $p = -n^2\pi^2 D/l^2, n = 1, 2, \cdots$, is

$$\frac{l + x}{l} + \sum_{n=1}^{\infty} (-1)^n \frac{2}{n\pi} e^{-n^2\pi^2 Dt/l^2} \sin \frac{n\pi(l + x)}{l},$$

that of $\dfrac{e^{pt} \cosh x\sqrt{p/D}}{p \cosh l\sqrt{p/D}}$ at the poles $p = 0$ and $p = -(n + \tfrac{1}{2})^2\pi^2 D/l^2$,

$n = 0, 1, 2, \cdots$, is

$$1 + \sum_{n=0}^{\infty} (-1)^{n+1} \frac{4}{(2n + 1)\pi} e^{-(n+\frac{1}{2})^2\pi^2 Dt/l^2} \cos x(n + \tfrac{1}{2})\pi/l,$$

and that of $\dfrac{e^{pt} \sinh x\sqrt{p/D}}{p \sinh l\sqrt{p/D}}$ at the poles $p = 0$, $p = -n^2\pi^2 D/l^2$,

$n = 1, 2, \cdots$, is

$$\frac{x}{l} + \sum_{n=1}^{\infty} (-1)^n \frac{2}{n\pi} e^{-n^2\pi^2 Dt/l^2} \sin \frac{n\pi x}{l}.$$

Taking the inverse transform of both sides of (7.4.14) and making use of the preceding results, we obtain after some simplifications

$$C(x,t) = \frac{2(C_0 - C_1)}{\pi} \sum_{n=1}^{\infty} (-1)^n \frac{e^{-n^2\pi^2 Dt/l^2}}{n} \sin \frac{n\pi}{2} \cos \frac{n\pi}{2l}(l + 2x)$$

$$- \frac{2(C_0 + C_1)}{\pi} \sum_{n=0}^{\infty} (-1)^{n+1} \frac{e^{-(n+\frac{1}{2})^2\pi^2 Dt/l^2}}{2n + 1} \cos \{x(n + \tfrac{1}{2})\pi/l\}$$

$$(-l < x < 0).$$

In the same manner we obtain

$$C(x,t) = \frac{2(C_0 - C_1)}{\pi} \sum_{n=1}^{\infty} (-1)^n e^{-n^2\pi^2 Dt/l^2} \sin \frac{n\pi}{2} \cos \frac{n\pi}{2l}(l - 2x)$$

$$- \frac{2(C_0 + C_1)}{\pi} \sum_{n=0}^{\infty} (-1)^{n+1} \frac{e^{-(n+\frac{1}{2})^2\pi^2 Dt/l^2}}{2n + 1} \cos \{x(n + \tfrac{1}{2})\pi/l\}$$

$$(0 < x < l).$$

Exercise. Solve the preceding problem in terms of the complementary error function.

7.5 Flow of Electricity in a Transmission Line

The study of the electrical behavior of linear conductors such as telephone wires, submarine cables, and transmission lines constitutes one of the most important problems arising in electrical engineering. We shall consider a *two-wire* transmission line which is *imperfectly* insulated and derive the pair of differential equations that must be satisfied by the current and voltage.   These equations will be *partial* rather than *ordinary* because the linear dimensions of the transmission line, unlike those of the electrical circuits considered heretofore, are so large that the variations of the voltage and current along the line can no longer be neglected.   Therefore, if x measures the distance along the wire from the source of voltage (e.g., a generator), then the voltage and current will be functions of x and t, say $V(x,t)$ and $I(x,t)$, respectively.

The quantities entering in the derivation of these equations are: the *resistance* R, the *inductance* L, the *capacitance* C between the two wires, and the *conductance* (leakage) G between the two wires, all per unit of length of the two-wire line.   Although these quantities, strictly speaking, are *not* constants, in many applications they can be considered as such and the results obtained on the basis of this assumption are good approximations.   In what follows we shall suppose that R, L, C, and G are constants.

Let us consider an element AB of the transmission line of length Δx (Fig. 7.5.1).   The change in potential along this element will be

$$\Delta V(x,t) = - (R\Delta x)I(x,t) - (L\Delta x)I_t(x,t),$$

where the first and second terms on the right are the voltage drops due

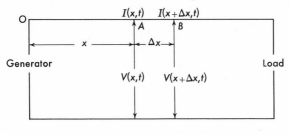

Fig. 7.5.1

to the resistance and inductance, respectively.   Similarly, the change in the current along Δx is

$$\Delta I(x,t) = - (G\Delta x)V(x,t) - (C\Delta x)V_t(x,t),$$

where the first term on the right is the current that leaks through the insulation due to the imperfections in the insulation of the line, and the second term is the current charging the capacitor formed by the adjacent wires.

Dividing each of the two preceding equations by Δx and passing to the limit as $\Delta x \to 0$, we obtain

(7.5.1) $$V_x(x,t) = - RI(x,t) - LI_t(x,t),$$

(7.5.2) $$I_x(x,t) = - GV(x,t) - CV_t(x,t).$$

These equations constitute a system of simultaneous linear partial differential equations for the voltage and current. By eliminating the current I between (7.5.1) and (7.5.2) we can get an equation involving only the voltage V. This is accomplished as follows. Differentiating equations (7.5.1) and (7.5.2) with respect to x and t, respectively, we find that

$$(7.5.3) \qquad V_{xx}(x,t) = -RI_x(x,t) - LI_{xt}(x,t),$$
$$(7.5.4) \qquad I_{tx}(x,t) = -GV_t(x,t) - CV_{tt}(x,t).$$

Substituting the right side of (7.5.2) for $I_x(x,t)$ in (7.5.3), eliminating the mixed partial derivatives between (7.5.3) and (7.5.4) (assuming that the order of differentiation is immaterial), and rearranging terms gives

$$(7.5.5) \quad V_{xx}(x,t) - LCV_{tt}(x,t) - (RC + LG)V_t(x,t) - RGV(x,t) = 0.$$

In a similar manner we obtain

$$(7.5.6) \quad I_{xx}(x,t) - LCI_{tt}(x,t) - (RC + LG)I_t(x,t) - RGI(x,t) = 0.$$

Both of these equations are homogeneous linear partial differential equations. Because they arise in problems in telephony they are known as the *telephone equations*.

In practice it is found that some of the so-called transmission line constants R, L, C, and G can be neglected, thus reducing the original equations to simpler ones. In this chapter we shall consider a few of these important special cases, leaving a discussion of the general equation to a subsequent chapter.

(a) $G = L = 0$. This case arises, e.g., in telegraph transmission where the leakage G and the inductance L are so small that they can be neglected. Upon substituting these values in (7.5.1), (7.5.2), (7.5.5), and (7.5.6), we get

$$(7.5.7) \qquad\qquad V_x(x,t) = -RI(x,t),$$
$$(7.5.8) \qquad\qquad I_x(x,t) = -CV_t(x,t),$$
$$(7.5.9) \qquad\qquad V_{xx}(x,t) = RCV_t(x,t),$$
$$(7.5.10) \qquad\qquad I_{xx}(x,t) = RCI_t(x,t).$$

These equations are known as the *telegraph equations*. It should be observed that equations (7.5.9) and (7.5.10) are of the same form as the diffusion equation with $D = 1/RC$. Thus the problem of propagation of current, in this case, is the same as that of the transport of a dissolved substance in one direction. Information about one yields information about the other.

Example 1. The potential of a semi-infinite line is initially V_1. At $t = 0$ a constant potential V_0 is impressed at one end. Find $V(x,t)$ for $t > 0$.

The equation to be solved is

$$V_t(x,t) = \frac{1}{RC} V_{xx}(x,t),$$

and the boundary conditions are

$$V(x,0) = V_1, \qquad V(0,t) = V_0, \quad \text{and} \quad \lim_{x \to \infty} V(x,t) = V_1.$$

But this problem is the same as Example 1, section 7.1, where $D = 1/RC$ in this case. Therefore the solution is

$$V(x,t) = V_1 + (V_0 - V_1) \operatorname{erfc}\left(\frac{x}{2}\sqrt{\frac{RC}{t}}\right).$$

Example 2. The initial potential of a line of length l is V_0, and the ends $x = 0$, $x = l$ are kept at zero potential. Find $V(x,t)$ and $I(x,t)$ for $t > 0$.

The equation is the same as in the preceding example and the boundary conditions are:

$$V(x,0) = V_0, \quad (0 < x < l); \qquad V(0,t) = 0, \qquad V(l,t) = 0, \quad (t > 0).$$

This problem, however, is the same as the one-dimensional diffusion problem given as an exercise at the end of section 7.3. Hence in the present case we have

$$V(x,t) = \frac{4V_0}{\pi} \sum_{n=0}^{\infty} \frac{1}{2n+1} e^{-[(2n+1)\pi/l]^2 t/RC} \sin \frac{2n+1}{l} \pi x.$$

Making use of differential equation (7.5.7), we obtain

$$I(x,t) = -\frac{1}{R} V_x(x,t) = -\frac{4V_0}{Rl} \sum_{n=0}^{\infty} e^{-[(2n+1)\pi/l]^2 t/RC} \cos \frac{2n+1}{l} \pi x.$$

Example 3. A transmission line of length l is grounded at $x = l$, and the initial potential is zero. At $t = 0$ an alternating voltage $b \sin \omega t$ is applied at the end $x = 0$. Obtain $V(x,t)$ for $t > 0$.

The potential $V(x,t)$ satisfies the following conditions

$$\begin{aligned}
V_{xx}(x,t) &= RC V_t(x,t) && (0 < x < l, t > 0), \\
V(x,0) &= 0 && (0 < x < l), \\
V(0,t) = b \sin \omega t, \qquad V(l,t) &= 0 && (t > 0).
\end{aligned}$$

Therefore, upon taking transforms of the preceding equations with respect to t, we get

(7.5.11)
$$\frac{d^2 v(x,p)}{dx^2} - RCp v(x,p) = 0,$$

(7.5.12)
$$v(0,p) = \frac{b\omega}{p^2 + \omega^2}, \quad v(l,p) = 0,$$

where $L_t\{V(x,t)\} = v(x,p)$.

The general solution of (7.5.11) is

$$(7.5.13) \qquad v(x,p) = c_1 \cosh x\sqrt{RCp} + c_2 \sinh x\sqrt{RCp}.$$

Applying conditions (7.5.12) to this equation yields

$$c_1 = b\omega/(p^2 + \omega^2), \qquad c_1 \cosh l\sqrt{RCp} + c_2 \sinh l\sqrt{RCp} = 0,$$

from which

$$c_2 = -\frac{b\omega \cosh l\sqrt{RCp}.}{(p^2 + \omega^2)\sinh l\sqrt{RCp}}$$

Substituting the values of c_1 and c_2 in (7.5.13) and simplifying gives

$$(7.5.14) \qquad v(x,p) = \frac{b\omega \sinh (l - x)\sqrt{RCp}}{(p^2 + \omega^2)\sinh l\sqrt{RCp}}.$$

The poles of this single-valued function occur at $p = \pm i\omega$ and $p = - (n^2\pi^2/l^2RC)$, $n = 1, 2, \cdots$. As before, taking the contour of Fig. 2.9.2 with radius $R_n = (n + \frac{1}{2})^2\pi^2/l^2RC$ and letting $n \to \infty$,

$$V(x,t) = \sum \text{Res} \frac{b\omega e^{pt} \sinh (l - x)\sqrt{RCp}}{(p^2 + \omega^2)\sinh l\sqrt{RCp}}.$$

At the pole $p = i\omega$ the residue is

$$(7.5.15) \qquad b\omega e^{i\omega t} \frac{\sinh (l - x)\sqrt{RC\omega i}}{2\omega i \sinh l\sqrt{RC\omega i}},$$

and at $p = - i\omega$ it is

$$(7.5.16) \qquad - b\omega e^{-i\omega t} \frac{\sinh (l - x)\sqrt{- RC\omega i}}{2\omega i \sinh l\sqrt{- RC\omega i}}.$$

Now, $\sqrt{i} = (e^{(\pi/2)i})^{\frac{1}{2}} = \cos \dfrac{\pi}{4} + i \sin \dfrac{\pi}{4} = \dfrac{1 + i}{\sqrt{2}}$ and $\sqrt{- i}$

$= (e^{-(\pi/2)i})^{\frac{1}{2}} = \dfrac{1 - i}{\sqrt{2}}$. Hence the sum of (7.5.15) and (7.5.16) gives

$$b e^{i\omega t} \frac{\sinh (l - x)(1 + i)\sqrt{RC\omega/2}}{2i \sinh l(1 + i)\sqrt{RC\omega/2}} - b e^{-i\omega t} \frac{\sinh (l - x)(1 - i)\sqrt{RC\omega/2}}{2i \sinh l(1 - i)\sqrt{RC\omega/2}}.$$

The residue at the pole $p = - (n^2\pi^2/l^2RC)$ is

$$b\omega e^{-n^2\pi^2 t/l^2 RC} \frac{\sinh (l - x)n\pi i/l}{\left[(p^2 + \omega^2)\dfrac{d}{dp} \sinh l\sqrt{RCp}\right]_{p = -(n^2\pi^2/l^2RC)}}$$

$$= (- 1)^{n+1} b\omega e^{-n^2\pi^2 t/l^2 RC} \frac{2 \sin (l - x)n\pi/l}{\dfrac{l^2}{n\pi}\left(\dfrac{n^4\pi^4}{l^4 R^2 C^2} + \omega^2\right)RC}.$$

Therefore

$$V(x,t) = be^{i\omega t}\frac{\sinh(l-x)(1+i)\sqrt{RC\omega/2}}{2i\sinh l(1+i)\sqrt{RC\omega/2}}$$

$$- be^{-i\omega t}\frac{\sinh (l-x)(1-i)\sqrt{RC\omega/2}}{2i\sinh l(1-i)\sqrt{RC\omega/2}}$$

$$+ 2\omega b\sum_{n=1}^{\infty}(-1)^{n+1}e^{-n^2\pi^2 t/(l^2 RC)}\frac{\sin (l-x)n\pi/l}{\dfrac{RCl^2}{n\pi}\left(\dfrac{n^4\pi^4}{R^2C^2l^4}+\omega^2\right)}.$$

By combining the first two terms and eliminating the imaginary unit i it can be shown that

$$V(x,t) = b\frac{(\alpha\gamma+\beta\delta)\sin\omega t + (\alpha\delta-\beta\gamma)\cos\omega t}{\alpha^2+\beta^2}$$

$$+ 2\omega b\sum_{n=1}^{\infty}(-1)^{n+1}e^{-(n\pi/l)^2 t/RC}\frac{\sin n\pi(l-x)/l}{\dfrac{RCl^2}{n\pi}\left(\dfrac{n^4\pi^4}{R^2C^2l^4}+\omega^2\right)},$$

where
$$\alpha = \sinh l\sqrt{RC\omega/2}\cos l\sqrt{RC\omega/2},$$
$$\beta = \cosh l\sqrt{RC\omega/2}\sin l\sqrt{RC\omega/2},$$
$$\gamma = \sinh (l-x)\sqrt{RC\omega/2}\cos (l-x)\sqrt{RC\omega/2},$$
$$\delta = \cosh (l-x)\sqrt{RC\omega/2}\sin (l-x)\sqrt{RC\omega/2}.$$

Exercise. Find the potential $V(x,t)$ for $t>0$ if the end $x=0$ of the transmission line of the preceding example is subjected to the pulse
$$V(0,t) = V_0 t[1(t) - 1(t-t_0)].$$

Ans.
$$V(x,t) = \frac{V_0(l-x)}{l}[t + x(x-2l)RC/6]$$

$$+ \frac{2l^2RC}{\pi^3}V_0\sum_{n=1}^{\infty}(-1)^{n+1}\frac{e^{-(n\pi/l)^2 t/RC}}{n^3}\sin\frac{n\pi(l-x)}{l}$$

$$- V_0\left\{\frac{l-x}{l}[t + x(x-2l)RC/6]\right.$$

$$+ \frac{2l^2RC}{\pi^3}\sum_{n=1}^{\infty}(-1)^{n+1}\frac{1}{n^3}e^{-(n\pi/l)^2(t-t_0)/RC}\sin\frac{n\pi(l-x)}{l}\Big\}1(t-t_0)$$

$$- \frac{2V_0 t_0}{\pi}\left\{\sum_{n=1}^{\infty}(-1)^n\frac{1}{n}e^{-(n\pi/l)^2(t-t_0)/RC}\sin\frac{n\pi x}{l}\right\}1(t-t_0).$$

(b) $L=0$. The equations corresponding to this case are

(7.5.17) $V_x(x,t) = -RI(x,t),$

(7.5.18) $I_x(x,t) = -GV(x,t) - CV_t(x,t),$

(7.5.19) $V_{xx}(x,t) - RCV_t(x,t) - RGV(x,t) = 0,$

(7.5.20) $I_{xx}(x,t) - RCI_t(x,t) - RGI(x,t) = 0.$

Example.   A semi-infinite line is initially at potential V_0.   At $t = 0$ the end $x = 0$ is grounded and the distant end is insulated.   Find $V(x,t)$ for $t > 0$.

The boundary conditions for this problem are

$$(7.5.21) \qquad\qquad V(x,0) = V_0 \qquad\qquad (x > 0),$$

$$(7.5.22) \qquad V(0,t) = 0, \qquad \lim_{x \to \infty} V_x(x,t) = 0 \qquad (t > 0),$$

where the second one of the conditions (7.5.22) is obtained from (7.5.17) because the insulated end implies that the current there is zero.

For the transformed problem we have

$$(7.5.23) \qquad v_{xx}(x,p) - R(Cp + G)v(x,p) = - RCV_0,$$

$$(7.5.24) \qquad v(0,p) = 0, \qquad \lim_{x \to \infty} v_x(x,p) = 0.$$

The solution of the differential equation (6.5.23) is

$$(7.5.25) \qquad v(x,p) = c_1 e^{x\sqrt{R(Cp+G)}} + c_2 e^{-x\sqrt{R(Cp+G)}} + \frac{CV_0}{Cp + G}.$$

The second one of the conditions (7.5.24) implies that $c_1 = 0$ and the first that $c_2 = - \dfrac{CV_0}{Cp + G}$.   Therefore (7.5.25) becomes

$$(7.5.26) \qquad v(x,p) = \frac{V_0}{p + G/C}(1 - e^{-x\sqrt{RC}\sqrt{p+G/C}}).$$

Now

$$L^{-1}\left\{\frac{e^{-x\sqrt{RCp}}}{p}\right\} = \mathrm{erfc}\left(\frac{x}{2}\sqrt{\frac{RC}{t}}\right),$$

and consequently by Translation Theorem II

$$L^{-1}\left\{\frac{e^{-x\sqrt{RC}\sqrt{p+G/C}}}{p + G/C}\right\} = e^{-(G/C)t}\,\mathrm{erfc}\left(\frac{x}{2}\sqrt{\frac{RC}{t}}\right).$$

Since $L^{-1}\left\{\dfrac{1}{p + G/C}\right\} = e^{-(G/C)t}$, upon taking the inverse transform of both sides of (7.5.26), we obtain

$$V(x,t) = V_0 e^{-(G/C)t}\left[1 - \mathrm{erfc}\left(\frac{x}{2}\sqrt{\frac{RC}{t}}\right)\right].$$

Exercise.   Solve the following boundary value problem

$$V_{xx}(x,t) - RCV_t(x,t) - RGV(x,t) = 0 \quad (x > 0, t > 0),$$

$$V(x,0) = V_0 \qquad\qquad (x > 0),$$

$$V(0,t) = V_1[1(t) - 1(t - t_0)], \qquad \lim_{x \to \infty} V_x(x,t) = 0 \quad (t > 0).$$

$$\left[\textit{Hint:} \text{ Make use of the identity } \frac{1}{p} \equiv \frac{1}{p + G/C} + \frac{G/C}{p(p + G/C)}\right].$$

$$\textit{Ans.} \quad V(x,t) = V_0 e^{-(G/C)t}\left[1 - \text{erfc}\left(\frac{x}{2}\sqrt{\frac{RC}{t}}\right)\right]$$

$$+ V_1 e^{-(G/C)t} \text{erfc}\left(\frac{x}{2}\sqrt{\frac{RC}{t}}\right) + \frac{V_1 G}{C}\int_0^t e^{-(G/C)\tau} \text{erfc}\left(\frac{x}{2}\sqrt{\frac{RC}{\tau}}\right) d\tau$$

$$- V_1 e^{-(G/C)(t-t_0)} \text{erfc}\left(\frac{x}{2}\sqrt{\frac{RC}{t - t_0}}\right) 1(t - t_0)$$

$$- \frac{V_1 G}{C}\int_0^t e^{-(G/C)(\tau-t_0)} \text{erfc}\left(\frac{x}{2}\sqrt{\frac{RC}{\tau - t_0}}\right) 1(\tau - t_0)\, d\tau.$$

(c) $G = R = 0$. This is the case of the so-called *dissipationless* line. The differential equations satisfied by the potential and current are:

(7.5.27) $$V_x(x,t) = - LI_t(x,t),$$

(7.5.28) $$I_x(x,t) = - CV_t(x,t),$$

(7.5.29) $$V_{xx}(x,t) = LCV_{tt}(x,t),$$

(7.5.30) $$I_{xx}(x,t) = LCI_{tt}(x,t).$$

Since the one-dimensional wave equation is of the form $\dfrac{\partial^2 \Phi}{\partial x^2} = \dfrac{1}{c^2}\dfrac{\partial^2 \Phi}{\partial t^2}$, where c is the velocity of the wave, it follows that equations (7.5.29) and (7.5.30) are of this type with $c = 1/\sqrt{LC}$. Hence we shall be able to give the distribution of current and potential along the line a vivid physical interpretation in terms of traveling waves.

Example I. Initially, a semi-infinite line is dead, i.e., $V(x,0) = V_t(x,0) = I(x,0) = I_t(x,0) = 0$. At $t = 0$ a variable potential $F(t)$ is impressed at $x = 0$. If the circuit at the distant end is open (implying no current there), find $V(x,t)$ for $t > 0$.

In this problem $V(x,t)$ satisfies the differential equation

(7.5.31) $$V_{xx}(x,t) = LCV_{tt}(x,t) \qquad (x > 0, t > 0),$$

and the conditions

(7.5.32) $\quad V(x,0) = V_t(x,0) = 0, \qquad I(x,0) = I_t(x,0) = 0 \qquad (x > 0),$

(7.5.33) $$V(0,t) = F(t), \qquad \lim_{x\to\infty} I(x,t) = 0 \qquad (t > 0).$$

If we let $L_t\{F(t)\} = f(p)$, $L_t\{V(x,t)\} = v(x,p)$ and $L_t\{I(x,t)\} = i(x,p)$, then the problem in the transform is

(7.5.34) $$v_{xx}(x,p) - LCp^2 v(x,p) = 0,$$

(7.5.35) $v(0,p) = f(p),$

(7.5.36) $\lim_{x \to \infty} i(x,p) = 0.$

Condition (7.5.36) must be transformed into one containing $v(x,p)$ if equation (7.5.34) is to be solved. This is done by making use of equation (7.5.27), whose Laplace transform with respect to t is

(7.5.37) $v_x(x,p) = - Lpi(x,p),$

since $I(x,0) = 0$. Therefore, condition (7.5.36) is equivalent to

(7.5.38) $\lim_{x \to \infty} v_x(x,p) = 0.$

The solution of equation (7.5.34) is

$$v(x,p) = c_1 e^{px\sqrt{LC}} + c_2 e^{-px\sqrt{LC}}.$$

Condition (7.5.38) implies that $c_1 = 0$ and condition (7.5.35) that $c_1 = f(p)$. Thus

(7.5.39) $v(x,p) = e^{-px\sqrt{LC}} f(p),$

and hence

(7.5.40) $V(x,t) = L^{-1}\{e^{-px\sqrt{LC}} f(p)\} = F(t - x\sqrt{LC})1(t - x\sqrt{LC}).$

Let us consider several special cases.

(i) $F(t) = 1$. Equation (7.5.40) becomes

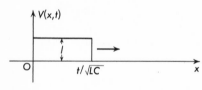

$$V(x,t) = 1(t - x\sqrt{LC}),$$

which represents a wave of amplitude one moving to the right with velocity $1/\sqrt{LC}$ (Fig. 7.5.2).

(ii) $F(t) = t$. In this case we have

$$V(x,t) = (t - x\sqrt{LC})1(t - x\sqrt{LC}),$$

Fig. 7.5.2

whose graph is shown in Fig. 7.5.3.

(iii) $F(t) = \sin \omega t$. Here

$$V(x,t) = \sin \omega (t - x\sqrt{LC})1(t - x\sqrt{LC}),$$

whose graph is shown in Fig. 7.5.4.

To obtain the current $I(x,t)$, we have from (7.5.37) and (7.5.39)

$$i(x,p) = - \frac{1}{Lp}v_x(x,p) = \sqrt{\frac{C}{L}}e^{-px\sqrt{LC}} f(p),$$

the inverse of which is

$$I(x,t) = \sqrt{\frac{C}{L}}F(t - x\sqrt{LC})1(t - x\sqrt{LC}).$$

As in the expression for $V(x,t)$ this solution may be interpreted as a wave moving to the right with a velocity $v = 1/\sqrt{LC}$.

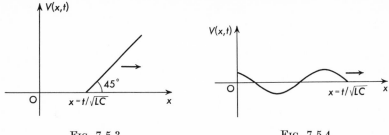

FIG. 7.5.3   FIG. 7.5.4

Example 2. Solve the problem of Example 1 if the line is of finite length l.

The potential is now the solution of the following boundary value problem

$$V_{xx}(x,t) = LCV_{tt}(x,t) \qquad (0 < x < l, t > 0),$$

$$V(x,0) = 0, \qquad V_t(x,0) = 0 \qquad (0 < x < l),$$

$$V(0,t) = F(t), \qquad I(l,t) = 0 \qquad (t > 0).$$

The problem in the transform $v(x,p)$ becomes

(7.5.41) $$v_{xx}(x,p) - LCp^2v(x,p) = 0,$$

(7.5.42) $$v(0,p) = f(p), \qquad i(l,p) = 0,$$

where $f(p) = L\{F(t)\}$ and $i(l,p) = L\{I(l,t)\}$. Solving equation (7.5.41), we obtain

(7.5.43) $$v(x,p) = c_1 \cosh px\sqrt{LC} + c_2 \sinh px\sqrt{LC}.$$

From (7.5.37) we see that the second condition in (7.5.42) is equivalent to the condition $v_x(l,p) = 0$. Using this and the first of the conditions (7.5.42) we obtain from (7.5.43)

$$0 = c_1 \sinh pl\sqrt{LC} + c_2 \cosh pl\sqrt{LC}, \quad f(p) = c_1,$$

from which $c_2 = -f(p) \sinh pl\sqrt{LC}/\cosh pl\sqrt{LC}$. Upon substituting these values in (7.5.43) and combining terms, we get

(7.5.44) $$v(x,p) = f(p) \frac{\cosh (l - x)p\sqrt{LC}}{\cosh pl\sqrt{LC}}.$$

Let us consider the case of the constant potential, i.e., $F(t) = V_0$. Then $f(p) = V_0/p$ and (7.5.44) becomes

(7.5.45) $$v(x,p) = V_0 \frac{\cosh (l - x)p\sqrt{LC}}{p \cosh pl\sqrt{LC}}.$$

The poles of this single-valued function occur at $p = 0$ and $p = \pm (n + \frac{1}{2})\pi i / l\sqrt{LC}$, $n = 0, 1, 2, \cdots$. Hence

$$V(x,t) = V_0 \sum \text{Res} \, \frac{e^{pt} \cosh (l - x)p\sqrt{LC}}{p \cosh pl\sqrt{LC}}$$

at the poles mentioned above

At $p = 0$ the residue is 1, and at $p = \pm (n + \frac{1}{2})\pi i / l\sqrt{LC}$ it is

$$\frac{e^{\pm[(2n+1)/(2l\sqrt{LC})]\pi it} \cosh \left\{ \left(\dfrac{l - x}{l} \right)(n + \frac{1}{2})\pi i \right\}}{\left[p\dfrac{d}{dp} (\cosh pl\sqrt{LC}) \right]_{p=\pm(n+\frac{1}{2})\pi i/l\sqrt{LC}}}$$

$$= \frac{e^{\pm[(2n+1)/(2l\sqrt{LC})]\pi it} \cos \left(\dfrac{l - x}{l} \right)(n + \frac{1}{2})\pi}{\pm \dfrac{(2n + 1)\pi i}{2} \sinh \{ \pm (n + \frac{1}{2})\pi i \}}$$

$$= - \frac{e^{\pm[(2n+1)/(2l\sqrt{LC})]\pi it} \cos \left(\dfrac{l - x}{l} \right)(n + \frac{1}{2})\pi}{\dfrac{2n + 1}{2}\pi \sin (n + \frac{1}{2})\pi}$$

$$= (-1)^{n+1} \frac{e^{\pm[(2n+1)/(2l\sqrt{LC})]\pi it} \cos \left(\dfrac{l - x}{l} \right)(n + \frac{1}{2})\pi}{\dfrac{2n + 1}{2}\pi}$$

$$= (-1)^{n+1} \frac{\left[\cos \dfrac{(2n + 1)\pi}{2l\sqrt{LC}}t \pm i \sin \dfrac{(2n + 1)\pi}{2l\sqrt{LC}}t \right] \cos \left(\dfrac{l - x}{l} \right)(n + \frac{1}{2})\pi}{(2n + 1)\pi/2}.$$

Corresponding to each value of $n = 0, 1, 2, \cdots$, this last expression gives the residues at each of the two poles on the imaginary axis symmetrically situated with respect to the real axis. Therefore when it is summed from $n = 0$ to ∞, the cosine term in the bracket will be doubled and the sine terms will cancel. Consequently

$$V(x,t) = V_0 \left\{ 1 + \frac{4}{\pi} \sum_{n=0}^{\infty} \frac{(-1)^{n+1}}{2n + 1} \cos \frac{(2n + 1)\pi}{2l\sqrt{LC}}t \cos \frac{(l - x)(2n + 1)}{2l}\pi \right\}.$$

This is the solution of the problem in terms of a trigonometric series. Let us now represent the solution as a potential wave traveling with a velocity $1/\sqrt{LC}$.

Returning to equation (7.5.45), we have

$$(7.5.46) \qquad v(x,p) = V_0 \frac{\cosh(l-x)p\sqrt{LC}}{p \cosh pl\sqrt{LC}} = \frac{V_0}{p} \frac{e^{(l-x)p\sqrt{LC}} + e^{-(l-x)p\sqrt{LC}}}{e^{pl\sqrt{LC}} + e^{-pl\sqrt{LC}}}$$

$$= \frac{V_0 e^{-xp\sqrt{LC}}}{p} \cdot \frac{1 + e^{-2(l-x)p\sqrt{LC}}}{1 + e^{-2lp\sqrt{LC}}}.$$

Since

$$1/(1 + e^{-2lp\sqrt{LC}}) = 1 - e^{-2lp\sqrt{LC}} + e^{-4lp\sqrt{LC}} - e^{-8lp\sqrt{LC}} + \cdots$$

we may write (7.5.46) as follows

$$v(x,p) = \frac{V_0}{p}[e^{-xp\sqrt{LC}} - e^{-(x+2l)p\sqrt{LC}} + e^{-(x+4l)p\sqrt{LC}} \cdots$$

$$+ e^{-(2l-x)p\sqrt{LC}} - e^{-(4l-x)p\sqrt{LC}} + \cdots].$$

The inverse of the preceding expression yields

$$(7.5.47) \quad V(x,t) = V_0\{ 1(t - x\sqrt{LC}) + 1[t - (2l - x)\sqrt{LC}]$$
$$- 1[t - (x + 2l)\sqrt{LC}] - 1[t - (4l - x)\sqrt{LC}]$$
$$+ 1[t - (x + 4l)\sqrt{LC} + \cdots\}, \quad (0 < x < l, t > 0).$$

Consider now the points in the interval $0 < x < l$ of our transmission line. Then $0 < x\sqrt{LC} < l\sqrt{LC}$ and for time t such that $0 < t < l\sqrt{LC}$ we see that the first unit function in (7.5.47) is the only one that can be different from zero. Hence, in this time interval we have a wave of amplitude V moving to the right as $t \to l\sqrt{LC}$ (Fig. 7.5.5).

For the interval $l\sqrt{LC} < (2l - x)\sqrt{LC} < 2l\sqrt{LC}$ and time t such that $l\sqrt{LC} < t < 2l\sqrt{LC}$, the first unit function is always one, the

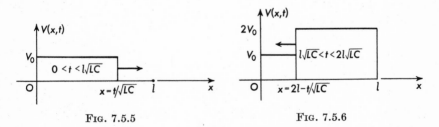

FIG. 7.5.5   FIG. 7.5.6

second can be different from zero, and all the other step functions are zero. Therefore, in this time interval we obtain a reflected wave of amplitude $2V_0$ moving to the left as $t \to 2l\sqrt{LC}$ (Fig. 7.5.6).

In the interval $2l\sqrt{LC} < (x + 2l)\sqrt{LC} < 3l\sqrt{LC}$ and time t such that $2l\sqrt{LC} < t < 3l\sqrt{LC}$, the first and second unit functions are always one, the third unit function can be different from zero, but the remaining unit functions are zero. However, this time the third unit

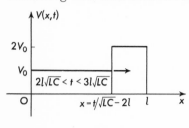

FIG. 7.5.7

function is prefixed by a minus sign. Hence we obtain a reflection at the left end with a change of sign, and the graph is that shown in Fig. 7.5.7.

For the interval $3l\sqrt{LC} < (4l - x)\sqrt{LC} < 4l\sqrt{LC}$ and time t such that $3l\sqrt{LC} < t < 4l\sqrt{LC}$, the first, second, and third unit functions

are always one, the fourth remaining functions are zero. also prefixed by a minus sign.

can be different from zero, and the In this case the fourth unit function is Thus a reflection with a change of sign

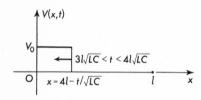

FIG. 7.5.8

occurs at the right end, and we obtain Fig. 7.5.8.

After this the pattern repeats itself. Thus the preceding graphs depict vividly the surge of voltage occurring along the line as time goes on.

The current $I(x,t)$ for this example can be obtained by taking the transform of equation (7.5.27) and the derivative of (7.5.44) with respect to x. We thus obtain

$$(7.5.47) \qquad i(x,p) = -\frac{1}{Lp}v_x(x,p) = f(p)\sqrt{\frac{C}{L}}\frac{\sinh{(l-x)p\sqrt{LC}}}{\cosh{pl\sqrt{LC}}}.$$

Exercise. Let $F(t) = V_0$ (constant), i.e., $f(p) = V_0/p$. Using equation (7.5.47), find $I(x,t)$:

(i)   as a trigonometric series,
(ii) as a series of unit functions.

Draw the traveling wave diagrams for the current $I(x,t)$.

(d) $RC = LG$. When this condition is satisfied we have what is called a *distortionless* line. The following equations obtain if G, for example, is replaced by its equal RC/L:

$$(7.5.48) \qquad V_x(x,t) = -RI(x,t) - LI_t(x,t),$$

$$(7.5.49) \qquad I_x(x,t) = -\frac{RC}{L}V(x,t) - CV_t(x,t),$$

$$(7.5.50) \qquad V_{xx}(x,t) - LCV_{tt}(x,t) - 2RCV_t(x,t) - \frac{R^2C}{L}V(x,t) = 0,$$

$$(7.5.51) \quad I_{xx}(x,t) - LCI_{tt}(x,t) - 2RCI_t(x,t) - \frac{R^2C}{L}I(x,t) = 0.$$

Example. Initially, a semi-infinite transmission line is dead, i.e., $V(x,0) = V_t(x,0) = I(x,0) = I_t(x,0) = 0$. At $t = 0$ a variable potential $F(t)$ is applied at $x = 0$. Find $V(x,t)$ for $t > 0$.

The boundary conditions for this problem are evidently

$$(7.5.52) \quad V(x,0) = V_t(x,0) = 0, \quad I(x,0) = I_t(x,0) = 0 \quad (x > 0),$$

$$(7.5.53) \quad V(0,t) = F(t), \quad \lim_{x \to \infty} V(x,t) = 0 \quad (t > 0).$$

In addition, the function $V(x,t)$ must satisfy the equation

$$(7.5.54) \quad V_{xx}(x,t) - LCV_{tt}(x,t) - 2RCV_t(x,t) - \frac{R^2C}{L}V(x,t) = 0,$$

whose transform with respect to t is

$$(7.5.55) \quad v_{xx}(x,p) - LC[p^2v(x,p) - pV(x,0) - V_t(x,0)]$$
$$- 2RC[pv(x,p) - V(x,0)] - \frac{R^2C}{L}v(x,p) = 0.$$

Now, since $V(x,0) = V_t(x,0) = 0$, then (7.5.55) becomes

$$(7.5.56) \quad v_{xx}(x,p) - \frac{C}{L}(Lp + R)^2v(x,p) = 0,$$

whose solution is

$$(7.5.57) \quad v(x,p) = c_1 e^{x(p+R/L)\sqrt{LC}} + c_2 e^{-x(p+R/L)\sqrt{LC}}.$$

From (7.5.53) we have

$$v(0,p) = f(p), \quad \lim_{x \to \infty} v(x,p) = 0.$$

These conditions applied to (7.5.57) give

$$c_1 = 0, \quad c_2 = f(p).$$

Therefore

$$(7.5.58) \quad v(x,p) = f(p)e^{-x(p+R/L)\sqrt{LC}}.$$

Suppose that $F(t) = b \sin \omega t$, then $f(p) = L\{F(t)\} = \dfrac{b\omega}{p^2 + \omega^2}$. Consequently (7.5.58) becomes

$$(7.5.59) \quad v(x,p) = \frac{b\omega}{p^2 + \omega^2}e^{-x(p+R/L)\sqrt{LC}}$$

and hence

$$(7.5.60) \quad V(x,t) = be^{-xR\sqrt{C/L}} \sin \omega(t - x\sqrt{LC})1(t - x\sqrt{LC}).$$

The graph of equation (7.5.60) is shown at two different times t_0 and

t_1 $(t_1 > t_0)$ in Fig. 7.5.9. Clearly the potential is an "attenuated" (damped) wave moving to the right with velocity $1/\sqrt{LC}$ and preserving its shape (i.e., without being distorted). The points P_1', P_2'

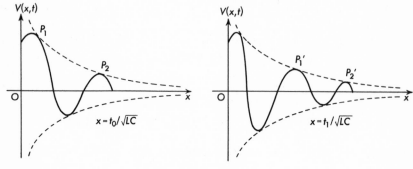

FIG. 7.5.9

on the wave at time t_1 correspond to the points P_1, P_2 on the wave at time t_0. Such waves are said to be *relatively undistorted*.

Exercise. Find the solution to the preceding example if
$$F(t) = V_0[1(t) + 1(t - t_0) - 2 \cdot 1(t - t_1)], \quad (t_1 > t_0),$$
and draw its graph.

Ans. $V(x,t) = V_0 e^{-xR\sqrt{C/L}}\{ 1(t - x\sqrt{LC}$
$$+ 1[t - (t_0 + x\sqrt{LC})] - 2 \cdot 1[t - (t_1 + x\sqrt{LC})]\}.$$

7.6 The Dissipationless Line with Different Transmission Line Constants

In practice it is frequently necessary to determine the manner in which waves are propagated when traveling in media having different physical characteristics. For example, suppose that a dissipationless line (initially dead) is such that its transmission line constants are L_1, C_1 over the distance $(-l,0)$ and L_2, C_2 over the distance $(0,\infty)$. If the distant end is *open* and the left end is subjected to a variable potential $F(t)$ at time $t = 0$, it is required to find the potential $V(x,t)$ for $t > 0$. The waves in the two parts of the cable have different velocities and the boundary value problem to be solved is the following:

(7.6.1) $V_{xx}(x,t) = L_1 C_1 V_{tt}(x,t)$ $(-l < x < 0, t > 0)$,

(7.6.2) $V_{xx}(x,t) = L_2 C_2 V_{tt}(x,t)$ $(0 < x < \infty, t > 0)$,

(7.6.3) $V(x,0) = V_t(x,0) = 0$ $(-l < x < \infty)$,

(7.6.4) $V(-l,t) = F(t)$, $\lim_{x \to \infty} I(x,t) = 0$ $(t > 0)$.

$$\text{(7.6.5)} \qquad V(0-,t) = V(0+,t) \qquad (t > 0),$$

$$\text{(7.6.6)} \qquad V_x(0-,t) = V_x(0+,t) \qquad (t > 0).$$

Condition (7.6.3) is a consequence of the fact that the line is initially dead, the second condition in (7.6.4) expresses the definition of an open end, and (7.6.5) and (7.6.6) are the continuity conditions that must hold across the boundary $x = 0$.

Taking the Laplace transform of the preceding conditions with respect to t, we obtain

$$\text{(7.6.7)} \qquad v_{xx}(x,p) - L_1 C_1 p^2 v(x,p) = 0 \qquad (-l < x < 0),$$

$$\text{(7.6.8)} \qquad v_{xx}(x,p) - L_2 C_2 p^2 v(x,p) = 0 \qquad (0 < x < \infty),$$

$$\text{(7.6.9)} \qquad v(-l,p) = f(p), \qquad \lim_{x \to \infty} v_x(x,p) = 0,$$

$$\text{(7.6.10)} \qquad v(0-,p) = v(0+,p),$$

$$\text{(7.6.11)} \qquad v_x(0-,p) = v_x(0+,p).$$

For a justification of the second condition in (7.6.9) see Example 1, case (c). Solving equations (7.6.7) and (7.6.8), we obtain

$$\text{(7.6.12)} \qquad v(x,p) = c_1 \cosh px\sqrt{L_1 C_1} + c_2 \sinh px\sqrt{L_1 C_1}$$
$$(-l < x < 0),$$

and

$$\text{(7.6.13)} \qquad v(x,p) = c_1' e^{px\sqrt{L_2 C_2}} + c_2' e^{-px\sqrt{L_2 C_2}} \qquad (0 < x < \infty).$$

Employing conditions (7.6.9), the preceding equations become

$$\text{(7.6.14)} \qquad f(p) = c_1 \cosh pl\sqrt{L_1 C_1} - c_2 \sinh pl\sqrt{L_1 C_1},$$

$$\text{(7.6.15)} \qquad 0 = c_1',$$

so that

$$\text{(7.6.16)} \qquad v(x,p) = c_2' e^{-px\sqrt{L_2 C_2}} \qquad (0 < x < \infty).$$

Finally, conditions (7.6.10) and (7.6.11) give

$$\text{(7.6.17)} \qquad c_1 = c_2', \qquad \sqrt{L_1 C_1}\, c_2 = -\sqrt{L_2 C_2}\, c_2'.$$

Solving the simultaneous equations (7.6.14) and (7.6.17), we find that

$$c_1 = c_2' = \frac{f(p)}{\cosh pl\sqrt{L_1 C_1} + \sqrt{L_2 C_2/L_1 C_1} \sinh pl\sqrt{L_1 C_1}},$$

and

$$c_2 = -\sqrt{\frac{L_2 C_2}{L_1 C_1}} \frac{f(p)}{\cosh pl\sqrt{L_1 C_1} + \sqrt{L_2 C_2/L_1 C_1} \sinh pl\sqrt{L_1 C_1}}.$$

Substituting these values in (7.6.12) and (7.6.16), we get
(7.6.18)

$$v(x,p) = f(p)\frac{\cosh px\sqrt{L_1C_1} - \lambda\sinh px\sqrt{L_1C_1}}{\cosh pl\sqrt{L_1C_1} + \lambda\sinh pl\sqrt{L_1C_1}} \quad (-l < x < 0),$$

(7.6.19)

$$v(x,p) = f(p)\frac{e^{-px\sqrt{L_2C_2}}}{\cosh pl\sqrt{L_1C_1} + \lambda\sinh pl\sqrt{L_1C_1}} \quad (0 < x < \infty),$$

where $\lambda = \sqrt{L_2C_2/L_1C_1}$.

To obtain a traveling wave solution we express the hyperbolic functions in terms of exponentials. Thus for (7.6.18) we have

$$v(x,p) = f(p)\frac{(1-\lambda)e^{px\sqrt{L_1C_1}} + (1+\lambda)e^{-px\sqrt{L_1C_1}}}{(1+\lambda)e^{pl\sqrt{L_1C_1}} + (1-\lambda)e^{-pl\sqrt{L_1C_1}}}$$

$$= f(p)\frac{\dfrac{1-\lambda}{1+\lambda}e^{-p(l-x)\sqrt{L_1C_1}} + e^{-p(l+x)\sqrt{L_1C_1}}}{1 + \dfrac{1-\lambda}{1+\lambda}e^{-2pl\sqrt{L_1C_1}}}$$

$$= f(p)\left\{\frac{1-\lambda}{1+\lambda}e^{-p(l-x)\sqrt{L_1C_1}}\right.$$

$$\left. + e^{-p(l+x)\sqrt{L_1C_1}}\right\}\sum_{n=0}^{\infty}(-1)^n\left(\frac{1-\lambda}{1+\lambda}\right)^n e^{-2npl\sqrt{L_1C_1}}$$

$$= \sum_{n=0}^{\infty}\left(\frac{\lambda-1}{\lambda+1}\right)^n e^{-p\{[(2n+1)l+x]\sqrt{L_1C_1}\}}f(p)$$

$$- \sum_{n=0}^{\infty}\left(\frac{\lambda-1}{\lambda+1}\right)^{n+1} e^{-p\{[(2n+1)l-x]\sqrt{L_1C_1}\}}f(p).$$

Therefore, upon taking the inverse Laplace transform of the preceding expression, we obtain

$$(7.6.20)\quad V(x,t) = \sum_{n=0}^{\infty}\left(\frac{\lambda-1}{\lambda+1}\right)^n F\{t - [(2n+1)l + x]\sqrt{L_1C_1}\}$$

$$1\{t - [(2n+1)l + x]\sqrt{L_1C_1}\}$$

$$- \sum_{n=0}^{\infty}\left(\frac{\lambda-1}{\lambda+1}\right)^{n+1} F\{t - [(2n+1)l - x]\sqrt{L_1C_1}\}$$

$$1\{t - [(2n+1)l - x]\sqrt{L_1C_1}\}, \quad (-l < x < 0)$$

Similarly for (7.6.19) we have

$$v(x,p) = f(p)\frac{2e^{-px\sqrt{L_2C_2}}}{(1+\lambda)e^{pl\sqrt{L_1C_1}} + (1-\lambda)e^{-pl\sqrt{L_1C_1}}}$$

$$= \frac{2f(p)}{1+\lambda}\frac{e^{-(l+\lambda x)p\sqrt{L_1C_1}}}{1 + \frac{1-\lambda}{1+\lambda}e^{-2pl\sqrt{L_1C_1}}}$$

$$= \frac{2f(p)}{1+\lambda}e^{-(l+\lambda x)p\sqrt{L_1C_1}}\sum_{n=0}^{\infty}(-1)^n\left(\frac{1-\lambda}{1+\lambda}\right)^n e^{-2npl\sqrt{L_1C_1}}$$

$$= \frac{2}{1+\lambda}\sum_{n=0}^{\infty}\left(\frac{\lambda-1}{\lambda+1}\right)^n e^{-p\{[(2n+1)l+\lambda x]\sqrt{L_1C_1}\}}f(p).$$

Therefore

$$(7.6.21) \quad V(x,t) = \frac{2}{\lambda+1}\sum_{n=0}^{\infty}\left(\frac{\lambda-1}{\lambda+1}\right)^n F\{t - [(2n+1)l + \lambda x]\sqrt{L_1C_1}\}$$

$$1\{t - [(2n+1)l + \lambda x]\sqrt{L_1C_1}\}, \quad (0 < x < \infty).$$

The results obtained may now be interpreted physically as waves that suffer partial reflection and partial transmission at $x = 0$, where the change in the transmission characteristics of the wire takes place. For equation (7.6.20) represents $V(x,t)$ as the superposition of waves that are reflected over and over again at the ends $x = -l$ and $x = 0$. Equation (7.6.21), on the other hand, represents the part of the wave that has been transmitted at $x = 0$. Thus we have a reflected part in the first medium and a transmitted part in the second medium with the amplitudes of the reflected and transmitted parts of the wave undergoing changes in magnitude at $x = 0$.

The ratio $2/(\lambda + 1)$ is called the *coefficient of reflection* and $(\lambda - 1)/(\lambda + 1)$ the *coefficient of transmission*.

Exercise. Solve the preceding problem when $F(t) = F_0$ by employing the complex inversion integral.

7.7 Longitudinal Oscillations of a Bar

Let us derive the differential equation which governs the longitudinal motion of the sections of an elastic bar (not necessarily of uniform cross section). Consider a portion of such a bar as that shown in Fig. 7.7.1. Let $A(x)$ be the area (assumed not to vary during the motion of the bar) at x measured from some fixed cross section, E

the modulus of elasticity, and $U(x,t)$ the displacement of the section at x at time t. If the sections at x and $x + dx$ undergo displacements $U(x,t)$ and $U(x + dx,t)$, respectively, then the sections are acted upon by the forces F_L and F_R as shown. Assuming that Hooke's law

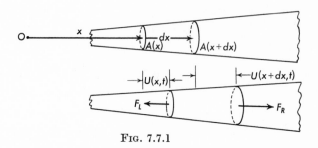

FIG. 7.7.1

applies, we know that the total force exerted by the left-hand portion on $A(x)$ is

$$F_L = EA(x)\frac{\partial U(x,t)}{\partial x},$$

and similarly the force exerted by the right-hand portion on $A(x + dx)$ is

$$F_R = EA(x + dx)\frac{\partial U(x + dx,t)}{\partial x} = E\left[A(x)\frac{\partial U(x,t)}{\partial x} + \frac{\partial}{\partial x}\left(A(x)\frac{\partial U(x,t)}{\partial x}\right)dx\right],$$

where we have made use of Taylor's expansion and dropped differentials of power higher than one. Therefore, the resultant force in the x direction is

$$F_R - F_L = E\frac{\partial}{\partial x}\left(A(x)\frac{\partial U(x,t)}{\partial x}\right)dx,$$

and hence according to Newton's law

$$E\frac{\partial}{\partial x}\left(A(x)\frac{\partial U(x,t)}{\partial x}\right)dx = \rho A(x)\frac{\partial^2 U(x,t)}{\partial t^2}dx,$$

or

(7.7.1) $$E\frac{\partial}{\partial x}\left(A(x)\frac{\partial U(x,t)}{\partial x}\right) = \rho A(x)\frac{\partial^2 U(x,t)}{\partial t^2},$$

where ρ is the density of the bar.

If the bar is of uniform cross section, then $A(x) = A$ (constant) and equation (7.7.1) becomes

(7.7.2) $$U_{tt}(x,t) = a^2 U_{xx}(x,t),$$

where $a = \sqrt{E/\rho}$. We recognize this equation to be the one-dimensional wave equation met previously, where in this case a represents the velocity of the elastic wave.

Equations (7.7.1) and (7.7.2) govern the behavior of an elastic bar when no external forces (such as gravitational or magnetic forces) act on it. If $F(x,t)$, denotes the *force per unit mass* acting parallel to the x-axis of Fig. 7.7.1, then equation (7.7.1) would be replaced by,

$$(7.7.3) \qquad F(x,t)\rho A(x) + E\frac{\partial}{\partial x}\left(A(x)\frac{\partial U(x,t)}{\partial x}\right) = \rho A(x)\frac{\partial^2 U(x,t)}{\partial t^2},$$

and (7.7.2) by

$$(7.7.4) \qquad\qquad F(x,t) + a^2 U_{xx}(x,t) = U_{tt}(x,t).$$

Example I. A uniform bar of length l is fixed at $x = 0$ (Fig. 7.7.2) and the end $x = l$ is stretched uniformly to l_0 and released at $t = 0$. Find the longitudinal displacement $U(x,t)$ for $t > 0$.

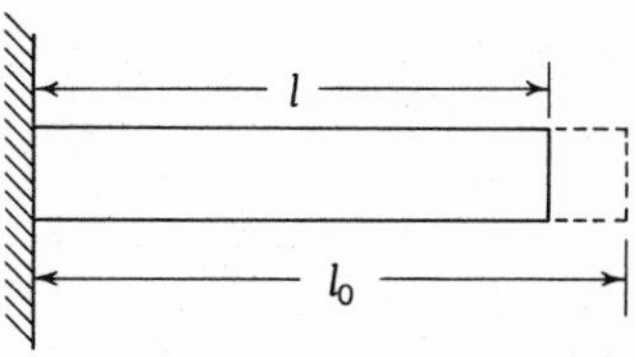

As initial and boundary conditions we have

$$U(x,0) = \frac{l_0 - l}{l}x, \qquad U_t(x,0) = 0$$

$$(0 < x < l),$$

$$U(0,t) = 0, \qquad U_x(l,t) = 0 \qquad (t > 0).$$

Fig. 7.7.2

In addition, $U(x,t)$ satisfies the differential equation

$$U_{tt}(x,t) = a^2 U_{xx}(x,t) \qquad (0 < x < l,\, t > 0).$$

The transforms of the preceding expressions with respect to t yield

$$(7.7.5) \qquad\qquad \frac{d^2 u(x,p)}{dx^2} - \frac{p^2}{a^2}u(x,p) = -\frac{l_0 - l}{la^2}xp,$$

$$(7.7.6) \qquad\qquad u(0,p) = 0, \qquad u_x(l,p) = 0.$$

One verifies readily that the solution of the linear differential equation (7.7.5) is

$$(7.7.7) \qquad u(x,p) = c_1 \cosh\frac{p}{a}x + c_2 \sinh\frac{p}{a}x + \frac{(l_0 - l)x}{lp}.$$

Conditions (7.7.6) yield the following equations

$$0 = c_1, \qquad 0 = c_1\frac{p}{a}\sinh\frac{l}{a}p + c_2\frac{p}{a}\cosh\frac{l}{a}p + \frac{l_0 - l}{lp},$$

from which

$$c_2 = -\frac{(l_0 - l)a}{lp^2 \cosh\frac{l}{a}p}.$$

These values for c_1 and c_2 when substituted in (7.7.7) give

$$(7.7.8) \qquad u(x,p) = \frac{(l_0 - l)x}{lp} - \frac{(l_0 - l)a}{l} \frac{\sinh \frac{x}{a}p}{p^2 \cosh \frac{l}{a}p}.$$

Therefore

$$(7.7.9) \quad U(x,t) = \frac{(l_0 - l)x}{l} - \frac{(l_0 - l)a}{l} \frac{1}{2\pi i} \int_{c-i\infty}^{c+i\infty} \frac{e^{pt} \sin \frac{x}{a}p}{p^2 \cosh \frac{l}{a}p} dp.$$

The function $\dfrac{e^{pt} \sinh \frac{x}{a}p}{p^2 \cosh \frac{l}{a}p}$ has a simple pole at $p = 0$, since

$$\lim_{p \to 0} \frac{\sinh \frac{x}{a}p}{p} = \lim_{p \to 0} \frac{x}{a}\left(1 + \frac{1}{3!}\left(\frac{x}{a}p\right)^2 + \cdots\right) = \frac{x}{a},$$

and simple poles at $p = \pm (n + \frac{1}{2})\pi i \frac{a}{l}$, $n = 0, 1, 2, \cdots$.

The residue at $p = 0$ is

$$\lim_{p \to 0} \frac{e^{pt} \sinh \frac{x}{a}p}{p \cosh \frac{l}{a}p} = \frac{x}{a},$$

and that at $p = \pm(n + \frac{1}{2})\pi i \frac{a}{l}$ is

$$\frac{e^{pt} \sinh \frac{x}{a}p}{\left[p^2 \frac{d}{dp}\left(\cosh \frac{l}{a}p\right)\right]_{p=\pm(n+\frac{1}{2})\pi i(a/l)}} = - \frac{e^{\pm(n+\frac{1}{2})\pi iat/l} \sin (n + \frac{1}{2})\pi \frac{x}{l}}{\frac{l}{a}(n + \frac{1}{2})^2\pi^2 \sin (n + \frac{1}{2})\pi}.$$

Therefore the sum of the residues at these poles is

$$\frac{x}{a} - \frac{2a}{l} \sum_{n=0}^{\infty} (-1)^n \frac{\sin (n + \frac{1}{2})\pi \frac{x}{l} \cos (n + \frac{1}{2})\pi a \frac{t}{l}}{\pi^2(n + \frac{1}{2})^2}.$$

and hence from (7.7.9) the solution is

$$U(x,t) = \frac{2(l_0 - l)a^2}{\pi^2 l^2} \sum_{n=0}^{\infty} (-1)^n \frac{\sin (n + \frac{1}{2})\pi \frac{x}{l} \cos (n + \frac{1}{2})\pi a \frac{t}{l}}{(n + \frac{1}{2})^2}.$$

We shall now determine the solution in terms of waves. We have

$$\frac{\sinh \frac{x}{a}p}{p^2 \cosh \frac{l}{a}p} = \frac{e^{-(p/a)(l-x)} - e^{-(p/a)(l+x)}}{p^2(1 + e^{-(2l/a)p})}$$

$$= \frac{1}{p^2}[(e^{-(p/a)(l-x)} - e^{-(p/a)(l+x)})(1 - e^{-(2l/a)p} + e^{-(4l/a)p}$$

$$- e^{-(6l/a)p} + \cdots]$$

$$= \frac{e^{-(p/a)(l-x)} - e^{-(p/a)(l+x)}}{p^2} - \frac{e^{-(p/a)(3l-x)} - e^{-(p/a)(3l+x)}}{p^2}$$

$$+ \frac{e^{-(p/a)(5l-x)} - e^{-(p/a)(5l+x)}}{p^2} + \cdots .$$

Therefore

$$L^{-1}\left\{ \frac{\sinh \frac{x}{a}p}{p^2 \cosh \frac{l}{a}p} \right\} = \left(t - \frac{l-x}{a}\right)1\left(t - \frac{l-x}{a}\right) - \left(t - \frac{l+x}{a}\right)1\left(t - \frac{l+x}{a}\right)$$

$$- \left(t - \frac{3l-x}{a}\right)1\left(t - \frac{3l-x}{a}\right) + \left(t - \frac{3l+x}{a}\right)1\left(t - \frac{3l+x}{a}\right)$$

$$+ \left(t - \frac{5l-x}{a}\right)1\left(t - \frac{5l-x}{a}\right) - \left(t - \frac{5l+x}{a}\right)1\left(t - \frac{5l+x}{a}\right) - \cdots ,$$

and consequently from (7.7.8)

$$U(x,t) = \frac{(l_0 - l)x}{l} - \frac{(l_0 - l)a}{l}\left\{\left(t - \frac{l-x}{a}\right)1\left(t - \frac{l-x}{a}\right)\right.$$

$$- \left(t - \frac{l+x}{a}\right)1\left(t - \frac{l+x}{a}\right) - \left(t - \frac{3l-x}{a}\right)1\left(t - \frac{3l-x}{a}\right)$$

$$+ \left(t - \frac{3l+x}{a}\right)1\left(t - \frac{3l+x}{a}\right) + \left(t - \frac{5l-x}{a}\right)1\left(t - \frac{5l-x}{a}\right)$$

$$\left. - \left(t - \frac{5l+x}{a}\right)1\left(t - \frac{5l+x}{a}\right) - \cdots \right\}, \quad 0 < x < l.$$

In order to graph this function we consider its value in the various time intervals shown below. It is readily verified that

$$U(x,t) = \frac{(l_0 - l)}{l}x, \qquad \text{when } 0 < t < \frac{l-x}{a},$$

$$U(x,t) = \frac{(l_0 - l)}{l}x - \frac{(l_0 - l)a}{l}\left(t - \frac{l-x}{a}\right),$$

$$\text{when } \frac{l-x}{a} < t < \frac{l+x}{a},$$

$$U(x,t) = -\frac{(l_0 - l)x}{a}, \qquad \text{when } \frac{l+x}{a} < t < \frac{3l-x}{a},$$

$$U(x,t) = \frac{l_0 - l}{l}x + \frac{(l_0 - l)a}{l}\left(t - \frac{3l+x}{a}\right),$$

$$\text{when } \frac{3l-x}{a} < t < \frac{3l+x}{a},$$

$$U(x,t) = \frac{(l_0 - l)x}{l}, \qquad \text{when } \frac{3l+x}{a} < t < \frac{5l-x}{a},$$

$$U(x,t) = \frac{(l_0 - l)x}{l} - \frac{(l_0 - l)a}{l}\left(t - \frac{5l-x}{a}\right),$$

$$\text{when } \frac{5l-x}{a} < t < \frac{5l+x}{a},$$

$$U(x,t) = -\frac{(l_0 - l)x}{a}, \qquad \text{when } \frac{5l+x}{a} < t < \frac{7l-x}{a}, \text{ etc.}$$

Hence the displacement of any section x at time t is that shown in Fig. 7.7.3.

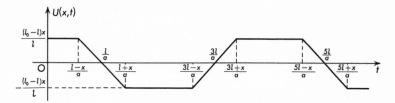

Fig. 7.7.3

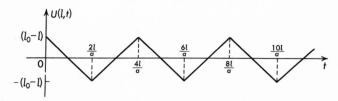

Fig. 7.7.4

The displacement of the end of the bar $x = l$ is of some interest. Its graph is shown in Fig. 7.7.4.

Example 2. A uniform bar of length l stands vertically on one end as shown in Fig. 7.7.5. At time $t = 0$ a heavy block of weight W_0 falls on the end $x = l$ with a velocity $- v_0$. Determine the displacement at any point for $t > 0$.   (Neglect the weight of the bar as being small compared with the weight W_0.)

For the motion of the bar $U(x,t)$ must satisfy the following conditions

$$U_{tt}(x,t) = a^2 U_{xx}(x,t)$$
$$(0 < x < l,\ t > 0),$$

$$U(x,0) = 0, \qquad U_t(x,0) = 0$$
$$(0 < x < l),$$

$$U(0,t) = 0 \qquad (t > 0).$$

The corresponding problem in the transform $u(x,t)$ is

$$u_{xx}(x,p) - \frac{p^2}{a^2} u(x,p) = 0$$
$$(0 < x < l),$$

with

$$u(0,p) = 0.$$

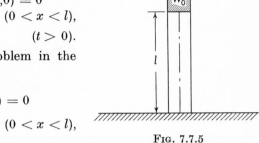

Fig. 7.7.5

When the differential equation is solved we find that

$$(7.7.10) \qquad u(x,p) = c_1 \sinh \frac{p}{a} x.$$

By Newton's law the equation governing the motion of the heavy block is

$$(7.7.11) \qquad -EA\, U_x(x,t)\Big]_{x=l} = \frac{W_0}{g} U_{tt}(x,t)\Big]_{x=l}$$

with the initial conditions at $x = l$

$$(7.7.12) \qquad U(x,0)]_{x=l} = 0, \qquad U_t(x,0)]_{x=l} = -v_0.$$

The transform of (7.7.11) is

$$-EA u_x(x,t)\Big]_{x=l} = \frac{W_0}{g}\Big[p^2 u(x,p) - pU(x,0) - U_t(x,0)\Big]_{x=l}.$$

Using conditions (7.7.12) we obtain

$$(7.7.13) \qquad -EA u_x(l,t) = \frac{W_0}{g}[p^2 u(l,p) + v_0].$$

From (7.7.10)

$$u_x(x,p) = c_1 \frac{p}{a} \cosh \frac{p}{a} x.$$

Substituting this and (7.7.10) in (7.7.13) and solving the resulting equation for c_1, we get

$$c_1 = \frac{-v_0 W_0}{gp\left[\dfrac{W_0}{g} p \sinh \dfrac{p}{a} l + \dfrac{EA}{a} \cosh \dfrac{p}{a} l\right]},$$

which when substituted in (7.7.10) gives

$$u(x,p) = \frac{-\,v_0 l \sinh \dfrac{p}{a}x}{ap\left[\dfrac{pl}{a}\sinh\dfrac{pl}{a} + \lambda \cosh\dfrac{pl}{a}\right]},$$

where $\lambda = (lgEA)/a^2 W_0 = \dfrac{Alp}{W_0/g} = \dfrac{m}{M}$, m is the mass of the bar and M that of the block. Consequently

(7.7.14)
$$U(x,t) = -\,\frac{-\,v_0 l}{2\pi i a}\int_{c-i\infty}^{c+i\infty}\frac{e^{pt}\sinh\dfrac{p}{a}x\,dp}{p\left[\dfrac{pl}{a}\sinh\dfrac{pl}{a} + \lambda\cosh\dfrac{pl}{a}\right]}.$$

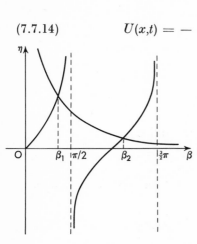

FIG. 7.7.6

The only poles of the integrand are the roots of $(pl/a)\tanh(pl/a) = -\lambda$. An analysis of this equation shows that it has only pure imaginary roots which can be written as $p = \pm\, ia\beta_n/l$, where β_n, $n = 1, 2, 3, \cdots$, are the positive roots of $\beta \tan\beta = \lambda$ which are the abscissas of the points of intersection of $\eta = \tan\beta$ and $\eta = \lambda/\beta$ (Fig. 7.7.6). The residue at the pole $p = \pm ia\beta_n/l$ is

$$\left[\frac{e^{pt}\sinh px/a}{p\dfrac{d}{dp}\left[\dfrac{pl}{a}\sinh\dfrac{pl}{a} + \lambda\cosh\dfrac{pl}{a}\right]}\right]_{p=\pm ia\beta_n/l}$$

$$= \frac{\pm\, e^{\pm ia\beta_n t/l}\sin x\beta_n/l}{i\beta_n[\beta_n\cos\beta_n + (1+\lambda)\sin\beta_n]}$$

$$= \frac{\pm\, e^{\pm ia\beta_n t/l}\sin x\beta_n/l}{i[\beta_n^2 + (1+\lambda)\lambda]\cos\beta_n},$$

where we have made use of the fact that $\beta_n\tan\beta_n = \lambda$ to simplify the denominator. Therefore, upon summing these residues, we have from (7.7.14)

$$U(x,t) = \frac{-\,2v_0 l}{a}\sum_{n=1}^{\infty}\frac{\sin a\beta_n t/l\,\sin x\beta_n/l}{[\beta_n^2 + (1+\lambda)\lambda]\cos\beta_n}.$$

Exercise. Find the longitudinal displacement $U(x,t)$ of a bar for which

$$U_{tt}(x,t) = a^2 U_{xx}(x,t) \qquad (0 < x < l,\, t > 0),$$

$$U(x,0) = \frac{1}{10}x\left[1(x) - 1\left(x - \frac{l}{2}\right) \right] - \frac{1}{10}(x - l)\left[1\left(x - \frac{l}{2}\right) \right.$$

$$\left. - 1(x - l) \right], \quad U_t(x,0) = 0 \qquad (0 < x < l),$$

$$U(0,t) = 0, \qquad U_x(l,t) = 0 \qquad (t > 0).$$

Draw the graph corresponding to Fig. 7.7.3.

Ans. $\quad U(x,t) = U(x,0) - \dfrac{x}{10}$

$$+ \frac{a^2}{5l\pi^2} \sum_{n=0}^{\infty} (-1)^n \frac{\sin (n + \frac{1}{2})\pi\frac{x}{l} \cos (n + \frac{1}{2})\pi a\frac{t}{l}}{(n + \frac{1}{2})^2} \qquad \left(0 < x < \frac{l}{2}\right),$$

$$U(x,t) = U(x,0) + \frac{x}{10}$$

$$- \frac{a^2}{5l\pi^2} \sum_{n=0}^{\infty} (-1)^n \frac{\sin (n + \frac{1}{2})\pi\frac{x}{l} \cos (n + \frac{1}{2})\pi a\frac{t}{l}}{(n + \frac{1}{2})^2} \qquad \left(\frac{l}{2} < x < l\right).$$

7.8 Transverse Vibrations of a Beam

In section 4.8 we considered the deflection of a beam when subjected to a static load $W(x)$ (load per unit length). The differential equation giving the displacement $Y(x)$ at any section x is

$$(7.8.1) \qquad \frac{d^2}{dx^2}\left(EI\frac{d^2 Y(x)}{dx^2}\right) = W(x).$$

This equation may be used to determine the transverse vibrations of a beam by using d'Alembert's principle which states that the equations of motion in dynamics can be obtained in the same way as equations in statics provided we take into consideration forces of inertia. Since the displacement is now a function of x and t, the equation of motion will be a partial differential equation. In applying this principle, the load is considered to be the inertial force $- m\dfrac{\partial^2 Y(x,t)}{\partial t^2}$, where m is the mass of the beam per unit length. Therefore, if $F(x,t)$ represents an external force, the equation for the transverse vibration of a beam is given by

$$(7.8.2) \qquad \frac{\partial^2}{\partial x^2}\left(EI\frac{\partial^2 Y(x,t)}{\partial x^2}\right) = - m\frac{\partial^2 Y(x,t)}{\partial t^2} + F(x,t).$$

If the cross section of the beam is uniform, EI is constant, and we have

(7.8.3) $$\frac{\partial^4 Y(x,t)}{\partial x^4} + a^2 \frac{\partial^2 Y(x,t)}{\partial t^2} = \frac{F(x,t)}{EI},$$

where $a^2 = m/EI$.

The equations involving the bending moment $M(x,t)$ and shearing force $S(x,t)$ are (for a uniform beam)

(7.8.4) $$EI \frac{\partial^2 Y(x,t)}{\partial x^2} = - M(x,t),$$

(7.8.5) $$EI \frac{\partial^3 Y(x,t)}{\partial x^3} = -S(x,t).$$

Upon taking the Laplace transform of both sides of (7.8.3) with respect to t, we obtain

(7.8.6) $$\frac{d^4 y(x,p)}{dx^4} + a^2 p^2 y(x,p) = a^2[p Y(x,0) + Y_t(x,0)] + f(x,p)/(EI),$$

where $f(x,p) = L_t\{F(x,t)\}$. $Y(x,0)$ and $Y_t(x,0)$ are the initial displacement and velocity, respectively, of any point x of the beam.

If we make the convenient substitutions

(7.8.7) $$q = \sqrt{iap}, \text{ i.e., } a^2 p^2 = -q^4,$$

and

(7.8.8) $$g(x,p) = a^2[p Y(x,0) + Y_t(x,0)] + f(x,p)/(EI),$$

then equation (7.8.6) may be written as

(7.8.9) $$\frac{d^4 y(x,p)}{dx^4} - q^4 y(x,p) = g(x,p).$$

Its general solution (see equation (4.1.8)) is

(7.8.10) $$y(x,p) = c_1 \sin qx + c_2 \cos qx + c_3 \sinh qx + c_4 \cosh qx$$
$$+ \frac{1}{2q^3} \int_0^x g(\xi,p)[\sinh q(x - \xi) - \sin q(x - \xi)]\, d\xi.$$

The following derivatives of (7.8.10) are listed for convenience:

(7.8.11) $$\frac{dy(x,p)}{dx} = q(c_1 \cos qx - c_2 \sin qx + c_3 \cosh qx + c_4 \sinh qx)$$
$$+ \frac{1}{2q^2} \int_0^x g(\xi,p)[\cosh q(x - \xi) - \cos q(x - \xi)]\, d\xi,$$

(7.8.12) $$\frac{d^2 y(x,p)}{dx^2} = q^2(- c_1 \sin qx - c_2 \cos qx + c_3 \sinh qx$$
$$+ c_4 \cosh qx) + \frac{1}{2q} \int_0^x g(\xi,p)[\sinh q(x - \xi) + \sin q(x - \xi)]\, d\xi,$$

$$(7.8.13) \quad \frac{d^3y(x,p)}{dx^3} = q^3(-c_1 \cos qx + c_2 \sin qx + c_3 \cosh qx$$

$$+ c_4 \sinh qx) + \tfrac{1}{2}\int_0^x g(\xi,p)[\cosh q(x-\xi) + \cos q(x-\xi)]\,d\xi,$$

The constants c_1, c_2, c_3, and c_4 are determined from the conditions at the ends of the beam. At an end which is freely hinged (e.g., $x = 0$) the deflection and bending moment are zero and hence

$$Y(0,t) = Y_{xx}(0,t) = 0.$$

At a built-in end ($x = 0$) the deflection and slope of a curve are zero and therefore

$$Y(0,t) = Y_x(0,t) = 0.$$

At a free end (e.g., $x = l$) the bending moment and shearing force are equal to zero and consequently

$$Y_{xx}(l,t) = Y_{xxx}(l,t) = 0.$$

Example I. A beam with hinged ends is initially straight and at rest (Fig. 7.8.1). At $t = 0$ a concentrated load F_0 is applied at $x = x_0$. Determine the subsequent vibration of the beam.

Clearly, $Y(x,0) = Y_t(x,0) = 0$ and since the ends are hinged

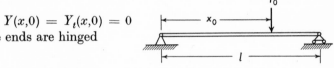

$$(7.8.14)$$

$$Y(0,t) = Y_{xx}(0,t) = Y(l,t)$$
$$= Y_{xx}(l,t) = 0.$$

FIG. 7.8.1

The transforms of the preceding four equations are

$$(7.8.15) \qquad y(0,p) = \frac{d^2y(0,p)}{dx^2} = y(l,p) = \frac{d^2y(l,p)}{dx^2} = 0.$$

Now, since $F(x,t) = F_0 1'(x - x_0)$, then $f(x,p) = \dfrac{F_0}{p}1'(x - x_0)$ and therefore

$$(7.8.16) \qquad g(x,p) = \frac{F_0}{EIp}1'(x - x_0).$$

Hence from (7.8.10) and (7.8.16) we have

$$(7.8.17) \quad y(x,p) = c_1 \sin qx + c_2 \cos qx + c_3 \sinh qx + c_4 \cosh qx$$

$$+ \frac{F_0}{2q^3pEI}\int_0^x 1'(\xi - x_0)[\sinh q(x-\xi) - \sin q(x-\xi)]\,d\xi.$$

The first two conditions in (7.8.15) yield the following system of equations

$$0 = c_2 + c_4, \qquad 0 = -c_2 + c_4,$$

whose solution is $c_2 = c_4 = 0$. These values together with the last two conditions in (7.8.15) result in the equations

$$(7.8.18) \quad 0 = c_1 \sin ql + c_3 \sinh ql + \frac{F_0}{2q^3 pEI} \int_0^l 1'(\xi - x_0)$$
$$[\sinh q(l - \xi) - \sin q(l - \xi)] \, d\xi,$$

$$0 = - c_1 \sin ql + c_3 \sinh ql + \frac{F_0}{2q^3 pEI} \int_0^l 1'(\xi - x_0)$$
$$[\sinh q(l - \xi) + \sin q(l - \xi)] \, d\xi.$$

Now, by (3.4.3) we have

$$\int_0^x \phi(\xi) \cdot 1'(\xi - x_0) \, d\xi = \phi(x_0) \cdot 1(x - x_0).$$

Using this result, we find from (7.8.18) that
(7.8.19)

$$c_1 \sin ql + c_3 \sinh ql = - \frac{F_0}{2q^3 pEI}[\sinh q(l - x_0) - \sin q(l - x_0)],$$

$$-c_1 \sin ql + c_3 \sinh ql = - \frac{F_0}{2q^3 pEI}[\sinh q(l - x_0) + \sin q(l - x_0)],$$

from which we obtain

$$c_1 = \frac{F_0}{2q^3 pEI} \frac{\sin q(l - x_0)}{\sin ql}, \qquad c_3 = - \frac{F_0}{2q^3 pEI} \frac{\sinh q(l - x_0)}{\sinh ql}.$$

From (7.8.17), therefore, we have

$$y(x,p) = \frac{F_0}{2q^3 pEI} \left[\frac{\sin q(l - x_0) \sinh ql \sin qx - \sinh q(l - x_0) \sin ql \sin qx}{\sin ql \sinh ql} \right]$$
$$+ \frac{F_0}{2q^3 pEI} \int_0^x 1'(\xi - x_0)[\sinh q(x - \xi) - \sin q(x - \xi)] \, d\xi$$

(7.8.20)

$$= \frac{F_0}{2q^3 pEI} \left[\frac{\sin q(l - x_0) \sinh ql \sin qx - \sinh q(l - x_0) \sin ql \sinh qx}{\sin ql \sinh ql} \right]$$
$$+ \frac{F_0}{2q^3 pEI}[\sinh q(x - x_0) - \sin q(x - x_0)] \, 1(x - x_0).$$

Therefore

$$(7.8.21) \quad Y(x,t) = \frac{F_0 1(x - x_0)}{4\pi i EI} \int_{c-i\infty}^{c+i\infty} e^{pt} \frac{\sinh q(x - x_0) - \sin q(x - x_0)}{q^3 p} dp$$

$$+ \frac{F_0}{4\pi i EI} \int_{c-i\infty}^{c+i\infty} e^{pt} \frac{\sin q(l - x_0) \sinh ql \sin qx - \sinh q(l - x_0) \sin ql \sinh qx}{q^3 p \sin ql \sinh ql} dp,$$

where $q = \sqrt{iap}$.

By expanding $\sinh q(x - x_0)$ and $\sin q(x - x_0)$ in power series of $q(x - x_0)$ it can be readily verified that the integrand of the first integral has a simple pole at $p = 0$. For the residue at $p = 0$ we have

$$(7.8.22) \quad \text{Res } (0) = \lim_{p \to 0} 2e^{pt}\{(x - x_0)^3/3! + q^4(x - x_0)^7/7! + \cdots$$
$$= \tfrac{1}{3}(x - x_0)^3.$$

In a similar manner, the integrand of the second integral is found to have a simple pole at $p = 0$ and at those values (other than zero) which make $\sin ql \sinh ql$ vanish. To find the residue at $p = 0$ we expand the terms in the numerator and denominator in power series and simplify. We thus obtain

$$\text{Res } (0) = \lim_{p \to 0} 2e^{pt} \frac{\left[-\dfrac{lx(l - x_0)^3}{3!} + \dfrac{xl^3(l - x_0)}{3!} - \dfrac{lx^3(l - x_0)}{3!} + \text{terms in powers of } q \right]}{l^2[1 + \text{terms in powers of } q]}$$

$$= \frac{x(l - x_0)}{3l}[2lx_0 - x_0{}^2 - x^2].$$

The problem now is that of finding the zeros of $\sin ql$ and $\sinh ql$. To do this we must find the region in the q-plane which corresponds to the region of the p-plane, since p and q are connected by the relation

$$(7.8.23) \qquad\qquad q^2 = iap.$$

This can be done by letting $p = Re^{i\Phi}$ and $q = re^{i\phi}$, where $\Phi = \text{amp } p$ and $\phi = \text{amp } q$. Therefore, since $e^{-(\pi/2)i} = -i$, we have from (7.8.23)

$$Re^{i\Phi} = \frac{r^2}{a}e^{[2\phi - (\pi/2)]i},$$

whence $R = r^2/a$ and $\Phi = 2\phi - \pi/2$. Hence, corresponding to the region

$$-\pi < \text{amp } p \leqslant \pi$$

of the p-plane, we have the region

$$-\frac{\pi}{4} < \text{amp } q \leqslant \frac{3}{4}\pi,$$

in the q-plane. It is in this region that we must seek the solutions (other than 0) of

$$\sin ql = 0 \quad \text{and} \quad \sinh ql = 0.$$

The zeros of the first equation are

$$q = i\frac{n\pi}{l}, \quad \text{or} \quad p = -i\frac{n^2\pi^2}{l^2a}, \quad n = 1, 2, 3, \cdots$$

and those of the second equation are

$$q = i\frac{n\pi}{l} \quad \text{or} \quad p = i\frac{n^2\pi^2}{l^2 a}, \quad n = 1, 2, 3, \cdots.$$

Evaluating the derivative of the denominator of the second integrand of (7.8.21) at $p = -i\dfrac{n^2\pi^2}{l^2 a}$, we have (remembering that $q^2 = iap$)

$$\frac{d}{dp}(q^3 p \sin ql \sinh ql)\bigg]_{q=n\pi/l} = \frac{d}{dq}(q^3 p \sin ql \sinh ql)\frac{dq}{dp}\bigg]_{q=n\pi/l}$$

$$= \frac{n^4\pi^4}{2l^3}(\cos n\pi \sinh n\pi).$$

Therefore

$$\text{Res}\left(-i\frac{n^2\pi^2}{l^2 a}\right) = \frac{e^{-n^2\pi^2 it/(l^2 a)} \sin \dfrac{n\pi(l - x_0)}{l} \sin \dfrac{n\pi}{l}x}{\dfrac{n^4\pi^4}{2l^3}\cos n\pi}$$

$$= -\frac{2l^3}{n^4\pi^4}e^{-n^2\pi^2 it/(l^2 a)} \sin \frac{n\pi}{l}x_0 \sin \frac{n\pi}{l}x.$$

A similar evaluation at $p = i\dfrac{n^2\pi^2}{l^2 a}$ shows that

$$\text{Res}\left(i\frac{n^2\pi^2}{l^2 a}\right) = -\frac{2l^3}{n^4\pi^4} e^{n^2\pi^2 it/(l^2 a)} \sin \frac{n\pi}{l}x_0 \sin \frac{n\pi}{l}x.$$

Hence, upon summing the residues previously obtained, we get

$$Y(x,t) = \frac{F_0}{6EI}\left\{\frac{x(l - x_0)}{l}(2lx_0 - x_0{}^2 - x^2) + (x - x_0)^3 1(x - x_0)\right\}$$

$$- \frac{2F_0 l^3}{EI\pi^4}\sum_{n=1}^{\infty}\frac{1}{n^4} \sin \frac{n\pi}{l}x_0 \sin \frac{n\pi}{l}x \cos \frac{n^2\pi^2}{al^2}t.$$

Example 2. A straight beam of length l, hinged at both ends, is initially

FIG. 7.8.2

at rest (Fig. 7.8.2). At $t = 0$ an oscillating bending moment of magnitude M and frequency ω is applied to the end $x = 0$. Determine the resulting motion.

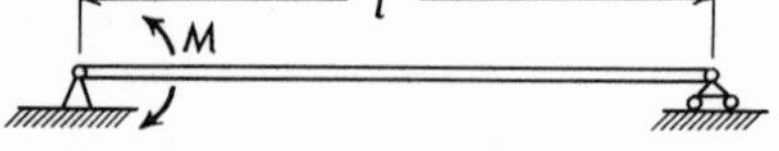

The initial and boundary conditions are

$$Y(x,0) = Y_t(x,0) = 0 \qquad (0 < x < l),$$

$$(7.8.24) \qquad Y(0,t) = 0, \qquad EI Y_{xx}(0,t) = -M \sin \omega t, \qquad (t > 0),$$

$$Y(l,t) = 0, \qquad Y_{xx}(l,t) = 0. \qquad (t > 0),$$

Since there are no external forces the equation governing the motion of the beam is

$$\frac{\partial^4 Y(x,t)}{\partial x^4} + a^2 \frac{\partial^2 Y(x,t)}{\partial t^2} = 0 \qquad (0 < x < l, t > 0)$$

whose transform for this problem is

$$\frac{d^4 y(x,p)}{dx^4} - q^4 y(x,p) = 0,$$

where as before $q^4 = -ap$. The solution of this equation is

(7.8.25) $\quad y(x,p) = c_1 \sin qx + c_2 \cos qx + c_3 \sinh qx + c_4 \cosh qx.$

The Laplace transforms of the last four conditions in (7.8.24) are

$$y(0,p) = 0, \qquad EIy_{xx}(0,p) = -M\omega/(p^2 + \omega^2),$$
$$y(l,p) = 0, \qquad y_{xx}(l,p) = 0.$$

When these are applied to equation (7.8.25) we obtain the following system of four equations

$$c_2 + c_4 = 0,$$
$$-c_2 + c_4 = -M\omega/[EI(p^2 + \omega^2)q^2],$$
$$c_1 \sin ql + c_2 \cos ql + c_3 \sinh ql + c_4 \cosh ql = 0,$$
$$-c_1 \sin ql - c_2 \cos ql + c_3 \sinh ql + c_4 \cosh ql = 0,$$

the solution of which is

$$c_2 = \frac{M\omega}{2EIq^2(p^2 + \omega^2)}, \qquad c_4 = -\frac{M\omega}{2EIq^2(p^2 + \omega^2)},$$

$$c_1 = -\frac{M\omega \cos ql}{2EIq^2(p^2 + \omega^2) \sin ql}, \qquad c_3 = \frac{M\omega \cosh ql}{2EIq^2(p^2 + \omega^2) \sinh ql}.$$

Substituting these values in (7.8.25), we find that

$$y(x,p) = \frac{M\omega(\cos qx - \cosh qx)}{2EIq^2(p^2 + \omega^2)}$$

$$+ \frac{M\omega(\cosh ql \sin ql \sinh qx - \cos ql \sinh ql \sin qx)}{2EIq^2(p^2 + \omega^2) \sin ql \sinh ql}$$

and therefore

(7.8.26) $\quad Y(x,t) = \dfrac{M\omega}{2EI} \cdot \dfrac{1}{2\pi i} \displaystyle\int_{c-i\infty}^{c+i\infty} e^{pt} \dfrac{(\cos qx - \cosh qx)}{q^2(p^2 + \omega^2)} dp$

$$+ \frac{M\omega}{2EI} \cdot \frac{1}{2\pi i} \int_{c-i\infty}^{c+i\infty} e^{pt} \frac{(\cosh ql \sin ql \sinh qx - \cos ql \sinh ql \sin qx)}{q^2(p^2 + \omega^2) \sin ql \sinh ql} dp.$$

The integrands are clearly single valued functions of p. By considering the expansions of $\cos qx$ and $\cosh qx$ it is easily seen that the only poles of the first integrand are $p = \pm i\omega$. Hence we have

$$\text{Res } (i\omega) = \left[\frac{e^{pt}(\cos qx - \cosh qx)}{q^2 \dfrac{d}{dp}(p^2 + \omega^2)} \right]_{p=i\omega}$$

$$= \frac{e^{i\omega t}(\cos x\sqrt{a\omega} - \cosh x\sqrt{a\omega})}{2ia\omega^2},$$

$$\text{Res } (-i\omega) = \left[\frac{e^{pt}(\cos qx - \cosh qx)}{q^2 \dfrac{d}{dp}(p^2 + \omega^2)} \right]_{p=-i\omega}$$

$$= - \frac{e^{-i\omega t}(\cos x\sqrt{a\omega} - \cosh x\sqrt{a\omega})}{2ia\omega^2}.$$

In a similar manner, it can be shown that the only poles of the second integrand in (7.8.26) occur at $p = \pm i\omega$ and at those values of q (other than 0) for which $\sin ql = 0$ and $\sinh ql = 0$. These are, respectively,

$$q = \frac{n\pi}{l} \quad \text{or} \quad p = -i\frac{n^2\pi^2}{al^2}, \quad n = 1, 2, 3, \cdots,$$

$$q = i\frac{n\pi}{l} \quad \text{or} \quad p = i\frac{n^2\pi^2}{al^2}, \quad n = 1, 2, 3, \cdots.$$

To evaluate the residues at these points we need

$$\left[q^2(p^2 + \omega^2) \sinh ql \frac{d}{dp} \sin ql \right]_{p=-in^2\pi^2/(al^2)}$$

$$= ia\frac{n\pi}{2}\left(\omega^2 - \frac{n^4\pi^4}{a^2l^4} \right) \sinh n\pi \cos n\pi,$$

$$\left[q^2(p^2 + \omega^2) \sin ql \frac{d}{dp} \sinh ql \right]_{p=in^2\pi^2/(al^2)}$$

$$= - ia\frac{n\pi}{2}\left(\omega^2 - \frac{n^4\pi^4}{a^2l^4} \right) \sinh n\pi \cos n\pi.$$

Therefore

$$\text{Res } \left(-i\frac{n^2\pi^2}{al^2} \right) = - e^{-n^2\pi^2 it/(al^2)} \frac{\sin \dfrac{n\pi}{l}x}{ia\dfrac{n\pi}{2}\left(\omega^2 - \dfrac{n^4\pi^4}{a^2l^4} \right)},$$

$$\text{Res } \left(i\frac{n^2\pi^2}{al^2} \right) = e^{+n^2\pi^2 it/(al^2)} \frac{\sin \dfrac{n\pi}{l}x}{ia\dfrac{n\pi}{2}\left(\omega^2 - \dfrac{n^4\pi^4}{a^2l^4} \right)}.$$

Similarly, the residues at $p = \pm\, i\omega$ are:

$$\text{Res}\,(i\omega) = -\,e^{i\omega t}\,\frac{\cos l\sqrt{a\omega}\,\sinh l\sqrt{a\omega}\,\sin x\sqrt{a\omega}\; -\cosh l\sqrt{a\omega}\,\sin l\sqrt{a\omega}\,\sinh x\sqrt{a\omega}}{2a\omega^2 i\,\sinh l\sqrt{a\omega}\,\sin l\sqrt{a\omega}},$$

$$\text{Res}\,(-\,i\omega) = e^{-i\omega t}\,\frac{\cos l\sqrt{a\omega}\,\sinh l\sqrt{a\omega}\,\sin x\sqrt{a\omega}\; -\cosh l\sqrt{a\omega}\,\sin l\sqrt{a\omega}\,\sinh x\sqrt{a\omega}}{2a\omega^2 i\,\sinh l\sqrt{a\omega}\,\sin l\sqrt{a\omega}}.$$

Summing the above residues and simplifying, we finally have

$$Y(x,t) = \frac{M\sin\omega t}{2EIa\omega}\left[\frac{\sin(l-x)\sqrt{a\omega}}{\sin l\sqrt{a\omega}} - \frac{\sinh(l-x)\sqrt{a\omega}}{\sinh l\sqrt{a\omega}}\right]$$

$$+\,\frac{2M\omega}{EI\pi a}\sum_{n=1}^{\infty}\frac{\sin\dfrac{n\pi}{l}x\,\sin\dfrac{n^2\pi^2}{al^2}t}{n\left(\omega^2 - \dfrac{n^4\pi^4}{a^2 l^4}\right)},$$

provided $\omega^2 \neq \dfrac{n^4\pi^4}{a^2 l^4}$ for any one of the integral values $n = 1, 2, 3, \cdots$.

If the frequency ω of the external bending moment is equal to $n^2\pi^2/(al^2)$, then we have *resonance* and to find the solution for this case the residues would have to be computed at the double poles $\pm\, i\omega$.

Exercise. Find the solution to the preceding problem for the *resonance* case.

7.9 Transverse Vibrations of a Stretched String

Let an elastic string of length l be tightly stretched between two points O and A (Fig. 7.9.1). If it is now distorted in some prescribed manner and released, then it will vibrate. Let us assume that the vibrations of the string are small as compared with the length l of the string, and the tension T (considered constant) is so large as compared with the force of gravity that the latter may be neglected. From

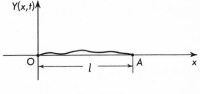

FIG. 7.9.1

these assumptions it follows that we may consider the length of the string as sensibly equal to l and that the longitudinal displacements can be neglected as compared with the transverse displacements. Thus, we shall consider the motion to be due to the vertical component of the tension.

Let us suppose that the motion of the string takes place in the xy-

plane.   Since the vertical displacement of any point on the string is a
function of x and t, we shall get a partial differential equation.   From
Fig. 7.9.2, which shows (greatly exaggerated) an element of string of

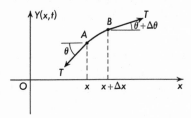

length $\varDelta x$ approximately, we see that
the resultant of the Y-components of
the tensions at the ends A and B in the
Y-direction is

$$T[\sin (\theta + \varDelta \theta) - \sin \theta].$$

Since θ is small for the type of vibrations we are considering, we may
replace $\sin \theta$ by $\tan \theta$ which is equal
to $Y_x(x,t)$.   Also

Fig. 7.9.2

$\sin (\theta + \varDelta \theta)$
$\quad = Y_x(x + \varDelta x,t) = Y_x(x,t) + Y_{xx}(x,t)\varDelta x + $ (higher powers of $\varDelta x$).
Therefore the resultant force is

$$T Y_{xx}(x,t)\varDelta x + \text{(higher powers of } \varDelta x).$$

Now, the mass of the element $\varDelta x$ under consideration is $M\varDelta x/l$,
where M is the total mass of the string.   Hence, by Newton's law of
motion

$$\frac{M}{l}Y_{tt}(x,t)\varDelta x = T Y_{xx}(x,t)\varDelta x + \text{(higher powers of } \varDelta x).$$

Dividing by $\varDelta x$ and passing to the limit as $\varDelta x \to 0$, we have

(7.9.1) $Y_{tt}(x,t) = a^2 Y_{xx}(x,t),$

where $a^2 = Tl/M$.

Example.   A taut string of length l, initially at rest, has one end
fixed, the other being subjected to a given motion.
For the initial and boundary conditions we have

(7.9.2) $Y(x,0) = 0, \qquad Y_t(x,0) = 0,$

(7.9.3) $Y(0,t) = F(t), \qquad Y(l,t) = 0,$

where $F(t)$ (continuous and such that $F(0) = 0$) is the motion given to
the left end.   The transforms of the conditions (7.9.3) are

(7.9.4) $y(0,p) = f(p), \qquad y(l,p) = 0,$

where $L_t\{F(t)\} = f(p)$.   Making use of conditions (7.9.2), the transform
of equation (7.9.1) is

(7.9.5) $y_{xx}(x,p) - \dfrac{p^2}{a^2}y(x,p) = 0,$

whose solution is

(7.9.6) $y(x,p) = c_1 \cosh \dfrac{p}{a}x + c_2 \sinh \dfrac{p}{a}x.$

Conditions (7.9.4) applied to (7.9.6) yield the equations

$$f(p) = c_1, \qquad c_1 \cosh \frac{p}{a}l + c_2 \sinh \frac{p}{a}l = 0.$$

Therefore

$$(7.9.7) \quad y(x,p) = f(p) \cosh \frac{p}{a}x - f(p) \frac{\sinh \frac{p}{a}x \cosh \frac{p}{a}l}{\sinh \frac{p}{a}l} = f(p) \frac{\sinh \frac{l-x}{a}p}{\sinh \frac{p}{a}l},$$

from which

$$(7.9.8) \qquad Y(x,t) = \frac{1}{2\pi i} \int_{c-i\infty}^{c+i\infty} f(p) e^{pt} \frac{\sinh \frac{l-x}{a}p}{\sinh \frac{p}{a}l} dp.$$

Let us consider the case when the left end is subjected to an oscillatory motion given by the function $F(t) = F_0 \sin \omega t$. Therefore, $f(p) = F_0/(p^2 + \omega^2)$ and

$$(7.9.9) \qquad Y(x,t) = \frac{1}{2\pi i} \int_{c-i\infty}^{c+i\infty} e^{pt} \frac{F_0 \omega \sinh \frac{l-x}{a}p}{(p^2 + \omega^2) \sinh \frac{l}{a}p} dp.$$

The poles of the integrand occur at $p = \pm i\omega$ and $p = \pm \dfrac{n\pi ai}{l}$, $n = 1, 2, \cdots$. An examination of the ratio of the series expansions for $\sinh (l - x)p/a$ and $\sinh pl/a$ shows that $p = 0$ is not a pole.

For the residues at $p = i\omega$ and $p = -i\omega$ we have, respectively,

$$\text{Res } (i\omega) = \left[\frac{F_0 \omega e^{pt} \sinh \frac{l-x}{a}p}{\sinh \frac{l}{a}p \frac{d}{dp}(p^2 + \omega^2)} \right]_{p=i\omega} = \frac{F_0 e^{i\omega t} \sinh i\frac{l-x}{a}\omega}{2i \sinh i\frac{\omega l}{a}},$$

$$\text{Res } (-i\omega) = \left[\frac{F_0 \omega e^{pt} \sinh \frac{l-x}{a}p}{\sinh \frac{l}{a}p \frac{d}{dp}(p^2 + \omega^2)} \right]_{p=-i\omega} = - \frac{F_0 e^{-i\omega t} \sinh i\frac{l-x}{a}\omega}{2i \sinh i\frac{\omega l}{a}}.$$

At the pole $p = n\pi ai/l$ the residue is

$$\left[\frac{F_0 \omega e^{pt} \sinh \frac{l-x}{a}p}{(p^2 + \omega^2) \frac{d}{dp} \sinh \frac{pl}{a}} \right]_{p=n\pi ai/l} = \frac{F_0 \omega e^{(n\pi ai/l)t} \sinh \frac{(l-x)n\pi i}{l}}{\frac{l}{a}\left(\omega^2 - \frac{n^2 \pi^2 a^2}{l^2} \right) \cosh n\pi i},$$

and at $p = -n\pi ai/l$ we have

$$\left[\frac{F_0\omega e^{pt}\sinh\dfrac{l-x}{a}p}{(p^2+\omega^2)\dfrac{d}{dp}\sinh\dfrac{pl}{a}}\right]_{p=-n\pi ai/l} = -\frac{F_0\omega e^{-(n\pi ai/l)t}\sinh\dfrac{(l-x)n\pi i}{l}}{\dfrac{l}{a}\left(\omega^2-\dfrac{n^2\pi^2a^2}{l^2}\right)\cosh n\pi i}.$$

Therefore

$$\text{Res}\,(i\omega) + \text{Res}\,(-i\omega) = F_0\frac{\sin\omega t\sin\dfrac{l-x}{a}\omega}{\sin\dfrac{\omega l}{a}},$$

and

$$\text{Res}\,(n\pi ai/l) + \text{Res}\,(-n\pi ai/l) = (-1)^{n+1}\frac{2F_0\omega a}{l}\cdot\frac{\sin\dfrac{n\pi a}{l}t\sin\dfrac{l-x}{l}n\pi}{\left(\omega^2-\dfrac{n^2\pi^2a^2}{l^2}\right)}.$$

Hence, finally,

$$Y(x,t) = F_0\frac{\sin\omega t\sin\dfrac{l-x}{a}\omega}{\sin\dfrac{\omega l}{a}} + \frac{2F_0\omega a}{l}\sum_{n=1}^{\infty}(-1)^{n+1}\frac{\sin\dfrac{n\pi a}{l}t\sin\dfrac{l-x}{l}n\pi}{(\omega^2-n^2\pi^2a^2/l^2)},$$

provided $\omega^2 \neq n^2\pi^2a^2/l^2$ for any one of the values $n = 1, 2, 3, \cdots$. Should this condition not be satisfied, we must make a separate calculation since $p = \pm i\omega$ would then be a double pole.

Exercise.   Find the solution to the previous problem if the left end of the string experiences a motion given by the function

$$F(t) = F_0t[1(t) - 1(t - t_0)] + F_01(t - t_0).$$

[*Hint:* In finding the inverse transform note the *Remark* (section 4.6.).]

$$Ans.\quad Y(x,t) = F_0\frac{l-x}{l}t + \frac{2F_0l}{a\pi^2}\sum_{n=1}^{\infty}(-1)^n\frac{\sin\dfrac{n\pi a}{l}t\sin\dfrac{n\pi(l-x)}{l}}{n^2}$$

$$- F_0\left\{\frac{l-x}{l}(t-t_0) + \frac{2l}{a\pi^2}\sum_{n=1}^{\infty}(-1)^n\frac{\sin\dfrac{n\pi a}{l}(t-t_0)\sin\dfrac{n\pi(l-x)}{l}}{n^2}\right\}1(t-t_0)$$

$$+ F_0(1-t_0)\left\{\frac{l-x}{l} + \frac{2}{\pi}\sum_{n=1}^{\infty}(-1)^n\frac{\cos\dfrac{n\pi a}{l}(t-t_0)\sin\dfrac{n\pi(l-x)}{l}}{n}\right\}1(t-t_0).$$

PROBLEMS

Solve the following boundary value problems which arise in connection with diffusion:

1.
$$C_t(x,t) = DC_{xx}(x,t) \qquad (0 < x < \infty, t > 0),$$
$$C(x,0) = C_0[1(x) - 1(x - l)] \qquad (0 < x < \infty),$$
$$\lim_{x \to \infty} C(x,t) = 0, \qquad C_x(0 +, t) = 0 \qquad (t > 0),$$
$$C(l -, t) = C(l +, t), \qquad C_x(l -, t) = C_x(l +, t) \qquad (t > 0).$$

Ans. $C(x,t) = \dfrac{C_0}{2}\left[\operatorname{erf}\dfrac{l + x}{2\sqrt{Dt}} + \operatorname{erf}\dfrac{l - x}{2\sqrt{Dt}}\right], \qquad (0 < x < \infty, t > 0).$

2.
$$C_t(x,t) = DC_{xx}(x,t) \qquad (0 < x < l, t > 0),$$
$$C(x,0) = C_0 \qquad (0 < x < l),$$
$$C(0,t) = 0, \qquad C(l,t) = C_1 \qquad (t > 0).$$

Ans. $C(x,t) = C_1\dfrac{x}{l} - \dfrac{2C_0}{\pi}\displaystyle\sum_{n=1}^{\infty}\dfrac{(-1)^n}{n}e^{-n^2\pi^2 Dt/l^2}\sin\dfrac{n\pi(l - x)}{l}$

$$+ \dfrac{2(C_1 - C_0)}{\pi}\sum_{n=1}^{\infty}\dfrac{(-1)^n}{n}e^{-n^2\pi^2 Dt/l^2}\sin\dfrac{n\pi x}{l}.$$

3.
$$C_t(x,t) = DC_{xx}(x,t) - kC(x,t) \qquad (-l < x < l, t > 0),$$
$$C(x,0) = C_0 \qquad (-l < x < l),$$
$$C(-l,t) = 0, \qquad C(l,t) = 0 \qquad (t > 0),$$
where k is a constant.

Ans. $C(x,t) = \dfrac{4C_0}{\pi}\exp(-kt)\displaystyle\sum_{n=0}^{\infty}\dfrac{(-1)^n}{(2n + 1)}\cos\dfrac{(2n + 1)\pi x}{2l}$

$$\exp\left(-\left[\dfrac{(2n + 1)\pi}{2l}\right]^2 Dt\right).$$

4.
$$C_t(x,t) = DC_{xx}(x,t) - kC(x,t) \qquad (-l < x < l, t > 0),$$
$$C(x,0) = C_0 \qquad (-l < x < l),$$
$$C_x(-l,t) = 0, \qquad C(l,t) = 0 \qquad (t > 0),$$
where k is a constant.

Ans. $C(x,t) = \dfrac{C_0}{\pi}\exp(-kt)\displaystyle\sum_{n=0}^{\infty}\dfrac{1}{2n + \frac{1}{4}}\exp(-[(2n + \tfrac{1}{4})\pi/l]^2 Dt)$

$$\cos[(2n + \tfrac{1}{4})\pi(x + l)/l] + \dfrac{C_0}{\pi}\exp(-kt)\sum_{n=0}^{\infty}\dfrac{1}{2n + \frac{3}{4}}$$

$$\exp(-[(2n + \tfrac{3}{4})\pi/l]^2 Dt)\cos[(2n + \tfrac{3}{4})\pi(x + l)/l].$$

5.
$$C_t(x,t) = DC_{xx}(x,t) - 2vC_x(x,t) - kC(x,t) \qquad (-l < x < l, t > 0),$$
$$C(x,0) = C_1 \qquad (-l < x < l),$$
$$C(-l,t) = 0, \qquad C(l,t) = 0 \qquad (t > 0),$$
where v and k are constants.

Ans. $C(x,t) = C_1 e^{-kt} - C_1 e^{(v/D)x - kt} \left(\cosh \dfrac{v}{D}x - \sinh \dfrac{v}{D}x \right)$

$$+ C_1 \pi e^{(v/D)x - [k + (v^2/D)]t} \cosh \frac{v}{D}l$$

$$\sum_{n=0}^{\infty} (-1)^n \frac{(2n+1)e^{-[(n+\frac{1}{2})^2\pi^2 D/l^2]t} \cos\left[(n+\frac{1}{2})\pi x/l\right]}{v^2 l^2/D^2 + (n+\frac{1}{2})^2\pi^2}$$

$$+ 2C_1 \pi e^{(v/D)x - [k + (v^2/D)]t} \sinh \frac{v}{D}l \sum_{n=1}^{\infty} (-1)^n \frac{n e^{-[n^2\pi^2 D/l^2]t} \sin\left[n\pi x/l\right]}{v^2 l^2/D^2 + n^2\pi^2}.$$

6. $C_t(x,t) = D_1 C_{xx}(x,t), \quad (x < 0); \quad C_t(x,t) = D_2 C_{xx}(x,t), \quad (x > 0),$
$\qquad C(x,0) = C_0, \quad (x < 0); \quad C(x,0) = 0, \quad (x > 0),$
$\qquad \lim\limits_{x \to -\infty} C(x,t) = C_0, \qquad \lim\limits_{x \to \infty} C(x,t) = 0, \quad (t > 0),$
$\lim\limits_{x \to 0-} C(x,t) = k \lim\limits_{x \to 0+} C(x,t), \; D_1 \lim\limits_{x \to 0-} C_x(x,t) = D_2 \lim\limits_{x \to 0+} C_x(x,t), \quad (t > 0).$

Ans. $\qquad C(x,t) = C_0 - \dfrac{C_0 \sqrt{D_2}}{k\sqrt{D_1} + \sqrt{D_2}} \operatorname{erfc}\left(-\dfrac{x}{2\sqrt{D_1 t}} \right), \quad (x < 0),$

$$C(x,t) = \frac{C_0 \sqrt{D_1}}{k\sqrt{D_1} + \sqrt{D_2}} \operatorname{erfc}\left(\frac{x}{2\sqrt{D_2 t}} \right), \quad (x > 0).$$

7. Initially, a distortionless line of length l is dead. At $t = 0$ a sinusoidal voltage $V_0 \sin \omega t$ is applied at the end $x = 0$. If the end $x = l$ is grounded, find the voltage $V(x,t)$ for $t > 0$.

8. Solve problem 7 if all other conditions remain the same except that
$$\begin{aligned} V(0,t) &= V_0, \quad 0 < t < t_0, \\ &= 2V_0, \quad t_0 < t < t_1, \\ &= 0, \quad t > t_1. \end{aligned}$$

9. Solve the problem of section 7.6 if all other conditions remain the same except that the semi-infinite line is replaced by a finite line of length l.

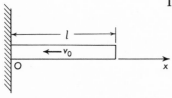

10. A uniform bar of length l, moving axially with a constant velocity $-v_0$, is brought to a sudden stop at $t = 0$ (Fig. 7.9.3). Find the displacement $U(x,t)$ for $t > 0$.

Ans. $U(x,t) = \dfrac{2v_0 l}{a\pi^2} \displaystyle\sum_{n=0}^{\infty} \dfrac{(-1)^{n+1}}{(n+\frac{1}{2})^2} \sin$

Fig. 7.9.3

$$\{(n+\tfrac{1}{2})a\pi t/l\} \cos\{(l-x)(n+\tfrac{1}{2})\pi/l\}.$$

11. Solve problem 10 if the bar is of infinite length.
    Ans. $U(x,t) = -v_0 t + v_0(t - x/a)\, 1(t - x/a).$

12. A uniform bar of length l lying on a horizontal frictionless plane is initially at rest and unstrained. At $t = 0$ the end $x = 0$ is subjected to an axial impact of impulse I_0 per unit cross-sectional area (Fig. 7.9.4). Determine the longitudinal displacement $U(x,t)$ for $t > 0$.

[*Hint:* The boundary value problem to be solved is:
$$U_{tt}(x,t) = a^2 U_{xx}(x,t) \qquad (0 < x < l, t > 0),$$
$$U(x,0) = 0, \qquad U_t(x,0) = 0 \qquad (0 < x < l),$$
$$EU_x(0,t) = -I_0 I'(t), \qquad U_x(l,t) = 0 \qquad (t > 0).]$$

Ans. $U(x,t) = \dfrac{I_0 a}{E}\left[\dfrac{at}{l} + \dfrac{2}{\pi}\sum_{n=1}^{\infty}\dfrac{(-1)^n}{n}\sin n\pi\dfrac{a}{l}t\cos n\pi\dfrac{l-x}{l}\right].$

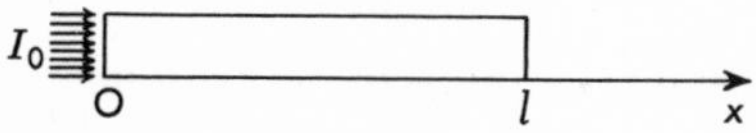

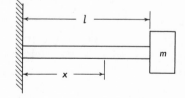

Fig. 7.9.4 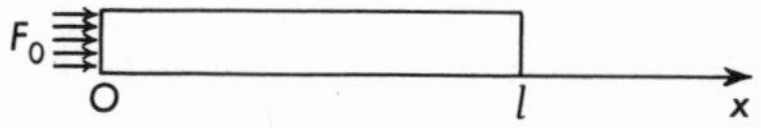 Fig. 7.9.5

13. Initially, a uniform bar of length l lies unstrained and at rest on a horizontal frictionless plane. Determine the displacement of any section x if the constant force $F(t) = F_0$ per unit cross-sectional area is applied axially to the end $x = 0$ at $t = 0$ (Fig. 7.9.5).

Ans. $U(x,t) = \dfrac{F_0 a^2}{2El}\left[\dfrac{2l^2 - 6lx + 3x^2}{3a^2} + t^2\right] + \dfrac{2F_0 l}{E\pi^2}\sum_{n=1}^{\infty}\dfrac{(-1)^{n+1}}{n^2}\cos\dfrac{n\pi a}{l}t\cos n\pi\dfrac{l-x}{l}.$

14. Solve problem 13 if $F(t) = F_0\sin\omega t$ per unit cross-sectional area.

15. A uniform prismatic bar of length l is initially clamped so that its longitudinal displacement is zero at all points. It is then hung from the end $x = 0$ and at $t = 0$ the clamps are released. Determine the subsequent motion of the bar as it vibrates under its own weight.

[*Hint:* The differential equation is $U_{tt}(x,t) = a^2 U_{xx}(x,t) + g$ $(0 < x < l, t > 0)$, where g is the acceleration due to gravity.]

Ans. $U(x,t) = \dfrac{gx}{2a^2}(2l - x) - \dfrac{16gl^2}{\pi^3 a^2}\sum_{n=1}^{\infty}\dfrac{1}{(2n-1)^3}\sin\dfrac{(2n-1)\pi x}{2l}\cos\dfrac{(2n-1)\pi at}{2l}.$

16. A heavy mass m is attached to the end $x = l$ of a uniform bar of cross-sectional area A which is fixed at the end $x = 0$. A constant force F_0 acts on m as shown in Fig. 7.9.6. If the system was initially at rest, find the displacement of any section x for $t > 0$.
[*Hint:* The boundary value problem to be solved is:

$$U_{tt}(x,t) = a^2 U_{xx}(x,t)$$
$$(0 < x < l, t > 0),$$

Fig. 7.9.6

$$U(x,0) = 0, \qquad U_t(x,0) = 0 \qquad (0 < x < l),$$
$$U(0,t) = 0, \qquad mU_{tt}(l,t) = -EAU_x(l,t) + F_0 \qquad (t > 0).]$$

Ans. $\quad U(x,t) = \dfrac{F_0 x}{EA} - \dfrac{2F_0 l^2}{a^2} \displaystyle\sum_{n=1}^{\infty} \dfrac{\cos \dfrac{a\beta_n}{l}t \sin \dfrac{\beta_n}{l}x}{m\beta_n \cos \beta_n + (1 + EAl/a^2) \sin \beta_n},$

where β_n are the positive roots of $\tan \beta = (EAl)/(a^2 m\beta)$.

17. Solve problem 16 when the mass m is acted upon by a force given by $F_0 t[1(t) - 1(t - t_0)]$.

18. The initial position of a string, tightly stretched between two fixed points $x = 0$ and $x = l$, is given by $Y(x,0) = A_0 \sin \dfrac{\pi x}{l}$. Find the displacement $Y(x,t)$ if it is released from rest from this position.

Ans. $\quad Y(x,t) = A_0 \sin \dfrac{\pi x}{l} \cos \dfrac{\pi a t}{l}.$

19. The initial velocity of any point x of a string stretched between two fixed points $x = 0$ and $x = l$ is given by $Y_t(x,0) = A_0 x(l - x)$. If the initial displacement of each point of the string is zero, find $Y(x,t)$ for $t > 0$.

Ans. $\quad Y(x,t) = \dfrac{4l^3 A_0}{\pi^4 a} \displaystyle\sum_{n=1}^{\infty} \dfrac{1}{n^4} \sin n\pi \dfrac{x}{l} \sin n\pi \dfrac{a}{l} t.$

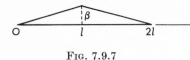

FIG. 7.9.7

20. A stretched string of length $2l$ is drawn aside a distance β at $x = l$ as shown in Fig. 7.9.7 and then released. Determine the subsequent motion.
[*Hint:* The boundary value problem to be solved is:

$$Y_{tt}(x,t) = a^2 Y_{xx}(x,t) \qquad\qquad (0 < x < 2l, \, t > 0),$$
$$Y(0,t) = 0, \qquad Y(2l,t) = 0 \qquad\qquad (t > 0),$$
$$Y(x,0) = \beta x/l \qquad\qquad\qquad\qquad (0 < x < l),$$
$$\qquad = \beta(2l - x)/l \qquad\qquad\qquad (l < x < 2l),$$
$$Y(l -, t) = Y(l +, t), \qquad Y_x(l -, t) == Y_x(l +, t)$$
$$\text{(continuity conditions).}$$

Ans. $\quad Y(x,t) = \dfrac{8\beta}{\pi^2} \displaystyle\sum_{n=0}^{\infty} \dfrac{(-1)^n}{(2n + 1)^2} \sin \dfrac{(2n + 1)\pi}{2l} x \cos \dfrac{(2n + 1)\pi a}{2l} t.$

21. If the weight of the string is taken into account, the transverse vibrations of a tightly stretched string are governed by the equation

$$Y_{tt}(x,t) = a^2 Y_{xx}(x,t) - g,$$

where g is the acceleration due to gravity.

Suppose that the initial position of a string stretched between two fixed points $x = 0$ and $x = l$ is given by $Y(x,0) = A_0 \sin \dfrac{\pi x}{l}$. Find the displacement $Y(x,t)$ if it is released from rest from this position.

Ans. $Y(x,t) = A_0 \sin \dfrac{\pi x}{l} \cos \dfrac{\pi a}{l} t - \dfrac{x(l-x)}{2a^2} g + \dfrac{4l^2 g}{a^2 \pi^3} \sum\limits_{n=0}^{\infty} \dfrac{1}{(2n+1)^3}$

$$\cos(2n+1)\frac{\pi a}{l}t \sin(2n+1)\pi\frac{x}{l}.$$

22. A semi-infinite string is initially at rest along a horizontal support. At $t = 0$ the support is removed and the left end is subjected to an oscillatory motion given by the function $A_0 \sin \omega t$ whereas the distant end is attached to a ring which slides without friction along a vertical support, so that $\lim\limits_{x\to\infty} Y_x(x,t) = 0$ since the support exerts no vertical force on the string. If the weight of the string is taken into account, so that the equation of problem 21 obtains, solve the resulting boundary value problem and draw the graph of the solution.

Ans. $Y(x,t) = \left[\dfrac{g}{2}\left(t - \dfrac{x}{a}\right)^2 + A_0 \sin \omega\left(t - \dfrac{x}{a}\right)\right] 1\left(t - \dfrac{x}{a}\right) - \dfrac{gt^2}{2}.$

CHAPTER VIII

Gamma, Error, and Bessel Functions. Asymptotic Series. Non-Elementary Integrals. Integral Equations.

8.1 The Gamma Function

In this chapter we shall study a particular group of functions which is of great importance in applied mathematics. The first one of these functions, arising frequently in the applications, is the so-called Gamma function $\Gamma(p)$. Euler defined it as the Cauchy integral

$$(8.1.1) \qquad \Gamma(p) = \int_0^\infty t^{p-1} e^{-t}\, dt \qquad\qquad \mathrm{Re}(p) > 0,$$

where, as usual, $p = x + iy$. It can be shown that $\Gamma(p)$ is an analytic function when $\mathrm{Re}(p) > 0$.*

Since

$$(8.1.2) \qquad \Gamma(p+1) = \int_0^\infty t^p e^{-t}\, dt,$$

we have, integrating by parts,

$$\int_0^\infty t^p e^{-t}\, dt = -\left. t^p e^{-t}\right|_0^\infty + p \int_0^\infty t^{p-1} e^{-t}\, dt = p\Gamma(p).$$

Therefore

$$(8.1.3) \qquad \Gamma(p+1) = p\Gamma(p),$$

which is the difference equation satisfied by the function $\Gamma(p)$.

By a repeated use of (8.1.3) we find that

$$(8.1.4) \qquad \Gamma(p+1) = p(p-1)\cdots(p-m)\Gamma(p-m),$$

or

(8.1.5)

$$\Gamma(p) = \frac{\Gamma(p+1)}{p} = \frac{\Gamma(p+2)}{p(p+1)} = \frac{\Gamma(p+m)}{p(p+1)\cdots(p+m-2)(p+m-1)},$$

---

* See P. Franklin, *Treatise on Advanced Calculus*, p. 560.

where m is a positive integer. The last expression enables us to extend the definition of the Gamma function to values of p for which $\text{Re}(p) < 0$. For, since (8.1.3) and (8.1.4) hold when the real part of p is positive, by taking m such that $\text{Re}(p + m) > 0$, we see that (8.1.5) defines $\Gamma(p)$ for $\text{Re}(p) < 0$.

An examination of (8.1.5) reveals that $\Gamma(p)$ has simple poles at $p = 0, -1, -2, \cdots$, since it is at these points that the denominator vanishes. Hence (8.1.1) and (8.1.5) define $\Gamma(p)$ as an analytic function for all finite values of p except for 0 and the negative integers.

Let us now consider the Gamma function for real values, i.e., for $p = x$. In particular, when x is a positive integer n, we obtain from (8.1.4)

$$\Gamma(n + 1) = n(n - 1) \cdots 3 \cdot 2 \cdot 1 \cdot \Gamma(1).$$

By direct integration we find that $\Gamma(1) = 1$, therefore

$$\Gamma(n + 1) = n!$$

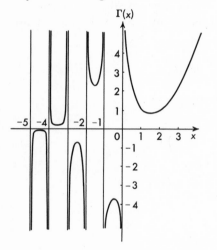

When $n = 0$, we have $0! = \Gamma(1) = 1$. The values of $\Gamma(x)$, for $1 < x < 2$, have been computed and can be found in various tables.* Consequently, from the recursion formula

$$(8.1.6) \quad \Gamma(x + 1) = x\Gamma(x)$$

we obtain the values of $\Gamma(x)$ for all other values of x. The graph of $\Gamma(x)$ is shown in Fig. 8.1.1.

Two very useful alternative definitions of the Gamma function are:

$$(8.1.7)$$

$$\Gamma(p) = \lim_{n \to \infty} \frac{n! n^p}{p(p + 1) \cdots (p + n)}$$

FIG. 8.1.1

and

$$(8.1.8) \qquad \frac{1}{\Gamma(p)} = e^{\gamma p} p \prod_{n=1}^{\infty} \left(1 + \frac{p}{n}\right)^{-p/n},$$

where in the latter, Π denotes the product of factors from one to infinity and γ is Euler's constant defined by

$$(8.1.9) \quad \gamma = \lim_{n \to \infty} \left(1 + \tfrac{1}{2} + \tfrac{1}{3} + \cdots + \frac{1}{n} - \ln n\right) = 0\cdot5772$$

$$\text{(approx.).}$$

* See e.g., B. O. Peirce, *Short Table of Integrals*, p. 140.

An important formula which is included here without proof is:

$$(8.1.10) \qquad \Gamma(p)\Gamma(1-p) = \frac{\pi}{\sin \pi p}.$$

Substituting $p = \frac{1}{2}$ in (8.1.10) we get the following useful result

$$\Gamma^2(\tfrac{1}{2}) = \pi,$$

whence

$$\Gamma(\tfrac{1}{2}) = \sqrt{\pi},$$

where the positive sign was chosen because $\Gamma(x) > 0$ for $x > 0$.

We have already seen (Example 1 (c), end of Chapter II) that

$$L\{t^n\} = \frac{n!}{p^{n+1}}, \quad n = 1, 2, 3, \cdots.$$

With the aid of the Gamma function it is now possible to generalize this formula to the case when the exponent of t is not necessarily an integer. To that end, let us consider

$$L\{t^r\} = \int_0^\infty e^{-pt}t^r \, dt \qquad (r > -1).$$

Making the substitution $pt = x$, we obtain

$$L\{t^r\} = \frac{1}{p^{r+1}} \int_0^\infty e^{-x}x^r \, dx,$$

or

$$L\{t^r\} = \frac{\Gamma(r+1)}{p^{r+1}} \qquad (r > -1).$$

Thus, for example,

$$\Gamma\{t^{\frac{1}{2}}\} = \frac{\Gamma(\tfrac{3}{2})}{p^{\frac{3}{2}}} = \frac{\tfrac{1}{2}\Gamma(\tfrac{1}{2})}{p^{\frac{3}{2}}} = \frac{\sqrt{\pi}}{2p^{\frac{3}{2}}}$$

and

$$L\{t^{-\frac{1}{2}}\} = \frac{\Gamma(\tfrac{1}{2})}{p^{\frac{1}{2}}} = \frac{\sqrt{\pi}}{p^{\frac{1}{2}}}.$$

8.2 The Error Function and Asymptotic Series

In order to introduce the topic of asymptotic series we shall find it convenient to discuss in somewhat more detail a function introduced in Chapter II, namely, the *error* or *probability* function defined there as

$$\operatorname{erf}(x) = \frac{2}{\sqrt{\pi}} \int_0^x e^{-\xi^2} \, d\xi.$$

Since the integrand can be expanded in a power series convergent everywhere, it may be integrated term by term. Performing this integration, we obtain

$$(8.2.2) \qquad \text{erf}(x) = \frac{2}{\sqrt{\pi}} \left[x - \frac{x^3}{3 \cdot 1!} + \frac{x^5}{5 \cdot 2!} - \frac{x^7}{7 \cdot 3!} + \cdots \right.$$

$$\left. + (-1)^{n+1} \frac{x^{2n+1}}{(2n+1) \cdot n!} + \cdots \right].$$

By means of this series the values of the error function have been tabulated* for various values of the argument x. When x is small the convergence is rapid and few terms are necessary to determine the value of erf x to a given number of decimal places. However, as x becomes large the number of terms required to obtain a given accuracy becomes prohibitively large and the resulting arithmetic calculation tedious and impractical. In such a case one may resort to so-called *asymptotic expansions*. Before defining such expansions formally, let us display one by making use of the error function.

We may clearly write (8.2.1) in the form

$$(8.2.3) \qquad \text{erf}(x) = \frac{2}{\sqrt{\pi}} \left[\int_0^\infty e^{-\xi^2}\, d\xi - \int_x^\infty e^{-\xi^2}\, d\xi \right].$$

By making the substitution $\xi = \sqrt{\lambda}$, $d\xi = d\lambda/2\sqrt{\lambda}$ in the first integral on the right side of (8.2.3) we see that

$$\int_0^\infty e^{-\xi^2}\, d\xi = \tfrac{1}{2} \int_0^\infty e^{-\lambda} \lambda^{-\frac{1}{2}}\, d\lambda = \tfrac{1}{2}\Gamma(-\tfrac{1}{2}) = \tfrac{1}{2}\Gamma(\tfrac{1}{2}) = \frac{\sqrt{\pi}}{2}.$$

Therefore (8.2.3) may be written as

$$(8.2.4) \qquad \text{erf}(x) = 1 - \frac{2}{\sqrt{\pi}} \int_x^\infty e^{-\xi^2}\, d\xi,$$

where

$$(8.2.5) \qquad \text{erfc}(x) = \frac{2}{\sqrt{\pi}} \int_x^\infty e^{-\xi^2}\, d\xi$$

is the *complementary error function* already met in Chapter II.

Integrating the right side of (8.2.5) by parts, we obtain

$$(8.2.6) \qquad \int_x^\infty e^{-\xi^2}\, d\xi = \frac{e^{-x^2}}{2x} - \tfrac{1}{2} \int_x^\infty \frac{e^{-\xi^2}}{2}\, d\xi.$$

* *Loc. cit.*, p. 240.

A repeated use of the integration by parts formula gives the following expression

$$(8.2.7) \quad \int_x^\infty e^{-\xi^2}\,d\xi = \frac{e^{-x^2}}{2x}\left[1 - \frac{1}{2x^2} + \frac{1\cdot 3}{(2x^2)^2} - \frac{1\cdot 3\cdot 5}{(2x^2)^3} + \cdots \right.$$

$$\left. + (-1)^{n-1}\frac{1\cdot 3\cdot 5\cdots(2n-3)}{(2x^2)^{n-1}}\right] + (-1)^n\frac{1\cdot 3\cdot 5\cdots(2n-1)}{2^n}\int_x^\infty\frac{e^{-\xi^2}}{\xi^{2n}}\,d\xi.$$

Therefore from (8.2.5) we get

$$(8.2.8) \quad \mathrm{erfc}\,(x) = \frac{e^{-x^2}}{x\sqrt{\pi}}\left[1 - \frac{1}{2x^2} + \frac{1\cdot 3}{(2x^2)^2} - \frac{1\cdot 3\cdot 5}{(2x^2)^3} + \cdots \right.$$

$$\left. + (-1)^{n-1}\frac{1\cdot 3\cdot 5(2n-3)}{(2x^2)^{n-1}}\right] + R(x,n),$$

where

$$(8.2.9) \quad R(x,n) = (-1)^n\frac{1\cdot 3\cdot 5\cdots(2n-1)}{2^{n-1}\sqrt{\pi}}\int_x^\infty\frac{e^{-\xi^2}}{\xi^{2n}}\,d\xi.$$

Now the series in the bracket is *divergent* for all values of x, since by the Cauchy ratio test $\lim\limits_{n\to\infty}\dfrac{2n-1}{2|x|^2}$ is infinite for every finite value of x, no matter how large. Nevertheless, for a *fixed* n we shall show that the remainder term $R(x,n)$ is smaller than the last term in the bracket of the expansion (8.2.8). Hence if x is large, the early terms will be small and the expansion may be used to compute the value of $\mathrm{erfc}\,(x)$.

To justify the statement made concerning the remainder, observe that the integral in (8.2.9) is increased by replacing ξ by x in $e^{-\xi^2}$. Therefore

$$(8.2.10) \quad |R(x,n)| < \frac{1\cdot 3\cdot 5\cdots(2n-1)}{2^{n-1}\sqrt{\pi}}e^{-x^2}\int_x^\infty \xi^{-2n}\,d\xi$$

$$= \frac{1\cdot 3\cdot 5\cdots(2n-3)e^{-x^2}}{2^{n-1}\sqrt{\pi}\,x^{2n-1}},$$

which is the numerical value of the term preceding $R(x,n)$ in (8.2.8).

In the case under consideration, relatively small values of x and n yield good approximations. For example, if $x = 2$ and $n = 3$, then

$$\mathrm{erfc}\,(2) = \frac{e^{-4}}{2\sqrt{\pi}}\left[1 - \frac{1}{8} + \frac{1\cdot 3}{8^2}\right] = 0\cdot 00476$$

and

$$\mathrm{erf}\,(2) = 1 - 0\cdot 00476 = 0\cdot 99524,$$

with an error $|R(2,3)| < \dfrac{3}{2^7\sqrt{\pi}}e^{-4} = 0\cdot 00024$. The value of $\mathrm{erf}\,(2)$ correct to 5 decimals is $0\cdot 99532$.

Let us now define formally what we mean by an asymptotic series. The series

$$a_0 + \frac{a_1}{x} + \frac{a_2}{x^2} + \cdots + \frac{a_n}{x^n} + \cdots ,$$

whether convergent or not, is said to be *asymptotic* to $f(x)$, and we write

$$f(x) \sim a_0 + \frac{a_1}{x} + \frac{a_2}{x^2} + \cdots + \frac{a_n}{x^n} + \cdots ,$$

if for a *fixed n*

$$\lim_{x \to \infty} \left[f(x) - \left(a_0 + \frac{a_1}{x} + \frac{a_2}{x^2} + \cdots + \frac{a_n}{x^n} \right) \right] = 0.$$

The distinction between a *convergent* series and an *asymptotic* series can be made clear as follows. Suppose that a function $f(x)$ is represented as an infinite power series which is written as a finite series $S_n(x)$ and a remainder $R(x,n)$. Thus

$$f(x) = S_n(x) + R(x,n)$$

or

$$R(x,n) = f(x) - S_n(x).$$

Then for the series to be *convergent* $\lim\limits_{n \to \infty} R(x,n) = 0$ *for a fixed value of* x, whereas, for the series to be *asymptotic* $\lim\limits_{x \to \infty} R(x,n) = 0$ *for a fixed value of* n.

8.3 The Bessel Functions $J_n(t)$ and $J_{-n}(t)$

A class of functions arising frequently in fluid dynamics, the theory of elasticity, acoustics, potential theory, etc., is the class of *Bessel functions*. These are defined by the linear differential equation

(8.3.1) $$t^2 Y''(t) + t Y'(t) + (t^2 - v^2) Y(t) = 0,$$

called *Bessel's equation of order* v after the German mathematician Friedrich Wilhelm Bessel. Here t is a real variable and the number v may be real or imaginary.

When v is *real and non-negative*, a particular solution of (8.3.1), known as the *Bessel Function of the first kind of order* v, turns out to be:*

(8.3.2) $$J_v(t) = \sum_{k=0}^{\infty} \frac{(-1)^k t^{v+2k}}{2^{v+2k} k! \Gamma(v + k + 1)} = \sum_{k=0}^{\infty} \frac{(-1)^k (t/2)^{v+2k}}{k! \Gamma(v + k + 1)}.$$

If $v = n$ is *zero* or a *positive* integer, $\Gamma(v + k + 1)$ can be replaced by $(n + k)!$ It can be shown that this series is uniformly convergent over

* See e.g., N. W. McLachlan, *Bessel Functions for Engineers.*

any finite interval and hence may be differentiated and integrated term by term.

Of special importance are the functions obtained from (8.3.2) by placing $\nu = 0$ and $\nu = 1$. Thus

$$(8.3.3) \qquad J_0(t) = 1 - \frac{t^2}{2^2} + \frac{t^4}{2^4(2!)^2} - \frac{t^6}{2^6(3!)^2} + \cdots$$
$$+ (-1)^k \frac{t^{2k}}{2^{2k}(k!)^2} + \cdots$$

and

$$(8.3.4) \qquad J_1(t) = \frac{t}{2} - \frac{t^3}{2^3 \cdot 2!} + \frac{t^5}{2^5 \cdot 2!3!} - \frac{t^7}{2^7 \cdot 3!4!} + \cdots$$
$$+ (-1)^k \frac{t^{2k+1}}{2^{2k+1} \cdot k!(k+1)!} + \cdots$$

From the preceding two series we immediately verify that

$$(8.3.5) \qquad\qquad J_0'(t) = -J_1(t).$$

The values of $J_\nu(t)$ for various orders have been tabulated and they, together with a great deal of other pertinent material, are to be found in Jahnke-Emde's *Tables of Functions*. Figure 8.3.1 shows the graphs

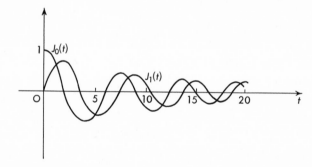

FIG. 8.3.1

of the functions $J_0(t)$ and $J_1(t)$. A detailed study reveals that: $J_0(t) = 0$ and $J_1(t) = 0$ each have an infinite number of distinct real roots; the roots of $J_0(t) = 0$ and $J_1(t) = 0$ interlace, i.e., between two successive roots of either of these equations there is exactly one root of the other; the distance between two consecutive zeros tends to π as $t \to \infty$. In this respect, $J_0(t)$ and $J_1(t)$ behave somewhat like the functions $\cos t$ and $\sin t$. Both pairs of functions have the first two properties, but $\sin t$ and $\cos t$ are periodic functions of period 2π, whereas $J_0(t)$ and $J_1(t)$ belong to the class of "almost periodic" functions, i.e., their period is "almost" 2π.

Another solution of equation (8.3.1), when ν is not zero or an integer, is obtained by replacing ν in (8.3.2) by $-\nu$.   Thus

$$(8.3.6) \qquad J_{-\nu}(t) = \sum_{k=0}^{\infty} \frac{(-1)^k(t/2)^{-\nu+2k}}{k!\Gamma(-\nu+k+1)}.$$

When $\nu = 0$ or an integer n, we have

$$(8.3.7) \qquad J_{-n}(t) = (-1)^n J_n(t).$$

This relation can be verified as follows.   Making use of (8.1.5), we have

$$\Gamma(-n+k+1) = (k-n)!$$

$$= \frac{k!}{(-n+k+1)(-n+k+2)\cdots(k-1)k},$$

which becomes ∞ as k tends to each of the values $0, 1, 2, \cdots, n-1$. Therefore, for $\nu = n$, all the terms from $k=0$ to $n-1$ in equation (8.3.6) vanish and we have

$$(8.3.8) \qquad J_{-n}(t) = \sum_{k=n}^{\infty} \frac{(-1)^k(t/2)^{-n+2k}}{k!(k-n)!} = \sum_{k=0}^{\infty} \frac{(-1)^{k+n}(t/2)^{n+2k}}{(k+n)!k!}.$$

But from (8.3.2) for $\nu = n$

$$(8.3.9) \qquad J_n(t) = \sum_{k=0}^{\infty} \frac{(-1)^k(t/2)^{n+2k}}{k!(n+k)!}.$$

Therefore, comparing (8.3.8) and (8.3.9), we obtain (8.3.7).

8.4 Identities.   The Function $Y_n(t)$

The Bessel functions are known to satisfy a number of important identities.   We shall derive a few of them.   To that end, consider

$$(8.4.1) \qquad t^\nu J_\nu(t) = \sum_{k=0}^{\infty} (-1)^k \frac{t^{2\nu+2k}}{2^{\nu+2k}k!\Gamma(\nu+k+1)},$$

and

$$(8.4.2) \qquad \frac{d}{dt}[t^\nu J_\nu(t)] = \sum_{k=0}^{\infty} (-1)^k \frac{(2\nu+2k)t^{2\nu+2k-1}}{2^{\nu+2k}k!\Gamma(\nu+k+1)}$$

$$= t^\nu \sum_{k=0}^{\infty} (-1)^k \frac{t^{\nu+2k-1}}{2^{\nu+2k-1}k!\Gamma(\nu+k)}.$$

Since the right side of the preceding equality is $t^\nu J_{\nu-1}(t)$, it follows that

$$(8.4.3) \qquad \frac{d}{dt}[t^\nu J_\nu(t)] = t^\nu J_{\nu-1}(t).$$

In a similar manner one can obtain

$$(8.4.4) \qquad \frac{d}{dt}[t^{-\nu}J_\nu(t)] = -t^{-\nu}J_{\nu+1}(t).$$

If the indicated differentiation of the product is carried out in these formulas, then

$$\frac{d}{dt}[J_\nu(t)] + \frac{\nu}{t}J_\nu(t) = J_{\nu-1}(t),$$

and

$$\frac{d}{dt}[J_\nu(t)] - \frac{\nu}{t}J_\nu(t) = -J_{\nu+1}(t),$$

from which

(8.4.5) $$2\frac{d}{dt}[J_\nu(t)] = [J_{\nu-1}(t) - J_{\nu+1}(t)]$$

and

(8.4.6) $$\frac{2\nu}{t}J_\nu(t) = J_{\nu-1}(t) + J_{\nu+1}(t).$$

Another useful relation, with the help of which the integral representation of the functions $J_n(t)$ of integral order can be obtained (see problem 7 at the end of this chapter), is the following:

(8.4.7) $$e^{(t/2)[k-(1/k)]} = J_0(t) + kJ_1(t) + k^2J_2(t) + k^3J_3(t) + \cdots$$

$$+ k^{-1}J_{-1}(t) + k^{-2}J_{-2}(t) + k^{-3}J_{-3}(t) + \cdots = \sum_{n=-\infty}^{\infty} k^nJ_n(t).$$

To prove this result, consider the series

$$e^{(t/2)k} = 1 + \left(\frac{t}{2}\right)k + \frac{1}{2!}\left(\frac{t}{2}\right)^2 k^2 + \cdots + \frac{1}{n!}\left(\frac{t}{2}\right)^n k^n + \cdots$$

and

$$e^{-(t/2)k^{-1}} = 1 - \left(\frac{t}{2}\right)k^{-1} + \frac{1}{2!}\left(\frac{t}{2}\right)^2 k^{-2} - \cdots + (-1)^n \frac{1}{n!}\left(\frac{t}{2}\right)^n k^{-n} + \cdots.$$

Upon multiplying these series, we find that the coefficient of k^n is:

$$\frac{(t/2)^n}{n!}\left[1 - \frac{(t/2)^2}{1!(n+1)} + \frac{(t/2)^4}{2!(n+1)(n+2)} - \cdots\right] = J_n(t).$$

From this formula (8.4.7) follows.

When ν is zero or a positive integer n, then another solution of Bessel's equation which is infinite at $t = 0$ is

(8.4.8) $$Y_n(t) = \frac{2}{\pi}\left(\ln\frac{t}{2} + \gamma\right)J_n(t)$$

$$+ \frac{1}{\pi}\sum_{k=0}^{\infty}(-1)^{k+1}\frac{t^{n+2k}}{2^{n+2k}k!(n+k)!}[\phi(k) + \phi(k+n)]$$

$$- \frac{1}{\pi}\sum_{k=0}^{n-1}\frac{(n-k-1)!t^{2k-n}}{2^{-n+2k}k!},$$

where γ is Euler's constant (the summation $\sum\limits_{k=0}^{n-1}$ is taken to be zero for $n = 0$),

$$\phi(k) = 1 + \tfrac{1}{2} + \cdots + \frac{1}{k}, \quad k \geqslant 1$$

and $\phi(0) = 0$. The expression $Y_n(t)$ is called Weber's form of the *Bessel function of the second kind of order n.* In particular, for $n = 0$.

$$(8.4.9) \qquad Y_0(t) = \frac{2}{\pi}\left[(\ln \frac{t}{2} + \gamma)J_0(t) + \sum_{k=0}^{\infty} (-1)^{n+1}\phi(k)\frac{t^{2k}}{2^{2k}(k!)^2}\right].$$

Unfortunately the notation for function (8.4.8) is not standard. Jahnke–Emde uses the notation $N_n(t)$ instead of $Y_n(t)$. The graphs of $Y_0(t)$ and $Y_1(t)$ are shown in Fig. 8.4.1.

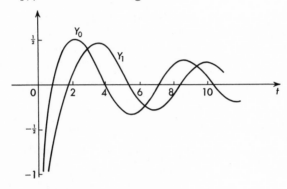

FIG. 8.4.1

8.5 The Inverse Transform of $1/\sqrt{p^2+1}$.

In this section we shall consider the problem of finding the inverse Laplace transform of a function having *two* branch points, namely, the function $f(p) = 1/\sqrt{p^2 + 1}$ having branch points at $p = \pm i$. A convenient cut to introduce in order to render $f(p)$ single valued is the line segment along the imaginary axis from $-i$ to i and an appropriate path of integration is that shown in Fig. 8.5.1, where $c > 0$ and $R > 1$.

Along the path $A_1A_2A_3A_{10}A_{11}$, $|f(p)| = \dfrac{1}{|\sqrt{p^2 + 1})|} < \dfrac{1}{|p|}$ so that

the conditions of Lemma III are satisfied and $\lim\limits_{R\to\infty} \displaystyle\int \dfrac{e^{pt}}{\sqrt{p^2 + 1}} dp$

along this path is zero. The integral of $e^{pt}/\sqrt{p^2 + 1}$ along A_3A_4 is negative that along A_4A_3 and hence their sum vanishes.

For any point on the small upper circle of radius r, $p - i = re^{i\theta}$ and $dp = rie^{i\theta}\,d\theta$, so that

$$\frac{1}{\sqrt{p^2 + 1}} = \frac{1}{\sqrt{p + i}\,\sqrt{p - i}} = \frac{1}{\sqrt{re^{i\theta}(2i + re^{i\theta})}}.$$

Thus, along this circle we have

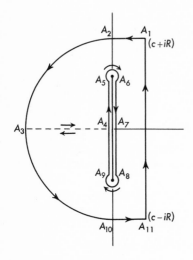

$$\int_{\frac{3}{2}\pi}^{-\pi/2} \lim_{r \to 0} \frac{e^{(i + re^{i\theta})t}\, rie^{i\theta}\,d\theta}{\sqrt{re^{i\theta}}\sqrt{2i + re^{i\theta}}}$$

$$= \int_{\frac{3}{2}\pi}^{-\pi/2} \lim_{r \to 0} \frac{e^{(i + re^{i\theta})t}\, i\sqrt{re^{i(\theta/2)}}}{\sqrt{2i + re^{i\theta}}}\,d\theta = 0.$$

A similar result is obtained for the lower circle of radius r.

  There remain to investigate the integrals along the paths $A_6 A_8$ and $A_9 A_5$ which tend to coincidence as $r \to 0$. For any point on $A_6 A_7$ or $A_4 A_5$, we have in the limit as $r \to 0$, $p = \rho i$, where ρ is the modulus of p. On the segments $A_7 A_8$, $A_9 A_4$, however, $p = -\rho i$. Moreover, in the limit as $r \to 0$, for any point on $A_6 A_8$, $\sqrt{p^2 + 1}$ $= \sqrt{1 - \rho^2}$ and on $A_9 A_5$, $\sqrt{p^2 + 1} = -\sqrt{1 - \rho^2}$. Consequently

$$\frac{1}{2\pi i}\int_{c - i\infty}^{c + i\infty} \frac{e^{pt}\,dp}{\sqrt{p^2 + 1}} + \frac{1}{2\pi i}\int_0^1 \frac{e^{i\rho t}i\,d\rho}{(-\sqrt{1 - \rho^2})} + \frac{1}{2\pi i}\int_1^0 \frac{e^{i\rho t}i\,d\rho}{\sqrt{1 - \rho^2}}$$

$$+ \frac{1}{2\pi i}\int_0^1 \frac{e^{-i\rho t}(-i\,d\rho)}{\sqrt{1 - \rho^2}} + \frac{1}{2\pi i}\int_1^0 \frac{e^{-i\rho t}(-i\,d\rho)}{(-\sqrt{1 - \rho^2})} = 0,$$

from which

$$L^{-1}\left\{\frac{1}{\sqrt{p^2 + 1}}\right\} = \frac{1}{\pi}\int_0^1 \frac{e^{i\rho t} + e^{-i\rho t}}{\sqrt{1 - \rho^2}}\,d\rho = \frac{2}{\pi}\int_0^1 \frac{\cos \rho t}{\sqrt{1 - \rho^2}}\,d\rho.$$

  By making the substitution $\rho = \cos \phi$, the integral

$$\frac{2}{\pi}\int_0^1 \frac{\cos \rho t}{\sqrt{1 - \rho^2}}\,d\rho = \frac{2}{\pi}\int_0^{\pi/2} \cos(t \cos \phi)\,d\phi = \frac{1}{\pi}\int_0^\pi \cos(t \cos \phi)\,d\phi = J_0(t),$$

where the last equality follows from problem 7 at the end of this chapter.

  Therefore,

(8.5.1) $$L^{-1}\left\{\frac{1}{\sqrt{p^2 + 1}}\right\} = J_0(t).$$

Fig. 8.5.1

We are now in the position to obtain the transforms of the higher integral order Bessel functions by means of the identities relating them. Thus, by Theorem 1 (section 3.1)

$$L\{J_1'(t)\} = pL\{J_0(t)\} - J_0(0),$$

and since $J_0(0) = 0$ and $J_0'(t) = -J_1(t)$ (formula (8.3.5)),

$$L\{-J_1(t)\} = \frac{p}{\sqrt{p^2 + 1}} - 1,$$

(8.5.2) $\quad L\{J_1(t)\} = \dfrac{\sqrt{p^2 + 1} - p}{\sqrt{p^2 + 1}} = \dfrac{1}{\sqrt{p^2 + 1}(\sqrt{p^2 + 1} + p)}.$

In order to determine $L\{J_2(t)\}$ we make use of formula (8.4.5), which for $\nu = 1$ gives

$$J_2(t) = J_0(t) - 2J_1'(t).$$

Therefore, by taking the transform of both sides, and using the formula for the transform of a derivative as well as the fact that $J_1(0) = 0$,

$$L\{J_2(t)\} = \frac{1}{\sqrt{p^2 + 1}} - 2L\{J_1'(t)\} = \frac{1}{\sqrt{p^2 + 1}} - 2[pL\{J_1(t)\} - J_1(0)]$$

$$= \frac{1}{\sqrt{p^2 + 1}} - \frac{2p}{\sqrt{p^2 + 1}(\sqrt{p^2 + 1} + p)}$$

$$= \frac{1}{\sqrt{p^2 + 1}(\sqrt{p^2 + 1} + p)^2}.$$

Proceeding similarly, we obtain

(8.5.3) $\quad L\{J_n(t)\} = \dfrac{1}{\sqrt{p^2 + 1}(\sqrt{p^2 + 1} + p)^n}, \quad n = 0, 1, 2, \cdots.$

Since $L\{F(at)\} = (1/a)f(p/a)$, where a is real and greater than zero, we obtain the more general formula

(8.5.4) $\quad L\{J_n(at)\} = \dfrac{a^n}{\sqrt{p^2 + a^2}(\sqrt{p^2 + a^2} + p)^n}, \quad n = 0, 1, 2, \cdots.$

8.6 Hankel Functions. Modified Bessel Functions. Asymptotic Expansions

In connection with the solution of problems in wave propagation it is convenient to define certain complex functions known as *Bessel Functions of order ν of the third kind* or *Hankel functions of order ν*, where ν is an arbitrary real number.   They have the following form:

(8.6.1) $\quad\quad\quad H_\nu^{(1)}(t) = J_\nu(t) + iY_\nu(t),$

$$H_\nu^{(2)}(t) = J_\nu(t) - iY_\nu(t),$$

where

(8.6.2) $\quad\quad\quad Y_\nu(t) = \dfrac{\cos \nu\pi \cdot J_\nu(t) - J_{-\nu}(t)}{\sin \nu\pi}.$

If ν is an integer n, $Y_n(t)$ assumes the indeterminate form $0/0$ and is in this case defined as $\lim\limits_{\nu \to n} Y_\nu(t)$.

The general solution of Bessel's equation

$$(8.6.3) \qquad t^2 Y''(t) + t Y'(t) + (t^2 - \nu^2) Y(t) = 0$$

can be shown to be

$$(8.6.4) \qquad Y(t) = A_1 J_\nu(t) + A_2 Y_\nu(t),$$

where A_1, A_2 are arbitrary constants. If ν is not zero or an integer the solution can be written in the form

$$(8.6.5) \qquad Y(t) = A_1 J_\nu(t) + A_2 J_{-\nu}(t).$$

A number of differential equations reduce to Bessel's equation after a suitable transformation of variables. For our purpose it will be sufficient to consider a simple but important case which leads to Bessel functions involving imaginary arguments. Thus, consider the equation

$$(8.6.6) \qquad t^2 Y''(t) + t Y'(t) - (t^2 + \nu^2) Y(t) = 0.$$

If we make the substitution $it = \tau$, then (8.6.6) becomes

$$\tau^2 Y''(-i\tau) + \tau Y'(-i\tau) + (\tau^2 - \nu^2) Y(-i\tau) = 0,$$

whose general solution is

$$Y(-i\tau) = A_\nu J_\nu(\tau) + A_2 Y_\nu(\tau).$$

Hence the solution of (8.6.6) is

$$(8.6.7) \qquad Y(t) = A_1 J_\nu(it) + A_2 Y_\nu(it).$$

As before, if ν is different from zero or an integer, the solution of (8.6.6) can be written as

$$(8.6.8) \qquad Y(t) = A_1 J_\nu(it) + A_2 J_{-\nu}(it).$$

In practice it is more convenient to define the function

$$(8.6.9) \qquad I_\nu(t) = i^{-\nu} J_\nu(it),$$

which is real, as a fundamental solution of equation (8.6.6). It is called the *modified Bessel function of the first kind of order* ν. A second fundamental solution of equation (8.6.6)—the *modified Bessel function of the second kind*—is defined to be

$$(8.6.10) \qquad K_\nu(t) = \frac{\pi/2}{\sin \nu\pi} [I_{-\nu}(t) - I_\nu(t)].$$

As in the case of $Y_\nu(t)$, when $\nu = n$ is an integer, $K_\nu(t)$ is defined to be $\lim\limits_{\nu \to n} K_\nu(t)$.

In terms of the new functions just defined, the solutions of (8.6.6) corresponding to the expressions (8.6.7) and (8.6.8) are

$$(8.6.11) \qquad Y(t) = A_1 I_\nu(t) + A_2 K_\nu(t),$$

and

(8.6.12) $Y(t) = A_1 I_\nu(t) + A_2 I_{-\nu}(t).$

In general, the series defining the Bessel functions converge very slowly for large values of t and hence it is important to obtain asymptotic expansions of these functions. Unfortunately, their analysis would take us outside the scope of this work and we therefore refer the student to standard works on Bessel functions such as Watson's *Theory of Bessel Functions* for their derivations. For future reference, however, we give the following asymptotic expansions of $J_0(t)$ and $Y_0(t)$:

$$(8.6.13) \quad J_0(t) \sim \frac{\cos(t - \pi/4)}{\sqrt{\pi t/2}}\left[1 - \frac{(1 \cdot 3)^2}{2!(8t)^2} + \frac{(1 \cdot 3 \cdot 5 \cdot 7)^2}{4!(8t)^4} - \cdots\right]$$

$$+ \frac{\sin(t - \pi/4)}{\sqrt{\pi t/2}}\left[\frac{1}{8t} - \frac{(3 \cdot 5)^2}{3!(8t)^3} + \cdots\right],$$

$$(8.6.14) \quad Y_0(t) \sim \frac{\sin(t - \pi/4)}{\sqrt{\pi t/2}}\left[1 - \frac{(1 \cdot 3)^2}{2!(8t)^2} + \frac{(1 \cdot 3 \cdot 5 \cdot 7)^2}{4!(8t)^4} - \cdots\right]$$

$$+ \frac{\sin(t - \pi/4)}{\sqrt{\pi t/2}}\left[\frac{1}{8t} - \frac{(3 \cdot 5)^2}{3!(8t)^3} + \cdots\right].$$

8.7 Some Non-Elementary Integrals

We shall now consider a group of integrals which arise frequently in the applications. The first of these is the so-called *sine-integral* defined by the expression

$$(8.7.1) \quad\quad SI(t) = \int_t^\infty \frac{\sin \tau}{\tau}\, d\tau, \quad t > 0.$$

To obtain a series convergent for all values of t we may proceed by writing (8.7.1) as follows:

$$(8.7.2) \quad\quad SI(t) = \int_0^\infty \frac{\sin \tau}{\tau}\, d\tau - \int_0^t \frac{\sin \tau}{\tau}\, d\tau.$$

Then, by expanding the integrand of the second integral as a power series and integrating term by term and making use of the fact that

$$(8.7.3) \quad\quad \int_0^\infty \frac{\sin \tau}{\tau}\, d\tau = \frac{\pi}{2},$$

(see Example 4, section 1.12), it follows that

$$(8.7.4) \quad SI(t) = \frac{\pi}{2} - t + \frac{t^3}{3 \cdot 3!} - \frac{t^5}{5 \cdot 5!} + \frac{t^7}{7 \cdot 7!} - \cdots.$$

This series converges rapidly for small values of t. To make it useful for large values of t, an asymptotic expansion is resorted to. By a repeated use of the integration by parts formula applied to (8.7.1), we obtain

$$(8.7.5) \qquad SI(t) = \frac{\cos t}{t} + \frac{\sin t}{t^2} - 2! \frac{\cos t}{t^3} - 3! \frac{\sin t}{t^4} + \cdots.$$

Let us now determine the transform of the sine-integral. From (8.7.2) and (8.7.3)

$$SI(t) = \frac{\pi}{2} - \int_0^t \frac{\sin \tau}{\tau} d\tau,$$

and therefore

$$(8.7.6) \qquad L\{SI(t)\} = \frac{\pi}{2p} - L\left\{ \int_0^t \frac{\sin \tau}{\tau} d\tau \right\}.$$

Now $L\{\sin t\} = \dfrac{1}{p^2 + 1}$ for $\mathrm{Re}(p) > 0$ and $\lim\limits_{t \to 0+} \dfrac{\sin t}{t} = 1$. Hence by Theorem 7,

$$(8.7.7) \qquad L\left\{\frac{\sin t}{t}\right\} = \int_p^\infty \frac{dp}{p^2 + 1} = \arctan p \Big]_p^\infty = \frac{\pi}{2} - \arctan p,$$

and by Theorem 3,

$$L\left\{ \int_0^t \frac{\sin \tau}{\tau} d\tau \right\} = \frac{1}{p}\left(\frac{\pi}{2} - \arctan p \right).$$

Substituting this result in (8.7.6), we see that

$$(8.7.8) \qquad L\{SI(t)\} = \frac{\arctan p}{p}, \quad \mathrm{Re}(p) > 0.$$

Another function of some importance is the following so-called *cosine-integral*

$$(8.7.9) \qquad CI(t) = \int_t^\infty \frac{\cos \tau}{\tau} d\tau, \quad t > 0.$$

To obtain its asymptotic expansion, we proceed as in connection with the sine-integral by making use of the integration by parts formula. This procedure yields the following expansion

$$(8.7.10) \quad CI(t) = -\frac{\sin t}{t} + \frac{\cos t}{t^2} + 2! \frac{\sin t}{t^3} - 3! \frac{\cos t}{t^4} - \cdots.$$

The transform of the cosine-integral can be obtained as follows. Making the substitution $\tau = \xi t$ in (8.7.9), we get

$$(8.7.11) \qquad CI(t) = \int_1^\infty \frac{\cos \xi t}{\xi} d\xi,$$

and therefore

$$L\{CI(t)\} = \int_0^\infty e^{-pt} \left\{ \int_1^\infty \frac{\cos \xi t}{\xi} d\xi \right\} dt = \int_1^\infty \frac{1}{\xi} \left\{ \int_0^\infty e^{-pt} \cos \xi t \, dt \right\} d\xi$$

$$= p \int_1^\infty \frac{d\xi}{\xi(p^2 + \xi^2)} = \frac{1}{2p} \ln \frac{\xi^2}{p^2 + \xi^2} \Big]_1^\infty.$$

When evaluated, the last expression gives

$$(8.7.12) \qquad L\{CI(t)\} = \frac{1}{2p} \ln (p^2 + 1), \quad \mathrm{Re}(p) > 0.$$

Remark. In obtaining this result an interchange of order of integration was made. For the validity of such a change of order we refer the reader, e.g., to H. S. Carslaw's *Fourier Series and Integrals* for a detailed discussion of this point.

The last non-elementary integral to be mentioned in this section is the *exponential-integral*

$$(8.7.13) \qquad\qquad EI(t) = \int_t^\infty \frac{e^{-\tau}}{\tau} d\tau, \quad t > 0.$$

The derivation of its asymptotic expansion and Laplace transform will be left to the student in the form of exercises at the end of this chapter.

8.8 The Fresnel Sine and Cosine Integrals

Two integrals of great importance in the theory of optics are the following:

$$(8.8.1) \qquad FS(t) = \int_0^t \sin \tau^2 \, d\tau, \qquad FC(t) = \int_0^t \cos \tau^2 \, d\tau,$$

known as Fresnel's sine and cosine integrals, respectively.

Expanding the integrands in each of the above integrals and integrating term by term, it is easy to verify the following expansions

$$(8.8.2) \quad FS(t) = \frac{t^3}{3} - \frac{t^7}{7 \cdot 3!} + \frac{t^{11}}{11 \cdot 5!} - \cdots$$
$$+ (-1)^{n+1} \frac{t^{4n-1}}{(4n-1)(2n-1)!} + \cdots$$

and

$$(8.8.3) \quad FC(t) = t - \frac{t^5}{5 \cdot 2!} + \frac{t^9}{9 \cdot 4!} - \cdots$$
$$+ (-1)^{n+1} \frac{(4n-3)(2n-2)!}{t^{4n-3}} + \cdots.$$

These power series are easily seen to be convergent for all values of t. Notice that both functions are odd, i.e., $FS(-t) = -FS(t)$ and $FC(-t) = -FC(t)$.

Of particular importance are the values of the infinite Fresnel integrals

$$(8.8.4) \qquad FS(\infty) = \int_0^\infty \sin \tau^2 \, d\tau \quad \text{and} \quad FC(\infty) = \int_0^\infty \cos \tau^2 \, d\tau.$$

We shall show how the Laplace transform can be used to evaluate integrals such as these. To evaluate the first integral in (8.8.4), say, we introduce the parameter t and write

$$(8.8.5) \qquad F(t) = \int_0^\infty \sin t\tau^2 \, d\tau, \quad t > 0.$$

Taking the Laplace transform and interchanging the order of integration, we get

$$(8.8.6) \qquad L\{F(t)\} = f(p) = \int_0^\infty \frac{\tau^2}{\tau^4 + p^2} \, d\tau.$$

By decomposition into partial fractions, the integrand can be written as follows

$$\frac{\tau^2}{\tau^4 + p^2} \equiv \frac{1}{2\sqrt{2p}} \left[\frac{\tau}{\tau^2 - \tau\sqrt{2p} + p} - \frac{\tau}{\tau^2 + \tau\sqrt{2p} + p} \right].$$

Substituting this result in (8.8.6) and integrating, we obtain

$$f(p) = \frac{1}{2\sqrt{2p}} \left[\frac{1}{2} \ln \frac{\tau^2 - \tau\sqrt{2p} + p}{\tau^2 + \tau\sqrt{2p} + p} + \arctan \left(\tau\sqrt{\frac{2}{p}} - 1 \right) \right.$$
$$\left. + \arctan \left(\tau\sqrt{\frac{2}{p}} + 1 \right) \right]_0^\infty = \frac{\pi}{2\sqrt{2p}}.$$

Therefore

$$\int_0^\infty \sin t\tau^2 \, d\tau = F(t) = L^{-1} \left\{ \frac{\pi}{2\sqrt{2p}} \right\} = \frac{1}{2}\sqrt{\frac{\pi}{2t}}, \quad t > 0.$$

In particular,

$$(8.8.7) \qquad FS(\infty) = \int_0^\infty \sin \tau^2 \, d\tau = \frac{1}{2}\sqrt{\frac{\pi}{2}}.$$

8.9 Abel's Integral Equation

An integral equation is one in which the unknown function appears under the integral sign. The great Norwegian mathematician Niels Abel (1802–1829) considered and solved the integral equation arising in what is now a classical problem, the so-called *tautochrone problem*.

This problem may be stated in the following way. A heavy bead of mass m slides (without friction) from rest down a curve to the origin O. Determine the curve for which the time required for the bead to descend to O is the same regardless of the starting position. Thus the name tautochrone, which literally means: *of same time.* We proceed to solve this problem by means of the Laplace transform.

In Fig. 8.9.1, $P(x,y)$ represents the starting point, $Q(\xi,\eta)$ any point between O and $P(x,y)$, and $s(\eta)$ the length of the arc OQ. Since the gain in kinetic energy is equal to the loss in potential energy, we have

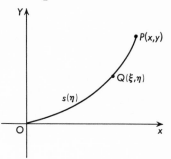

$$\tfrac{1}{2}m\left(\frac{ds}{dt}\right)^2 = mg(y - \eta),$$

from which

$$(8.9.1) \qquad \frac{ds}{dt} = -\sqrt{2g(y - \eta)}, \qquad\qquad \text{FIG. 8.9.1}$$

where the minus sign was chosen because s is a decreasing function of η. From (8.9.1)

$$dt = -\frac{ds(\eta)}{\sqrt{2g(y - \eta)}} = -\frac{s'(\eta)d\eta}{\sqrt{2g(y - \eta)}},$$

whence

$$\int_0^T dt = -\frac{1}{\sqrt{2g}}\int_y^0 (y - \eta)^{-\frac{1}{2}}s'(\eta)\, d\eta$$

and

$$(8.9.2) \qquad T(y) = \frac{1}{\sqrt{2g}}\int_0^y (y - \eta)^{-\frac{1}{2}}s'(\eta)\, d\eta.$$

The problem now is to solve this integral equation for the unknown $s'(\eta)$ when the function $T(y)$ is given. In our case $T(y) = T_0$, where T_0 is a constant. Thus

$$(8.9.3) \qquad T_0 = \frac{1}{\sqrt{2g}}\int_0^y (y - \eta)^{-\frac{1}{2}}s'(\eta)\, d\eta,$$

or, since the integral here is of the convolution type, it may also be written as

$$(8.9.4) \qquad T_0\sqrt{2g} = y^{-\frac{1}{2}}*s'(y).$$

Taking the transform of both sides with respect to y and making use of Theorem 5, we obtain

$$\frac{T_0\sqrt{2g}}{p} = \sqrt{\frac{\pi}{g}}L\{s'(y)\} = \sqrt{\frac{\pi}{g}}(pL\{s(y)\} - s(0)),$$

and since $s(0) = 0$, it follows that

$$L\{s(y)\} = \frac{T_0\sqrt{2g}}{p^{3/2}\sqrt{\pi}},$$

from which

(8.9.5) $$s(y) = \frac{2T_0\sqrt{2gy}}{\pi}.$$

It is readily verified that this function satisfies equation (8.9.3).

From (8.9.5), $\dfrac{ds}{dy} = \dfrac{\sqrt{2g}\,T_0}{\pi\sqrt{y}}$. Substituting this result in $(ds/dy)^2$

$= (dx/dy)^2 + 1$, and solving for dx/dy we get

$$\frac{dx}{dy} = \sqrt{\frac{2gT_0^2}{\pi^2 y} - 1} = \sqrt{\frac{a-y}{y}},$$

where $a = 2gT_0^2/\pi^2$. This leads to the equation

$$dx = \sqrt{\frac{a-y}{y}}\,dy,$$

which when integrated by elementary methods yields

(8.9.6) $$x = a \arccos \frac{a-y}{a} + \sqrt{2ay - y^2},$$

where the constant of integration turns out to be zero when evaluated since $x = 0$ when $y = 0$. The expression (8.9.6) is the Cartesian coordinate equation of the *cycloid*, one arch of which is the tautochrone of our problem.

Equation (8.9.2) is a particular case of the more general equation

(8.9.7) $$F(t) = \int_0^t (t - \tau)^{-k} Y'(\tau)\, d\tau, \quad (0 < k < 1),$$

which is called *Abel's integral equation*.

8.10 Integral Equations of the Convolution Type

The Abel integral equation of the preceding section is but a special case of the more general integral equation of the convolution type, namely,

(8.10.1) $$Y(t) = F(t) + \int_0^t K(t - \tau) Y(\tau)\, d\tau,$$

where $K(t - \tau)$, called the *kernel* of the integral equation, and $F(t)$ are *known* functions and $Y(t)$ is the *unknown* function.

This equation can also be written in the form

(8.10.2) $$Y(t) = F(t) + K(t) * Y(t),$$

the Laplace transform of which yields the algebraic equation

$$y(p) = f(p) + k(p)y(p).$$

Solving it for $y(p)$, we obtain

(8.10.3) $$y(p) = L\{Y(t)\} = \frac{f(p)}{1 - k(p)},$$

whence

(8.10.4) $$Y(t) = L^{-1}\left\{\frac{f(p)}{1 - k(p)}\right\}.$$

Example I.   Solve the integral equation

$$Y(t) = at + b^2 \int_0^t (t - \tau) Y(\tau) \, d\tau.$$

Since $L\{at\} = a/p^2$ and $L\{b^2t\} = b^2/p^2$, by formula (8.10.4) we have

$$Y(t) = L^{-1}\left\{\frac{a/p^2}{1 - b^2/p^2}\right\} = L^{-1}\left\{\frac{a}{p^2 - b^2}\right\} = \frac{a}{b} \sinh bt.$$

This result can be shown to be a solution by direct substitution in the given equation.

Example 2.   Find the solution of the *integro-differential* equation

$$Y'(t) + Y(t) = a - \int_0^t e^{(t-\tau)} Y(\tau) \, d\tau,$$

when $Y(0) = 0$.

The transform of both sides gives the following algebraic equation

$$py(p) + y(p) = \frac{a}{p} - \frac{y(p)}{p - 1},$$

which when solved for $y(p)$ yields

$$y(p) = \frac{a(p - 1)}{p^3}.$$

Taking the inverse transform of both sides, we obtain

$$Y(t) = a(t - t^2/2),$$

which can be shown to satisfy the given equation.

PROBLEMS

1. Find the residue of $\Gamma(p)$ at $p = -n$, where n is a non-negative integer.
   Ans. $(-1)^n/n! = (-1)^n/\Gamma(n + 1)$.

2. Find the sum of the residues of $\Gamma(p)$ at its poles.
   Ans. $1/e$.

3. (a) Show that $\Gamma\left(\dfrac{11}{2}\right) = \dfrac{1 \cdot 3 \cdot 5 \cdot 7 \cdot 9}{2^5} \sqrt{\pi}.$

   (b) Show that $\Gamma\left(\dfrac{n+1}{2}\right) = \dfrac{1 \cdot 3 \cdot 5 \cdots (n-3)(n-1)}{2^{n/2}} \sqrt{\pi}$, if n is an *even positive* integer.

4. Show that (a) $J_{1/2}(t) = \sqrt{2/(\pi t)} \sin t$,

        (b) $J_{-1/2}(t) = \sqrt{2/(\pi t)} \cos t$.

5. Prove that (a) $J_2(t) = J_0(t) + 2J_0''(t)$,

        (b) $J_0''(t) = J_2(t) + t^{-1}J_0'(t)$,

        (c) $\displaystyle\int_0^x \tau^\nu J_{\nu-1}(a\tau)\, d\tau = \dfrac{x^\nu}{a} J_\nu(ax), \ \nu \geqslant 0.$

6. By substituting $k = e^{i\phi}$ in formula (8.4.7), show that
   (a) $\cos (t \sin \phi) = J_0(t) + 2J_2(t) \cos 2\phi + 2J_4(t) \cos 4\phi + \cdots,$
   (b) $\sin (t \sin \phi) = 2J_1(t) + 2J_3(t) \sin 3\phi + 2J_5(t) \sin 5\phi + \cdots.$

7. Obtain the following integral representation:

$$J_n(t) = \frac{1}{\pi} \int_0^\pi \cos (n\phi - t \sin \phi)\, d\phi,$$

where $n = 0, 1, 2, \cdots$. In particular, verify that

$$J_0(t) = \frac{1}{\pi} \int_0^\pi \cos (t \cos \phi)\, d\phi.$$

8. Obtain the $L^{-1}\{1/\sqrt{p^2 + 1}\}$ in the following way. Write $1/\sqrt{p^2 + 1}$
$= \dfrac{1}{p}\left(1 + \dfrac{1}{p^2}\right)^{-\frac{1}{2}}$, expand by the binomial theorem and apply the inverse
transform to each of the resulting series. (Note that the last step involves the interchange of the operations Σ and L^{-1}, a step which can be justified rigorously.)

9. Making use of formula (8.4.6), show that

$$L\{nJ_n(at)/t\} = \frac{a^n}{(\sqrt{p^2 + a^2} + p)^n}, \quad n = 0, 1, 2, \cdots.$$

10. Show that $I_\nu(\tau)$ satisfies the following relations:

   (a) $\dfrac{d}{d\tau}[\tau^\nu I_\nu(\tau)] = \tau^\nu I_{\nu-1}(\tau),$

   (b) $\dfrac{d}{d\tau}[\tau^{-\nu} I_\nu(\tau)] = \tau^{-\nu} I_{\nu+1}(\tau),$

   (c) $\dfrac{dI_\nu}{d\tau} = \frac{1}{2}[I_{\nu-1} + I_{\nu+1}],$

   (d) $\dfrac{2\nu}{\tau} I_\nu = I_{\nu-1} - I_{\nu+1}.$

11. Derive the following asymptotic expansion of the exponential-integral

$$EI(t) = e^{-t}\left[\frac{1}{t} - \frac{1}{t^2} + \frac{2!}{t^3} - \cdots + (-1)^n\frac{n!}{t^{n+1}}\right] + R_{n+1},$$

where

$$R_{n+1} = (-1)^{n+1}(n+1)!\int_t^\infty e^{-\tau}\,\tau^{-n-2}\,d\tau.$$

Show that

$$|R_{n+1}| \leqslant (n+1)!\,e^{-t}\,t^{-n-2}.$$

12. Verify that

$$L\{EI(t)\} = \frac{\ln(p+1)}{p}, \quad \mathrm{Re}(p) > 0.$$

13. Verify the following asymptotic expansions:

(a) $\displaystyle\int_t^\infty \sin\tau^2\,d\tau = \frac{\cos t^2}{2t} + \frac{\sin t^2}{2^2 t^3} - \frac{3\cos t^2}{2^3 t^5} - \frac{3\cdot 5\sin t^2}{2^4 t^7} + \cdots,$

(b) $\displaystyle\int_t^\infty \cos\tau^2\,d\tau = -\frac{\sin t^2}{2t} + \frac{\cos t^2}{2^2 t^3} + \frac{3\sin t^2}{2^3 t^5} - \frac{3\cdot 5\cos t^2}{2^4 t^7} - \cdots.$

(c) Find $\displaystyle\int_{10}^\infty \sin\tau^2\,d\tau$ to three decimals.

(d) Using formula (8.8.7) and series (a) of this exercise, find the value $FS(10)$.

14. Obtain the following formulas:

(a) $\displaystyle\int_0^\infty \cos t\tau^2\,d\tau = \tfrac{1}{2}\sqrt{\frac{\pi}{2t}}, \quad t > 0.$

(b) $\displaystyle\int_0^\infty \frac{e^{-t\tau}}{\sqrt{\tau}}d\tau = \sqrt{\frac{\pi}{t}}, \quad t > 0.$

15. The *Laguerre polynomial* of degree n is defined as follows:

$$L_n(t) = \frac{e^t}{n!}\frac{d^n}{dt^n}(t^n e^{-t}), \quad n = 0, 1, 2, \cdots; \ -\infty < t < \infty.$$

(a) Find the first three Laguerre polynomials: $L_0(t)$, $L_1(t)$ and $L_2(t)$.
(b) Using Theorem 1, successively, and noting that $L_n(0) = 0$, show that

$$L\{L_n(t)\} = \frac{(p-1)^n}{p^{n+1}}, \quad \mathrm{Re}(p) > 0.$$

16. Show that the solution of Abel's integral equation:

$$F(t) = \int_0^t (t-\tau)^{-k} Y'(\tau)\,d\tau, \quad 0 < k < 1$$

is

$$Y(t) = Y(0) + \frac{\sin k\pi}{\pi}\int_0^t (t-\tau)^{k-1}F(\tau)\,d\tau.$$

17. Solve the following integral equations:

(a) $Y(t) = \cos t + \int_0^t (t - \tau) Y(\tau) \, d\tau,$

(b) $t = \int_0^t \sin (t - \tau) Y(\tau) \, d\tau,$

(c) $Y(t) = e^t + \int_0^t (t - \tau)^2 Y(\tau) \, d\tau.$

18. Find the solution of the following integro-differential equation

$$Y'(t) + a Y(t) = b + \int_0^t \cos (t - \tau) Y(\tau) \, d\tau.$$

CHAPTER IX

Further Problems in Partial Differential Equations

Bessel functions occur very frequently in the solution of a variety of problems, especially vibrating systems having symmetry about an axis. Such systems and others will form the subject matter of this chapter.

9.1 A Transmission Line Problem for Which G = 0

In chapter VII the transmission line equation

$$(9.1.1) \qquad V_{xx}(x,t) - LCV_{tt}(x,t) - (RC + LG)V_t(x,t) + RGV(x,t) = 0$$

was solved for a number of cases in which one or more of the transmission line constants R, L, C, and G were neglected. Another important problem arises when the leakage $G = 0$ and the remaining constants are present, so that equation (9.1.1) becomes

$$(9.1.2) \qquad V_{xx}(x,t) - LCV_{tt}(x,t) - RCV_t(x,t) = 0.$$

(a) *Semi-infinite Line.* Suppose now that a semi-infinite line is dead initially and that at $t = 0$ a constant voltage V_0 is impressed at the end $x = 0$. It is required to find the voltage $V(x,t)$ and the current $I(x,t)$ for $t > 0$. The boundary value problem for the voltage $V(x,t)$ is then

$$(9.1.3) \qquad V_{xx}(x,t) - LCV_{tt}(x,t) - RCV_t(x,t) = 0 \qquad (x > 0, t > 0),$$

$$(9.1.4) \qquad V(x,0) = V_t(x,0) = 0 \qquad (x > 0),$$

$$(9.1.5) \qquad V(0,t) = V_0, \qquad \lim_{x \to \infty} V(x,t) = 0 \qquad (t > 0).$$

If, as usual, we let $L_t\{V(x,t)\} = v(x,p)$ and take transforms of the terms of equations (9.1.3) and (9.1.5), then $v(x,p)$ must satisfy the following conditions:

$$(9.1.6) \qquad v_{xx}(x,p) - LCp(p + R/L)v(x,p) = 0 \qquad (x > 0),$$

$$(9.1.7) \qquad v(0,p) = V_0/p, \qquad \lim_{x \to \infty} v(x,p) = 0.$$

The general solution of (9.1.6) convenient for our problem is

$$v(x,p) = c_1 \exp\left(x\sqrt{LC}\sqrt{p(p + R/L)}\right) + c_2 \exp\left(-x\sqrt{LC}\sqrt{p(p + R/L)}\right),$$

where $\exp(\xi) = e^\xi$. Applying conditions (9.1.7) to it, we find that $c_1 = 0$ and $c_2 = V_0/p$. Therefore,

$$(9.1.8) \qquad v(x,p) = (V_0/p) \exp\left(-x\sqrt{LC}\sqrt{p(p + R/L)}\right)$$

and

$$(9.1.9) \quad V(x,t) = V_0 L^{-1}\{(1/p)\exp\left(-x\sqrt{LC}\sqrt{p(p + R/L)}\right)\}$$
$$= V_0 L^{-1}\{(1/p)\exp\left(-x\sqrt{LC}\sqrt{(p + R/2L)^2 - (R/2L)^2}\right)\}.$$

Now

$$(9.1.10) \quad L^{-1}\{(1/p)\exp\left(-x\sqrt{LC}\sqrt{(p + R/2L)^2 - (R/2L)^2}\right)\}$$
$$= L^{-1}\{(1/p)\exp\left(-x\sqrt{LC}(p + R/2L)\right)\}$$
$$+ L^{-1}\{(1/p)[\exp\left(-x\sqrt{LC}\sqrt{(p + R/2L)^2 - (R/2L)^2}\right)$$
$$- \exp\left(-x\sqrt{LC}(p + R/2L)\right)]\}.$$

Also, from Translation Theorem I

$$(9.1.11) \quad L^{-1}\{(1/p)\exp\left(-x\sqrt{LC}(p + R/2L)\right)\}$$
$$= \exp\left(-(R/2)x\sqrt{C/L}\right)1(t - x\sqrt{LC}).$$

and from (formula 79) as well as Translation Theorem II

$$L^{-1}\{\exp\left(-x\sqrt{LC}\sqrt{(p + R/2L)^2 - (R/2L)^2}\right)$$
$$- \exp\left(-x\sqrt{LC}(p + R/2L)\right)\}$$
$$= x(R/2)\sqrt{C/L}(t^2 - x^2 LC)^{-\frac{1}{2}}I_1(R\sqrt{t^2 - x^2 LC}/2L)$$
$$\exp\left(-Rt/2L\right)1(t - x\sqrt{LC}),$$

Moreover, from Theorem 3 (formula (3.2.2))

$$(9.1.12) \quad L^{-1}\{(1/p)[\exp\left(-x\sqrt{LC}\sqrt{(p + R/2L)^2 - (R/2L)^2}\right)$$
$$- \exp\left(-x\sqrt{LC}(p + R/2L)\right)]\}$$
$$= (R/2)x\sqrt{C/L}\left\{\int_0^t (\tau^2 - x^2 LC)^{-\frac{1}{2}}I_1(R\sqrt{\tau^2 - x^2 LC}/2L)\right.$$
$$\left. \exp\left(-R\tau/2L\right)d\tau\right\}1(t - x\sqrt{LC}).$$

Therefore, substituting (9.1.12) and (9.1.11) in (9.1.10) and the result in (9.1.9), we obtain

$$V(x,t) = V_0 \exp\left(-(R/2)x\sqrt{C/L}\right)1(t - x\sqrt{LC})$$
$$+ (V_0 R/2)x\sqrt{C/L}\left\{\int_0^t (\tau^2 - x^2 LC)^{-\frac{1}{2}}I_1(R\sqrt{\tau^2 - x^2 LC}/2L)\right.$$
$$\left. \exp\left(-R\tau/2L\right)d\tau\right\}1(t - x\sqrt{LC}),$$

where I_1 is the modified Bessel function of the *first* kind of order *one*.

In order to determine the current $I(x,t)$ we shall make use of equation (7.5.1), namely,

$$(9.1.13) \qquad V_x(x,t) = -RI(x,t) - LI_t(x,t),$$

whose transform with respect to t is

(9.1.14) $\qquad v_x(x,p) = -\,Ri(x,p) - L[pi(x,p) - I(x,0)].$

Since the line is initially dead, $I(x,0) = 0$ and from (9.1.8) by differentiating with respect to x,

$$v_x(x,p) = -\,V_0\sqrt{LC}p^{-\frac12}\sqrt{p + R/L}\,\exp\,(-\,x\sqrt{LC}\sqrt{p(p + R/L)}).$$

Hence from (9.1.14) we obtain

$$i(x,p) = V_0\sqrt{C/L}\,\exp\,(-\,x\sqrt{LC}\sqrt{p(p + R/L)})/\sqrt{p(p + R/L)}$$
$$= V_0\sqrt{C/L}\,\exp\,(-\,x\sqrt{LC}\sqrt{(p + R/2L)^2 - (R/2L)^2})/$$
$$\sqrt{(p + R/2L)^2 - (R/2L)^2}.$$

Translation Theorem II and formula 81 ($\nu = 0$) now yields

$$I(x,t) = V_0\sqrt{C/L}\,e^{-(R/2L)t}I_0(R\sqrt{t^2 - x^2LC}/2L)1(t - x\sqrt{LC}),$$

where I_0 is the modified Bessel function of the *first* kind of order *zero*.

(b) *Finite Line.* If initially a line of length l is dead, a constant voltage V_0 is impressed at $x = 0$ and the end $x = l$ is grounded, then the boundary value problem to be solved is

(9.1.15) $\qquad V_{xx}(x,t) - LCV_{tt}(x,t) - RCV_t(x,t) = 0$
$$(0 < x < l, \, t > 0),$$

(9.1.16) $\qquad V(x,0) = V_t(x,0) = 0 \qquad\qquad (0 < x < l),$

(9.1.17) $\qquad V(0,t) = V_0, \qquad V(l,t) = 0 \qquad\qquad (t > 0).$

The problem in the transform is

(9.1.18) $\qquad v_{xx}(x,p) - LCp(p + R/L)v(x,p) = 0 \qquad\qquad (x > 0),$

(9.1.19) $\qquad v(0,p) = V_0/p, \qquad v(l,p) = 0.$

A solution of (9.1.18) suitable for our purposes is the following

(9.1.20) $\quad v(x,p) = c_1 \cosh x\sqrt{LC}\sqrt{p(p + R/L)}$
$$+ \, c_2 \sinh x\sqrt{LC}\sqrt{p(p + R/L)}.$$

Conditions (9.1.19) applied to this equation yields the simultaneous system

$$c_1 \cosh l\sqrt{LC}\sqrt{p(p + R/L)} + c_2 \sinh l\sqrt{LC}\sqrt{p(p + R/L)} = 0,$$
$$V_0/p = c_1.$$

The values of c_1 and c_2 obtained from this system when substituted in (9.1.20) gives the equation

(9.1.21) $\qquad v(x,p) = \dfrac{V_0}{p}\,\dfrac{\sinh\,(l - x)\sqrt{LC}\sqrt{p(p + R/L)}}{\sinh l\sqrt{LC}\sqrt{p(p + R/L)}},$

from which

(9.1.22) $\qquad V(x,t) = V_0L^{-1}\left\{\dfrac{\sinh\,(l - x)\sqrt{LC}\sqrt{p(p + R/L)}}{p \sinh l\sqrt{LC}\sqrt{p(p + R/L)}}\right\}.$

Now

$$(9.1.23) \quad \frac{\sinh(l-x)\sqrt{LC}\sqrt{p(p+R/L)}}{p \sinh l\sqrt{LC}\sqrt{p(p+R/L)}}$$

$$= \frac{\exp[-x\sqrt{LC}\sqrt{p(p+R/L)}] - \exp[-(2l-x)\sqrt{LC}\sqrt{p(p+R/L)}]}{p(1-\exp[-2l\sqrt{LC}\sqrt{p(p+R/L)}])}$$

$$= (1/p)(\exp[-x\sqrt{LC}\sqrt{p(p+R/L)}]$$

$$- \exp[-(2l-x)\sqrt{LC}\sqrt{p(p+R/L)}]) \sum_{n=0}^{\infty} \exp[-2nl\sqrt{LC}\sqrt{p(p+R/L)}]$$

$$= (1/p)\sum_{n=0}^{\infty}\left\{\exp[-(x+2nl)\sqrt{LC}\sqrt{p(p+R/L)}]\right.$$

$$\left. - \exp[-(2(n+1)l-x)\sqrt{LC}\sqrt{p(p+R/L)}]\right\}$$

$$= (1/p)\sum_{n=0}^{\infty}\left\{\exp[-(x+2nl)\sqrt{LC}\sqrt{p(p+R/L)}]\right.$$

$$\left. - \exp[-(x+2nl)\sqrt{LC}(p+R/2L)]\right\}$$

$$- (1/p)\sum_{n=0}^{\infty}\left\{\exp[-(2(n+1)l-x)\sqrt{LC}\sqrt{p(p+R/L)}]\right.$$

$$\left. - \exp[-(2(n+1)l-x)\sqrt{LC}(p+R/2L)]\right\}$$

$$+ (1/p)\sum_{n=0}^{\infty}\exp[-(x+2nl)\sqrt{LC}(p+R/2L)]$$

$$- (1/p)\sum_{n=0}^{\infty}\exp[-(2(n+1)l-x)\sqrt{LC}(p+R/2L)].$$

Proceeding as in the derivation of the solution for $V(x,t)$ in the case of the semi-infinite line, we find, upon taking the inverse of the members of (9.1.23) and substituting in (9.1.22), that

$$V(x,t) = V_0 \sum_{n=0}^{\infty}\left\{e^{-\frac{1}{2}R(x+2nl)\sqrt{C/L}}\right.$$

$$+ \tfrac{1}{2}R(x+2nl)\sqrt{C/L}\int_0^t e^{-R\tau/(2L)}\frac{I_1(R\sqrt{\tau^2-(x+2nl)^2LC}/2L)}{\sqrt{\tau^2-(x+2nl)^2LC}}d\tau\right\}$$

$$1(t-(x+2nl)\sqrt{LC}) - V_0\sum_{n=0}^{\infty}\left\{e^{-\frac{1}{2}R[2(n+1)l-x]\sqrt{C/L}}\right.$$

$$+ \tfrac{1}{2}R[2(n+1)l-x]\sqrt{C/L}\int_0^t e^{-R\tau/(2L)}$$

$$\frac{I_1(R\sqrt{\tau^2-[2(n+1)l-x]^2LC}/2L)}{\sqrt{\tau^2-[2(n+1)l-x]^2LC}}d\tau\right\}1(t-[2(n+1)l-x]\sqrt{LC}).$$

For the determination of the current $I(x,t)$ we again make use of (9.1.13) and (9.1.14). The latter when solved for $i(x,p)$ yields

$$(9.1.23) \qquad i(x,p) = -\frac{v_x(x,p)}{L(p + R/L)}.$$

Differentiating (9.1.21) with respect to x and substituting in (9.1.23), we find that

$$(9.1.24) \qquad i(x,p) = V_0\sqrt{\frac{C}{L}}\frac{\cosh(l-x)\sqrt{LC}\sqrt{p(p+R/L)}}{\sqrt{p(p+R/L)}\sinh l\sqrt{LC}\sqrt{p(p+R/L)}},$$

and therefore

$$(9.1.25) \quad I(x,t = V_0\sqrt{\frac{C}{L}}L^{-1}\left\{\frac{\cosh(l-x)\sqrt{LC}\sqrt{p(p+R/L)}}{\sqrt{p(p+R/L)}\sinh l\sqrt{LC}\sqrt{p(p+R/L)}}\right\}.$$

Now it is easily verified that

$$(9.1.26) \qquad \frac{\cosh(l-x)\sqrt{LC}\sqrt{p(p+R/L)}}{\sqrt{p(p+R/L)}\sinh l\sqrt{LC}\sqrt{p(p+R/L)}}$$

$$= \sum_{n=0}^{\infty}\frac{\exp[-(x+2nl)\sqrt{LC}\sqrt{p(p+R/L)}] - \exp[-(2(n+1)l-x)\sqrt{LC}\sqrt{p(p+R/L)}]}{\sqrt{p(p+R/L)}}.$$

Again making use of Translation Theorem II and formula 81, we easily obtain the inverse of (9.1.26) which when substituted in (9.1.25) gives the solution

$$(9.1.27)$$

$$I(x,t) = V_0\sqrt{C/L}\sum_{n=0}^{\infty}\left\{e^{-(R/2L)t}I_0(R\sqrt{t^2 - (x+2nl)^2 LC}/2L)\right.$$

$$1[t - (x+2nl)\sqrt{LC}] - e^{-(R/2Lt)}I_0(R\sqrt{t^2 - [2(n+1)l-x]^2 LC}/2L)$$

$$\left.1[t - (2(n+1)l-x)\sqrt{LC}]\right\}.$$

Let us obtain an alternative solution for the voltage $V(x,t)$ by using the complex inversion integral. We have from (9.1.21)

$$(9.1.28) \qquad V(x,t) = \frac{V_0}{2\pi i}\int_{c-i\infty}^{c+i\infty}e^{pt}\frac{\sinh(l-x)\sqrt{LC}\sqrt{p(p+R/L)}}{p\sinh l\sqrt{LC}\sqrt{p(p+R/L)}}dp.$$

It is readily verified that the integrand is a single-valued function with a simple pole at $p = 0$ and simple poles at those values of p for which $l\sqrt{LC}\sqrt{p(p+R/L)} = n\pi i$, $n = 1, 2, 3, \cdots$, where, as usual, the principal value of the square root is taken. Solving the preceding equation for p, we find that

$$p = -(R/2L) \pm \sqrt{(R/2L)^2 - (n\pi/l\sqrt{LC})^2}, \quad n = 1, 2, 3, \cdots.$$

Now, the residues at the above mentioned poles are:

$$\text{Res } (0) = (l - x)/l,$$

$$\text{Res } [- (R/2L) + \sqrt{(R/2L)^2 - (n\pi/l\sqrt{LC})^2}]$$

$$= \left[\frac{e^{pt} \sinh (l - x)\sqrt{LC}\sqrt{p(p + R/L)}}{p(d/dp) \sinh l\sqrt{LC}\sqrt{p(p + R/L)}}\right]_{p=-(R/2L)+\sqrt{(R/2L)^2-(n\pi/l\sqrt{LC})^2}}$$

$$= (- 1)^{n+1}\frac{n\pi}{l^2 LC}$$

$$\frac{\sin \{n\pi(l - x)/l\} \exp [- (R/2L) + \sqrt{(R/2L)^2 - (n\pi/l\sqrt{LC})^2}]t}{\sqrt{(R/2L)^2 - (n\pi/l\sqrt{LC})^2}[- (R/2L) + \sqrt{(R/2L)^2 - (n\pi/l\sqrt{LC})^2}]},$$

and

$$\text{Res } [- (R/2L) - \sqrt{(R/2L)^2 - (n\pi/l\sqrt{LC})^2}]$$

$$= (- 1)^{n+1}\frac{n\pi}{l^2 LC}$$

$$\frac{\sin\{n\pi(l - x)/l\} \exp [- (R/2L) - \sqrt{(R/2L)^2 - (n\pi/l\sqrt{LC})^2}]t}{\sqrt{(R/2L)^2 - (n\pi/l\sqrt{LC})^2}[- (R/2L) - \sqrt{(R/2L)^2 - (n\pi/l\sqrt{LC})^2}]}.$$

Therefore, upon adding these residues and simplifying, we find from (9.1.28) that

$$V(x,t) = V_0(l - x)/l$$

$$- V_0\frac{e^{-(R/2L)t}}{\pi} \sum_{n=1}^{\infty} \frac{1}{n} \sin \frac{n\pi x}{l}\left(\frac{R}{L} \frac{\sinh \sqrt{(R/2L)^2 - (n\pi/l\sqrt{LC})^2}\, t}{\sqrt{(R/2L)^2 - (n\pi/l\sqrt{LC})^2}}\right.$$

$$\left. + 2 \cosh \sqrt{(R/2L)^2 - (n\pi l\sqrt{LC})^2}\, t\right).$$

An interesting feature of this solution is the fact that the hyperbolic functions in the infinite series do not persist but change to trigonometric functions when n becomes large enough. This transition occurs as soon as n is such that $4n^2\pi^2 L \geqslant l^2 CR^2$.

Exercise 1. Using the complex inversion integral, find an expression for the current $I(x,t)$ given by (9.1.25).

Exercise 2. Obtain the voltage and current for the semi-infinite and finite lines discussed in the preceding section if a finite pulse $V(0,t) = V_0[1(t - t_0) - 1(t - t_1)]$ is applied to the end $x = 0$. In the case of the finite line obtain solutions by both methods discussed in the text.

9.2 Symmetrical Vibrations of a Circular Membrane

It is shown in books on mechanics that the displacements U of a stretched thin elastic body (e.g., a drumhead) are governed by the equation

(9.2.1) $$\frac{1}{a^2}\frac{\partial^2 U}{\partial t^2} = \frac{\partial^2 U}{\partial x^2} + \frac{\partial^2 U}{\partial y^2} = \frac{1}{r}\frac{\partial}{\partial r}\left(r\frac{\partial U}{\partial r}\right) + \frac{1}{r^2}\frac{\partial^2 U}{\partial \theta^2},$$

where a is a constant. In particular, suppose that the membrane is circular and U is independent of θ, i.e., the vibrations are symmetrical with respect to a vertical axis passing through the center of the circle. Then equation (9.2.1) becomes

(9.2.2) $$U_{rr}(r,t) + \frac{1}{r}U_r(r,t) = \frac{1}{a^2}\,U_{tt}(r,t),$$

whose Laplace transform with respect to t is

(9.2.3) $$u_{rr}(r,p) + \frac{1}{r}u_r(r,p) - \frac{p^2}{a^2}u(r,p) = -\frac{pU(r,0) + U_t(r,0)}{a^2}.$$

If the initial conditions $U(r,0)$ and $U_t(r,0)$ are specified and appropriate boundary conditions given, then the symmetrical vibrations of a circular membrane can be obtained by solving (9.2.3) for $u(r,p)$ and inverting to get the displacement $U(r,t)$.

As a specific example, let us suppose that a circular membrane of radius R is such that

(9.2.4) $$U(r,0) = 0 \quad \text{and} \quad U_t(r,0) = k^2 \text{ (const.)} \quad (0 \leqslant r < R).$$

If the membrane is assumed to be clamped, then, in addition, we have

(9.2.5) $$U(R,t) = 0 \qquad\qquad (t > 0),$$

whose transform is

(9.2.6) $$u(R,p) = 0.$$

Substituting conditions (9.2.4) in (9.2.3), we see that the ordinary differential equation

(9.2.7) $$u_{rr}(r,p) + u_r(r,p)/r - p^2 u(r,p)/a^2 = -k^2/a^2$$

must be solved subject to condition (9.2.6). Now a solution of the Bessel equation of order zero

$$ru_{rr}(r,p) + u_r(r,p) - p^2 r u(r,p)/a^2 = 0,$$

which is finite at $r = 0$ is

$$u(r,p) = c_1 I_0(rp/a),$$

while a particular integral of (9.2.7) is clearly k^2/p^2. Therefore, the general solution of (9.2.7) is

(9.2.8) $$u(r,p) = c_1 I_0(rp/a) + k^2/p^2.$$

Making use of the condition $u(R,p) = 0$, we obtain

$$c_1 I_0(Rp/a) + k^2/p^2 = 0,$$

which when substituted in (9.2.8) yields the expression

(9.2.9) $u(r,p) = k^2[1 - I_0(rp/a)/I_0(Rp/a)]/p^2.$

Whence by inversion

(9.2.10) $U(r,t) = k^2 t - \dfrac{k^2}{2\pi i} \displaystyle\int_{c-i\infty}^{c+i\infty} \dfrac{e^{pt} I_0(rp/a)}{p^2 I_0(Rp/a)}\, dp.$

Let us denote the roots of $J_0(\zeta) = 0$ (real and infinite in number) by $\pm\alpha_n$, $n = 1, 2, 3, \cdots$. Then, since $I_0(\zeta) = J_0(i\zeta)$ (formula 8.6.9), $I_0(Rp/a) = 0$ when $p = \pm(a/R)\alpha_n i$, $n = 1, 2, 3, \cdots$. These values constitute the simple poles, and $p = 0$ is the double pole of the integrand in (9.2.10). The residue at the pole $p = (a/R)\alpha_n i$ is

$$\dfrac{e^{(a/R)\alpha_n it} I_0(r\alpha_n i/R)}{\left[p^2 \dfrac{d}{dp} I_0(Rp/a)\right]_{p=a\alpha_n i/R}} = \dfrac{e^{(a/R)\alpha_n it} J_0(r\alpha_n/R)}{(a/R)\alpha_n^2 i J_0'(\alpha_n)},$$

whereas that at $p = -(a/R)\alpha_n i$ is $-\dfrac{e^{-(a/R)\alpha_n it} J_0(r\alpha_n/R)}{(a/R)\alpha_n^2 i J_0'(\alpha_n)}$.   For the

residue at the double pole $p = 0$, we have

$$\lim_{p\to 0} \dfrac{d}{dp}\left[\dfrac{e^{pt} I_0(rp/a)}{I_0(Rp/a)}\right]$$

$$= \lim_{p\to 0} \dfrac{I_0(Rp/a)[te^{pt} I_0(rp/a) + (r/a)e^{pt} I_0'(rp/a)]}{I_0^2(Rp/a)}\begin{subarray}{l}\\ - (R/a)e^{pt} I_0(rp/a) I_0'(Rp/a)\end{subarray} = t.$$

Adding these residues and making use of the fact that $J_0'(\alpha_n) = -J_1(\alpha_n)$, we obtain from (9.2.10) the solution

$$U(r,t) = \dfrac{2Rk^2}{a} \sum_{n=1}^{\infty} \dfrac{\sin(a/R)\alpha_n t}{\alpha_n^2} \dfrac{J_0(r\alpha_n/R)}{J_1(\alpha_n)}.$$

Exercise. Solve the preceding problem for the case when $U(r,0) = k^2$ (const.) and $U_t(r,0) = 0$.

9.3 Diffusion in a Circular Cylinder and a Sphere

The general three-dimensional diffusion equation considered in Chapter VII, namely,

(9.3.1) $\dfrac{\partial C}{\partial t} = D\left[\dfrac{\partial^2 C}{\partial x^2} + \dfrac{\partial^2 C}{\partial y^2} + \dfrac{\partial^2 C}{\partial z^2}\right]$

can be transformed into other systems of coordinates such as cylindrical or spherical. Thus, in the former system equation (9.3.1) becomes

$$(9.3.2) \qquad \frac{\partial C}{\partial t} = \frac{D}{r}\left[\frac{\partial}{\partial r}\left(r\frac{\partial C}{\partial r}\right) + \frac{\partial}{\partial\theta}\left(\frac{1}{r}\frac{\partial C}{\partial\theta}\right) + \frac{\partial}{\partial z}\left(r\frac{\partial C}{\partial z}\right)\right],$$

and in the latter system we have

$$(9.3.3) \qquad \frac{\partial C}{\partial t} = \frac{D}{r^2}\left[\frac{\partial}{\partial r}\left(r^2\frac{\partial C}{\partial r}\right) + \frac{1}{\sin\theta}\frac{\partial}{\partial\theta}\left(\sin\theta\frac{\partial C}{\partial\theta}\right) + \frac{1}{\sin^2\theta}\frac{\partial^2 C}{\partial\phi^2}\right].$$

Of great practical importance are the cases when C in (9.3.2) and (9.3.3) depends only on r and t. In the first instance we have *axial symmetry* and in the second, *spherical* symmetry, and equations (9.3.2) and (9.3.3) reduce to the following:

$$(9.3.4) \qquad \frac{\partial C}{\partial t} = D\left[\frac{\partial^2 C}{\partial r^2} + \frac{1}{r}\frac{\partial C}{\partial r}\right],$$

$$(9.3.5) \qquad \frac{\partial C}{\partial t} = D\left[\frac{\partial^2 C}{\partial r^2} + \frac{2}{r}\frac{\partial C}{\partial r}\right].$$

Consider now the problem of determining the concentration in a right circular cylinder of radius R and infinite in extent if equation (9.3.4) obtains and the initial concentration as well as the concentration at the boundary are prescribed. The boundary value problem to be solved when these concentrations are distinct constants is then

$$(9.3.6) \qquad C_t(r,t) = D\left[C_{rr}(r,t) + \frac{1}{r}C_r(r,t)\right] \qquad (0 \leqslant r < R,\ t > 0),$$

$$(9.3.7) \qquad C(r,0) = C_0, \quad (0 \leqslant r < R); \qquad C(R,t) = C_1, \qquad (t > 0).$$

As is readily seen, the problem in the transform is

$$(9.3.8) \qquad c_{rr}(r,p) + \frac{1}{r}c_r(r,p) - \frac{p}{D}c(r,p) = -\frac{C_0}{D},$$

with

$$(9.3.9) \qquad c(R,p) = C_1/p.$$

A solution of Bessel's equation of order zero

$$c_{rr}(r,p) + \frac{1}{r}c_r(r,p) - \frac{p}{D}c(r,p) = 0$$

which is finite at $r = 0$ is

$$c(r,p) = c_1 I_0\left(r\sqrt{\frac{p}{D}}\right).$$

Therefore the general solution of (9.3.8) is

$$(9.3.10) \qquad c(r,p) = c_1 I_0\left(r\sqrt{\frac{p}{D}}\right) + \frac{C_0}{p}.$$

Applying condition (9.3.9) to this equation, we have

(9.3.11)
$$\frac{C_1}{p} = c_1 I_0\left(R\sqrt{\frac{p}{D}}\right) + \frac{C_0}{p},$$

which when solved for c_1 and substituted in (9.3.10) yields

$$c(r,p) = \frac{C_0}{p} + \frac{C_1 - C_0}{p}\, \frac{I_0\left(r\sqrt{\frac{p}{D}}\right)}{I_0\left(R\sqrt{\frac{p}{D}}\right)},$$

from which

(9.3.12)
$$C(r,t) = C_0 + \frac{C_1 - C_0}{2\pi i}\int_{c-i\infty}^{c+i\infty} e^{pt}\frac{I_0\left(r\sqrt{\frac{p}{D}}\right)}{p I_0\left(R\sqrt{\frac{p}{D}}\right)}\, dp.$$

The integrand in (9.3.12) is a single-valued function of p with poles at $p = 0$ and those values of p for which $I_0\left(R\sqrt{\frac{p}{D}}\right) = J_0\left(iR\sqrt{\frac{p}{D}}\right) = 0$. If we let $iR\sqrt{\frac{p}{D}} = \alpha_n$, $n = 1, 2, 3, \cdots$ be the positive roots of $J_0(\zeta) = 0$, then these values are $p = -\frac{D\alpha_n^2}{R^2}$. At $p = 0$ the residue of the integrand is

$$\lim_{p\to 0} e^{pt}\, \frac{I_0\left(r\sqrt{\frac{p}{D}}\right)}{I_0\left(R\sqrt{\frac{p}{D}}\right)} = 1,$$

since $I_0(0) = 1$, and at $p = -\frac{D\alpha_n^2}{R^2}$, we have

$$\left[\frac{e^{pt}\, I_0\left(r\sqrt{\frac{p}{D}}\right)}{p\dfrac{d}{dp}I_0\left(R\sqrt{\frac{p}{D}}\right)}\right]_{p=-D\alpha_n^2/R^2} = -\frac{2J_0\left(r\dfrac{\alpha_n}{R}\right)e^{-(D\alpha_n^2/R^2)t}}{\alpha_n J_1(\alpha_n)},$$

where use was made of the relations $I_0'(\zeta) = iJ_0'(i\zeta)$, $I_0'(i\zeta) = iJ_0'(-\zeta)$, $J_0'(\zeta) = -J_1(-\zeta) = J_1(-\zeta)$. Hence in the usual way, we have

$$C(r,t) = C_0 + (C_1 - C_0)\left[1 - 2\sum_{n=1}^{\infty}\frac{e^{-(D\alpha_n^2/R^2)t}J_0\left(r\dfrac{\alpha_n}{R}\right)}{\alpha_n J_1(\alpha_n)}\right],$$

or, finally,

$$(9.3.13) \quad C(r,t) = C_1 + 2(C_0 - C_1) \sum_{n=1}^{\infty} \frac{e^{-(D\alpha_n^2/R^2)t} J_0\left(r\frac{\alpha_n}{R}\right)}{\alpha_n J_1(\alpha_n)}.$$

For the corresponding problem of diffusion in a sphere of radius R, we must solve the boundary value problem

$$(9.3.14) \qquad C_t(r,t) = D[C_{rr}(r,t) + \frac{2}{r}C_r(r,t)] \qquad (0 \leqslant r < R, \, t > 0),$$

$$(9.3.15) \qquad C(r,0) = C_0, \quad (0 \leqslant r < R); \qquad C(R,t) = C_1, \qquad (t > 0).$$

Making use of the initial condition, the Laplace transform of (9.3.14) gives the equation

$$(9.3.16) \qquad c_{rr}(r,p) + \frac{2}{r}c_r(r,p) - \frac{p}{D}c(r,p) = -\frac{C_0}{D},$$

which must be solved together with the condition

$$(9.3.17) \qquad c(R,p) = C_1/p.$$

Equation (9.3.16) can be solved easily if we observe that

$$c_{rr}(r,p) + \frac{2}{r}c_r(r,p) = \frac{1}{r}[rc(r,p)]_{rr},$$

where the subscript in the bracket denotes differentiation with respect to r. Thus, upon substitution in (9.3.16) and multiplication by r, we obtain

$$[rc(r,p)]_{rr} - \frac{p}{D}[rc(r,p)] = -\frac{C_0 r}{D},$$

whose general solution is

$$(9.3.18) \quad rc(r,p) = c_1 \cosh r\sqrt{\frac{p}{D}} + c_2 \sinh r\sqrt{\frac{p}{D}} + \frac{rC_0}{p}.$$

Now, if $\lim_{r \to 0} c(r,p)$ is to be finite, c_1 must be equal to zero. Hence (9.3.18) becomes

$$(9.3.19) \qquad c(r,p) = \frac{C_2}{r} \sinh r\sqrt{\frac{p}{D}} + \frac{C_0}{p}.$$

From (9.3.17) and this equation, we obtain

$$c_2 = \frac{C_1 - C_0}{p} \frac{R}{\sinh R\sqrt{\frac{p}{D}}}.$$

which when substituted in (9.3.19) yields

$$c(r,p) = \frac{C_0}{p} + \frac{R(C_1 - C_0)}{r} \frac{\sinh r \sqrt{\dfrac{p}{D}}}{p \sinh R \sqrt{\dfrac{p}{D}}}.$$

Therefore,

$$C(r,t) = C_0 + \frac{R(C_1 - C_0)}{r} L^{-1} \left\{ \frac{\sinh r \sqrt{\dfrac{p}{D}}}{p \sinh R \sqrt{\dfrac{p}{D}}} \right\}.$$

Now the inverse transform of $\sinh r \sqrt{\dfrac{p}{D}} \Big/ \left(p \sinh R \sqrt{\dfrac{p}{D}} \right)$ has been
computed in section 7.3, both by the inversion integral and in terms
of error functions. Using the results obtained there we find that

$$C(r,t) = C_1 + \frac{2R(C_1 - C_0)}{\pi r} \sum_{n=1}^{\infty} (-1)^n \frac{1}{n} e^{-n^2\pi^2 Dt/R^2} \sin \frac{n\pi}{R} r$$

or

$$C(r,t) = C_0 + \frac{R(C_1 - C_0)}{r} \sum_{n=0}^{\infty} \left\{ \mathrm{erfc}\, \frac{(2n+1)R - r}{2\sqrt{Dt}} - \mathrm{erfc}\, \frac{(2n+1)R + r}{2\sqrt{Dt}} \right\}.$$

Exercise. Solve the preceding problem for the cylinder and sphere
if equations (9.3.4) and (9.3.5) are replaced by

$$C_t(r,t) = D\left[C_{rr}(r,t) + \frac{1}{r} C_r(r,t) \right] + f(C)$$

and

$$C_t(r,t) = D\left[C_{rr}(r,t) + \frac{2}{r} C_r(r,t) \right] + f(C),$$

where $f(C)$ (giving the rate of change of concentration due to chemical
reaction) is taken to be $- kC(r,t)$.

9.4 The Skin Effect Equation

When the non-uniform distribution of alternating current in a
cylindrical conductor is analyzed it is found to lead to a very important partial differential equa-
tion which is often referred to as
the *skin effect equation.*

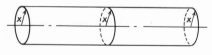

Let the *current density* in
amperes per square meter be
denoted by $C(x,t)$, where x is the

Fig. 9.4.1

radius of a cylinder (Fig. 9.4.1) and t is the time. If ρ denotes the
resistance of a cubic meter of the conductor and μ the *permeability*

(considered constant), then it can be shown* that the current density satisfies the following partial differential equation

$$(9.4.1) \qquad C_{xx}(x,t) + \frac{1}{x}C(x,t) = \frac{\mu}{\rho}C_t(x,t),$$

which we recognize to be of the same type as the diffusion equation (9.3.4) for axial symmetry. Furthermore, the total current $I(x,t)$ inside the cylinder of radius x is

$$(9.4.2) \qquad I(x,t) = 2\pi \int_0^x xC(x,t)\, dx \text{ amperes.}$$

An important problem in electrical engineering is that of determining the current density distribution along a cylinder of fixed radius r if, initially, the current density is zero and the total current varies sinusoidally, i.e., $I(r,t) = I_0 \sin \omega t$. To solve this problem by Laplace transforms let us, as usual, set $L_t\{C(x,t)\} = c(x,p)$. Then, upon transforming the members of (9.4.1) and making use of the initial condition $C(x,0) = 0$, we have

$$(9.4.3) \qquad c_{xx}(x,p) + \frac{1}{x}c_x(x,p) - \frac{\mu}{\rho}pc(x,p) = 0,$$

which is Bessel's equation of order zero. Its general solution is

$$(9.4.4) \qquad c(x,p) = c_1 J_0(ix\sqrt{\mu p/\rho}) + c_2 Y_0(ix\sqrt{\mu p/\rho}).$$

Now, the current $C(x,t)$ must exist for all x in the interval $0 \leqslant x \leqslant r$ and in particular $\lim_{x\to 0} C(x,t)$ and $\lim_{x\to 0} c(x,p)$ must also exist. But as $x \to 0$, $J_0(ix\sqrt{\mu p/\rho}) \to 1$ and $Y_0(ix\sqrt{\mu p/\rho}) \to \infty$. Hence, if $c(x,p)$ is to be finite as $x \to 0$, c_2 must be taken as zero. Consequently,

$$(9.4.5) \qquad c(x,p) = c_1 J_0(ix\sqrt{\mu p/\rho}).$$

Since we are assuming that $I(r,t) = I_0 \sin \omega t$, from (9.4.2) we have

$$I_0 \sin \omega t = 2\pi \int_0^r xC(x,t)\, dx.$$

The transform of both sides of this expression, after interchanging the order of integration, leads to the equality

$$\frac{I_0\omega}{p^2 + \omega^2} = 2\pi \int_0^r xc(x,p)\, dx,$$

which, upon making use of (9.4.5), becomes

$$\frac{I_0\omega}{p^2 + \omega^2} = 2\pi c_1 \int_0^r xJ_0(ix\sqrt{\mu p/\rho})\, dx.$$

---

* See e.g., M. B. Reed and G. B. Reed, *Mathematical Methods in Electrical Engineering*, Harper & Brothers, Chap. 12.

Utilizing formula 5(c), we obtain

$$\frac{I_0\omega}{p^2 + \omega^2} = \frac{2\pi\sqrt{\rho}}{i\sqrt{\mu p}} rc_1 J_1(ir\sqrt{\mu p/\rho}),$$

from which

$$c_1 = \frac{I_0\omega i\sqrt{\mu p}}{2\pi r\sqrt{\rho}(p^2 + \omega^2)J_1(ir\sqrt{\mu p/\rho})}.$$

This result when substituted in (9.4.5) finally gives

(9.4.6) $$c(x,p) = \frac{I_0\omega}{2\pi r} \cdot \frac{i\sqrt{\mu p/\rho}}{p^2 + \omega^2} \cdot \frac{J_0(ix\sqrt{\mu p/\rho})}{J_1(ir\sqrt{\mu p/\rho})}.$$

Therefore,

(9.4.7) $$C(x,t) = \frac{1}{2\pi i}\int_{c-i\infty}^{c+i\infty} \frac{I_0\omega}{2\pi r} \cdot \frac{i\sqrt{\mu p/\rho}}{p^2 + \omega^2} \cdot \frac{J_0(ix\sqrt{\mu p/\rho})}{J_1(ir\sqrt{\mu p/\rho})}\, dp.$$

By expanding the Bessel functions in the numerator and denominator it is seen that the integrand is a single-valued function of p. The poles occur at $p = \pm i\omega$ and $p = -\frac{\rho}{\mu}\left(\frac{\alpha_n}{r}\right)^2$, $n = 1, 2, 3, \cdots$, where $\alpha_1, \alpha_2, \cdots$ are the *positive* roots of $J_1(\alpha_n) = 0$. Note that $p = 0$ is not a pole of the integrand.

Computing residues, we have

$$\text{Res }(i\omega) = -\frac{I_0}{4\pi r} \cdot i^{-\frac{3}{2}}\sqrt{\mu\omega/\rho} \cdot \frac{J_0(i^{\frac{3}{2}}x\sqrt{\mu\omega/\rho})}{J_1(i^{\frac{3}{2}}r\sqrt{\mu\omega/\rho})}e^{i\omega t},$$

$$\text{Res }(-i\omega) = -\frac{I_0}{4\pi r} \cdot i^{\frac{3}{2}}\sqrt{\mu\omega/\rho} \cdot \frac{J_0(i^{-\frac{3}{2}}x\sqrt{\mu\omega/\rho})}{J_1(i^{-\frac{3}{2}}r\sqrt{\mu\omega/\rho})}e^{-i\omega t},$$

$$\text{Res }\left[-\frac{\rho}{\mu}\left(\frac{\alpha_n}{r}\right)^2\right] = \frac{I_0\omega}{2\pi r}\left[\frac{i\sqrt{\mu p/\rho}}{p^2 + \omega^2} \cdot \frac{J_0(ix\sqrt{\mu p/\rho})}{\frac{d}{dp}J_1(ir\sqrt{\mu p/\rho})}e^{pt}\right]_{p=-(\rho/\mu)(\alpha_n/r)^2}$$

where we have used the relation $i^{\frac{1}{2}} = -i^{-\frac{3}{2}}$ in writing the first two expressions. The sum of these residues can be represented suitably in terms of the ber and bei functions which are defined as follows:

$$\text{ber}_\nu(z) + i\,\text{bei}_\nu(z) = J_\nu(ze^{\frac{3}{4}\pi i}) = J_\nu(zi^{\frac{3}{2}}),$$

$$\text{ber}_\nu(z) - i\,\text{bei}_\nu(z) = J_\nu(ze^{-\frac{3}{4}\pi i}) = J_\nu(zi^{-\frac{3}{2}}).$$

We find that

$$C(x,t) =$$

$$\frac{I_0}{2\pi r}\left\{\frac{\text{bei}\,(x\sqrt{\mu\omega/\rho})\,\text{ber}_1\,(r\sqrt{\mu\omega/\rho}) - \text{ber}\,(x\sqrt{\mu\omega/\rho})\,\text{bei}_1\,(r\sqrt{\mu\omega/\rho})}{\text{ber}_1{}^2\,(r\sqrt{\mu\omega/\rho}) + \text{bei}_1{}^2\,(r\sqrt{\mu\omega/\rho})}\,\sin\omega t\right.$$

$$\left. - \frac{\text{ber}\,(x\sqrt{\mu\omega/\rho})\,\text{ber}_1\,(r\sqrt{\mu\omega/\rho}) + \text{bei}\,(x\sqrt{\mu\omega/\rho})\,\text{bei}_1\,(r\sqrt{\mu\omega/\rho})}{\text{ber}_1{}^2\,(r\sqrt{\mu\omega/\rho}) + \text{bei}_1{}^2\,(r\sqrt{\mu\omega/\rho})}\,\cos\omega t\right\}$$

$$- \frac{I_0\omega\rho}{\pi r^2\mu}\sum_{n=1}^{\infty}\frac{(\alpha_n/r)^2 J_0(x\alpha_n/r)e^{-(\rho/\mu)(\alpha_n/r)^2 t}}{[(\rho/\mu)^2(\alpha_n/r)^4 + \omega^2]J_1'(\alpha_n)}.$$

Exercise.   Solve the preceding problem if the total current $I(r,t)$ is the *square wave* of problem 5 given at the end of Chapter III.

9.5 A Certain Third Order Partial Differential Equation

The problem of determining the dynamic behavior of certain soils, and consequently the structures that rest on them, when these soils are subjected to an initial disturbance, say, an earthquake, is an important one.   If the soil is assumed to be visco-elastic, so that stresses are equal to linear combinations of strains and rates of strains, and if displacements of sections of a semi-inifinite slab are considered, then the following equation obtains*

$$(9.5.1) \qquad E\frac{\partial^2 U}{\partial x^2} + E'\frac{\partial^3 U}{\partial x^2\partial t} = \rho\frac{\partial^2 U}{\partial t^2},$$

where E and E' are characteristics of the material in question, ρ is the density of the material (mass/unit volume), U denotes the parallel displacement of a section x (Fig. 9.5.1), and t represents the time.   If suitable initial and boundary conditions are given, this equation can be used to establish a basis for the earthquake design of structures.†   For example, suppose that the section $x = 0$ of a

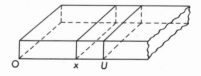

FIG. 9.5.1

semi-infinite visco-elastic slab is fixed and each section for which $x > 0$ is displaced a constant distance $k(> 0)$ and released from rest. Then the boundary value problem to be solved is

$$(9.5.2) \qquad EU_{xx}(x,t) + E'U_{xxt}(x,t) = \rho U_{tt}(x,t) \qquad (x > 0, t > 0),$$

$$(9.5.3) \quad U(x,0) = k, \qquad U_t(x,0) = 0, \quad (x > 0); \qquad U(0,t) = 0,$$
$$(t > 0).$$

* K. Sezawa, "On the Decay of Waves in Visco-Elastic Solid Bodies," *Bull. of the Earthquake Research Inst.*, Tokyo Imperial Univ., p. 3, 1927.

† An approximate solution of this problem is due to E. Rosenblueth, "A Basis for Aseismic Design of Structures," Doctoral Thesis, University of Illinois, 1951.

Let $L_t\{U(x,t)\} = u(x,p)$. Then, in view of the first two conditions in (9.5.3), the transform of the members of (9.5.2) is

$$Eu_{xx}(x,p) + E'[pu_{xx}(x,p)] = \rho[p^2u(x,p) - pk],$$

or

$$(9.5.4) \qquad u_{xx}(x,p) - \frac{\rho p^2}{E + E'p}u(x,p) = -\frac{\rho kp}{E + E'p},$$

whose general solution is

$$(9.5.5) \qquad u(x,p) = c_1 e^{xp\sqrt{\rho/E'}/\sqrt{p+E/E'}} + c_2 e^{-xp\sqrt{\rho/E'}/\sqrt{p+E/E'}} + \frac{k}{p}.$$

We now make the assumption that $\lim_{x\to\infty} U(x,t)$ be finite, so that $\lim_{x\to\infty} u(x,p)$ is finite. From this hypothesis it follows that $c_1 = 0$ and (9.5.5) becomes

$$(9.5.6) \qquad u(x,p) = \frac{k}{p} + c_2 e^{-xp\sqrt{\rho/E'}/\sqrt{p+E/E'}}.$$

From the third condition in (9.5.3) $L_t\{U(0,t)\} = u(0,p) = 0$. Therefore, from (9.5.6) $c_2 = -k/p$ and

$$(9.5.7) \qquad u(x,p) = \frac{k}{p} - \frac{k}{p}e^{-xp\sqrt{\rho/E'}/\sqrt{p+E/E'}},$$

whence

$$(9.5.8) \qquad U(x,t) = k - kL^{-1}\{e^{-x\alpha p/\sqrt{p+\beta}}/p\},$$

where $\alpha = \sqrt{\rho/E'}$ and $\beta = E/E'$. Making use of the identities

$$p/\sqrt{p+\beta} \equiv \sqrt{p+\beta} - \beta/\sqrt{p+\beta}$$

and

$$1/p \equiv 1/(p+\beta) + \beta/[p(p+\beta)],$$

we have

$$L^{-1}\left\{\frac{e^{-x\alpha p/\sqrt{p+\beta}}}{p}\right\}$$

$$= L^{-1}\left\{e^{-x\alpha\sqrt{p+\beta}} \cdot \frac{e^{x\alpha\beta/\sqrt{p+\beta}}}{p+\beta}\right\} + L^{-1}\left\{e^{-x\alpha\sqrt{p+\beta}} \cdot \frac{e^{x\alpha\beta/\sqrt{p+\beta}}}{p(p+\beta)}\right\}.$$

From the table of Laplace transforms (formulas 66 and 75) as well as Translation Theorem II,

$$L^{-1}\left\{e^{-x\alpha\sqrt{p+\beta}}\right\} = e^{-\beta t}\frac{x\alpha}{2\sqrt{\pi t^3}}\exp\left(-\frac{x^2\alpha^2}{4t}\right)$$

and

$$L^{-1}\left\{\frac{e^{x\alpha\beta/\sqrt{p+\beta}}}{p+\beta}\right\} = \frac{e^{-\beta t}}{2\sqrt{\pi x}\sqrt{\alpha\beta}\,t^{\frac{3}{4}}}\int_0^\infty \tau_1^{\frac{3}{4}}e^{-\tau_1^2/(4t)}I_1(2\sqrt{x\alpha\beta\tau_1})\,d\tau_1.$$

Therefore by the convolution theorem

$$L^{-1}\left\{e^{-x\sqrt{\alpha(p+\beta)}}\cdot\frac{e^{x\alpha\beta/\sqrt{p+\beta}}}{p+\beta}\right\}$$

$$=\int_0^t\left[\frac{\alpha x e^{-\beta(t-\tau)}\cdot e^{-(\alpha x/2)^2/(t-\tau)}}{2\sqrt{\pi}(t-\tau)^{\frac{3}{2}}}\cdot\frac{e^{-\beta\tau}}{2\tau^{\frac{3}{2}}\sqrt{\pi\alpha\beta x}}\right.$$

$$\left.\int_0^\infty \tau_1^{\frac{3}{2}}e^{-(\tau_1/2)^2/\tau}I_1(2\sqrt{\alpha\beta x\tau_1})\,d\tau_1\right]d\tau$$

$$=\frac{\sqrt{\alpha x}}{4\pi\sqrt{\beta}}\int_0^t\left\{\frac{e^{-\beta t-(\alpha x/2)^2/(t-\tau)}}{[\tau(t-\tau)]^{\frac{3}{2}}}\int_0^\infty \tau_1^{\frac{3}{2}}e^{-(\tau_1/2)^2/\tau}I_1(2\sqrt{\alpha\beta x\tau_1})\,d\tau_1\right\}d\tau,$$

and by Theorem 3

$$L^{-1}\left\{\frac{e^{-x\sqrt{\alpha(p+\beta)}}}{p}\cdot\frac{e^{x\alpha\beta/\sqrt{p+\beta}}}{p+\beta}\right\}$$

$$=\frac{\sqrt{\alpha x}}{4\pi\sqrt{\beta}}\int_0^t\left\{\int_0^\tau\left[\frac{e^{-\beta t-(\alpha x/2)^2/(t-\tau_2)}}{[\tau_2(t-\tau_2)]^{\frac{3}{2}}}\right.\right.$$

$$\left.\left.\left(\int_0^\infty \tau_1^{\frac{3}{2}}e^{-(\tau_1/2)^2/\tau_2}I_1(2\sqrt{\alpha\beta x\tau_1})\,d\tau_1\right)\right]d\tau_2\right\}d\tau.$$

Consequently from (9.5.8)

$$U(x,t)=k$$

$$-\frac{k\sqrt{\alpha x}}{4\pi\sqrt{\beta}}\int_0^t\left\{\frac{e^{-\beta t-(\alpha x/2)^2/(t-\tau)}}{[\tau(t-\tau)]^{\frac{3}{2}}}\int_0^\infty \tau_1^{\frac{3}{2}}e^{-(\tau_1/2)^2/\tau}I_1(2\sqrt{\alpha\beta x\tau_1})\,d\tau_1\right\}d\tau$$

$$-\frac{k\sqrt{\alpha x}}{4\pi\sqrt{\beta}}\int_0^t\left\{\int_0^\tau\left[\frac{e^{-\beta t-(\alpha x/2)^2/(t-\tau_2)}}{[\tau_2(t-\tau_2)]^{\frac{3}{2}}}\left(\int_0^\infty \tau_1^{\frac{3}{2}}e^{-(\tau_1/2)^2/\tau_2}I_1(2\sqrt{\alpha\beta x\tau_1})\,d\tau_1\right)\right]d\tau_2\right\}d\tau.$$

Exercise. Solve the following boundary value problem

$$EU_{xx}(x,t)+E'U_{xxt}(x,t)=\rho U_{tt}(x,t)\qquad(x>0,\,t>0),$$
$$U(x,0)=U_t(x,0)=0\qquad\qquad\qquad(x>0),$$
$$\lim_{x\to\infty}U(x,t)\text{ is finite},\qquad U(0,t)=1(t-t_0)\qquad(t>0).$$

9.6 A Pair of Equations Arising in Crossflow Heat Exchangers

Suppose that Fig. 9.6.1 represents two fluids passing in thin parallel layers in the directions shown and separated by the x,y-plane. If the temperature of the upper layer differs from that of the lower layer, then heat is exchanged through the separating surface—called the heat exchanger surface. By making suitable assumptions, into which we do not enter, it is possible to derive the following pair of partial differential equations for the steady-state temperature distribution for the upper and lower layers, namely,

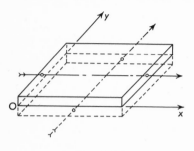

FIG. 9.6.1

(9.6.1)
$$T_y(x,y) + b[T(x,y) - \Theta(x,y)] = 0,$$

(9.6.2)
$$\Theta_x(x,y) + a[\Theta(x,y) - T(x,y)] = 0,$$

where a and b are constants while T and Θ are the temperatures of the upper and lower layers, respectively. By first eliminating Θ and then T between these equations we obtain the following second order partial differential equations

(9.6.3)
$$T_{xy}(x,y) + bT_x(x,y) + aT_y(x,y) = 0$$

and

(9.6.4)
$$\Theta_{xy}(x,y) + b\Theta_x(x,y) + a\Theta_y(x,y) = 0.$$

We shall determine formulas for $T(x,y)$ and $\Theta(x,y)$ when the following boundary conditions are stipulated

(9.6.5) $T(x,0) = k_1, \quad (x \geqslant 0); \qquad \Theta(0,y) = k_2, \quad (y \geqslant 0).$

Let $L_y\{T(x,y)\} = t(x,y)$. Then the transform of (9.6.3) with respect to y is

$$\frac{d}{dx}[pt(x,p) - T(x,0)] + b\frac{d}{dx}t(x,p) + a[pt(x,p) - T(x,0)] = 0$$

or, after simplification,

(9.6.6)
$$\frac{d}{dx}t(x,p) + \frac{ap}{p+b}t(x,p) = \frac{ak_1}{p+b}.$$

This first order linear differential equation has the solution

(9.6.7)
$$t(x,p) = \frac{k_1}{p} + c_1 e^{-axp/(p+b)}.$$

In order to determine the constant c_1 we must know $T(0,y)$, which is obtained from the differential equation (9.6.1) by substituting 0 for x. Thus

(9.6.8)
$$\frac{d}{dy}T(0,y) + bT(0,y) = bk_2,$$

from which

(9.6.9)
$$T(0,y) = k_2 + c_2 e^{-by}.$$

Substituting $y = 0$ in this equation and making use of the fact that $T(0,0) = k_1$, we find that $c_2 = k_1 - k_2$ and hence

(9.6.10) $$T(0,y) = k_2 + (k_1 - k_2)e^{-by}.$$

The Laplace transform of the preceding equation with respect to y is $t(0,p) = k_2/p + (k_1 - k_2)/(p + b)$ and from (9.6.7) $t(0,p) = k_1/p + c_1$. Therefore, by equating, we obtain

$$c_1 = \frac{k_2 - k_1}{p} - \frac{k_2 - k_1}{p + b} = \frac{(k_2 - k_1)b}{p(p + b)}.$$

This value when substituted in (9.6.7) yields the equation

$$t(x,p) = \frac{k_1}{p} + \frac{(k_2 - k_1)b}{p(p + b)} e^{-axp/(p+b)} = \frac{k_1}{p} + (k_2 - k_1)be^{-ax}\frac{e^{abx/(p+b)}}{p(p + b)},$$

whence

(9.6.11) $$T(x,y) = k_1 + (k_2 - k_1)he^{-ax}L_y^{-1}\left\{\frac{e^{abx/(p+b)}}{p(p + b)}\right\}.$$

Now from the table of transforms $L_y^{-1}\{e^{a/p}/p\} = I_0(2\sqrt{ay})$. Therefore, using Translation Theorem II and Theorem III

$$L_y^{-1}\left\{\frac{e^{abx/(p+b)}}{p(p + b)}\right\} = \int_0^y e^{-b\eta}I_0(2\sqrt{abx\eta})\,d\eta,$$

and

$$T(x,y) = k_1 + (k_2 - k_1)be^{-ax}\int_0^y e^{-b\eta}I_0(2\sqrt{abx\eta})\,d\eta.$$

In a similar manner, by operating on equation (9.6.2) with respect to x, one obtains

$$\Theta(x,y) = k_2 + a(k_1 - k_2)e^{-by}\int_0^x e^{-b\xi}I_0(2\sqrt{aby\xi})\,d\xi.$$

PROBLEMS

Solve the following boundary value problems which arise in various fields of engineering and in physics:

1. $$V_{xx}(x,t) - LCV_{tt}(x,t) - RCV_t(x,t) = 0 \qquad (x > 0, t > 0),$$
$$V(x,0) = V_t(x,0) = 0 \qquad (x > 0),$$
$$V(0,t) = V_0 I'(t), \lim_{x \to \infty} V(x,t) = 0 \qquad (t > 0).$$

Ans. $V(x,t) = V_0 e^{-(xR/2)\sqrt{C/L}} \cdot 1'(t - x\sqrt{LC})$

$$+ \frac{V_0 Rx}{2}\sqrt{\frac{C}{L}}e^{-(R/2L)t}\frac{I_1\left(\frac{R}{2L}\sqrt{t^2 - x^2LC}\right)}{\sqrt{t^2 - x^2LC}} \cdot 1(t - x\sqrt{LC}).$$

2. Solve the preceding problem if $V(0,t) = \sin \omega t$ and all the other conditions are the same.

[*Hint:* Use the convolution theorem.]

3.
$$D\left[C_{rr}(r,t) + \frac{1}{r}C_r(r,t)\right] = C_t(r,t) \qquad (0 \leqslant r < R, t > 0),$$

$$C(r,0) = C_0 \quad (0 \leqslant r < R), \quad C_r(R,t) = C_1 \qquad (t > 0).$$

4. $D\left[C_{rr}(r,t) + \frac{1}{r}C_r(r,t)\right] - vC_r(r,t) - kC(r,t) = C_t(r,t) \quad (0 \leqslant r < R, t > 0),$

$$C(r,0) = C_0, \quad (0 \leqslant r < R); \qquad C(R,t) = C_1, \qquad (t > 0),$$

where $v > 0$, $k > 0$. This is the case of diffusion, convection and chemical reaction when there is axial symmetry.

5. $D\left[C_{rr}(r,t) + \frac{2}{r}C_r(r,t)\right] - vC_r(r,t) - kC(r,t) = C_t(r,t) \quad (0 \leqslant r < R, t > 0),$

$$C(r,0) = C_0, \quad (0 \leqslant r < R); \qquad C(R,t) = C_1, \qquad (t > 0).$$

This is the case of diffusion, convection and chemical reaction when there is spherical symmetry.

6.
$$T_y(x,y) + b[T(x,y) - \Theta(x,y)] = 0,$$

$$\Theta(x,y) + a[\Theta(x,y) - T(x,y)] = 0,$$

$$T(x,0) = a_0 x, \quad (x \geqslant 0); \qquad \Theta(0,y) = b_0 y, \quad (y \geqslant 0).$$

Ans. $T(x,y) = a_0(ax - by)/a + \dfrac{a_0 b}{a}e^{-ax}\displaystyle\int_0^y e^{-b\eta}I_0(2\sqrt{abx\eta})\,d\eta$

$$+ \frac{(ab_0 + a_0 b)b}{a}e^{-ax}\int_0^y\int_0^\mu e^{-b\mu}I_0(2\sqrt{abx\mu})\,d\mu\,d\eta,$$

$$\Theta(x,y) = b_0(by - ax)/b + \frac{ab_0}{b}e^{-ay}\int_0^x e^{-a\xi}I_0(2\sqrt{aby\xi})\,d\xi$$

$$+ \frac{(ba_0 + b_0 a)a}{b}e^{-by}\int_0^x\int_0^\mu e^{-a\mu}I_0(2\sqrt{aby\mu})\,d\mu\,d\xi.$$

7.
$$C_t(r,t) = D\left[C_{rr}(r,t) + \frac{2}{r}C_r(r,t)\right] \qquad (r > R, t > 0),$$

$$C(r,0) = C_0, \quad (r > R); \quad \lim_{r \to \infty} C(r,t) = C_0, \qquad (t > 0),$$

$$C_r(R,t) = kC(R,t) \qquad (t > 0),$$

where k is a constant.

Ans. $C(r,t) = C_0 - \dfrac{kC_0 R^2}{r(1 + kR)}\left\{\text{erfc}\dfrac{r - R}{2\sqrt{Dt}}\right.$

$$- \exp\frac{1 + kR}{R}[r - R + (1 + kR)Dt/R] \times \text{erfc}\left.\left(\frac{r - R}{2\sqrt{Dt}} + \frac{1 + kR}{R}\sqrt{Dt}\right)\right\}.$$

8.
$$C_t(r,t) = D\left[C_{rr}(r,t) + \frac{2}{r}C_r(r,t)\right] + e^{-t} \qquad (r > R, t > 0),$$

$$C(r,0) = C_0, \quad (r > R); \quad \lim_{r \to \infty} C(r,t) = C_0 + 1 - e^{-t}, \qquad (t > 0),$$

$$C_r(R,t) = C(R,t) \qquad\qquad (t > 0).$$

Ans. $\displaystyle C(r,t) = C_0\left\{1 - \frac{R^2}{r(R+1)}Y(r,t)\right\}$

$$+ \int_0^t e^{-(t-\tau)}\left\{1 - \frac{R^2}{r(R+1)}Y(r,\tau)\right\} d\tau,$$

where

$$Y(r,t) = \text{erfc}\,\frac{r-R}{2\sqrt{Dt}} - \exp\frac{1+R}{R}[r - R + (1+R)Dt/R]$$

$$\times \text{erfc}\left(\frac{r-R}{2\sqrt{Dt}} + \frac{1+R}{R}\sqrt{Dt}\right).$$

9. Solve the following boundary value problem for $V_r(r,t)$.

$$[rV(r,t)]_{rr} = \frac{1}{C^2}[rV(r,t)]_{tt} \qquad (r > r_0, t > 0),$$

$$V(r,0) = V_t(r,0) = 0 \qquad (r > r_0),$$

$$V_r(r_0,t) = V_0[1(t) - 1(t - t_0)], \lim_{r \to \infty} V_r(r,t) \text{ finite} \qquad (t > 0).$$

$V_r(r,t)$ is the radial velocity of the points of a compressible fluid surrounding a sphere of radius r_0 when the radial velocity of the boundary of the sphere is given by the pulse $V_0[1(t) - 1(t - t_0)]$. c is the velocity of sound in the fluid.

Ans. $V_r(r,t) = V_0(r_0/r)\{[1 + (1 - r_0/r)(1 - e^{-(c/r_0)[t-(r-r_0)/c]})]$

$$1\,[t - (r - r_0)/c] - [1 + (1 - r_0/r)(1 - e^{-(c/r_0)[t-t_0-(r-r_0)/c]})]$$

$$1\,[t - t_0 - (r - r_0)/c]\}.$$

CHAPTER X

The Finite Fourier Sine, Cosine, and Hankel Transforms

The Laplace transform, because of its usefulness in solving ordinary differential equations and a large class of boundary value problems in partial differential equations, is the best known and most widely used transformation. In some cases, however, the use of other appropriate integral transforms may lead to a solution of a boundary value problem more quickly and easily than would be the case if a Laplace transform were employed. For this purpose the following integral transforms* have been used:

Complex Fourier transform

$$f(p) = \int_{-\infty}^{\infty} F(t)\, e^{ipt}\, dt,$$

Fourier sine transform

$$f(p) = \int_{0}^{\infty} F(t)\, \sin pt\, dt,$$

Fourier cosine transform

$$f(p) = \int_{0}^{\infty} F(t)\, \cos pt\, dt,$$

Mellin transform

$$f(p) = \int_{0}^{\infty} F(t)\, t^{p-1}\, dt,$$

Hankel transform

$$f(p) = \int_{0}^{\infty} F(t)\, tJ_{\nu}(pt)\, dt.$$

Together with the *Laplace transform*

$$f(p) = \int_{0}^{\infty} F(t)\, e^{-pt}\, dt,$$

* For an account of these transforms see the book by I. N. Sneddon, *Fourier Transforms*, McGraw-Hill Book Co., 1951, and the monograph by C. J. Tranter, *Integral Transforms in Mathematical Physics*, John Wiley & Sons, 1951.

we see that the range of integration in these integral transforms is infinite. Now, it may be that a boundary value problem is such that the variables involved range over finite intervals, in which case the preceding transforms do not apply. In other instances, where both finite and infinite intervals occur, it may be more convenient to work with the finite intervals. In such cases recourse is had to so-called *finite* transforms. The finite transforms involving the trigonometric functions sine and cosine were first suggested by Doetsch.* The extension to transforms involving Bessel functions is due to Sneddon.†

10.1 Finite Fourier Sine and Cosine Transforms

Let $F(x)$ be a sectionally continuous function over the interval $0 < x < l$. Then the *finite sine transform* of $F(x)$ is defined by

$$(10.1.1) \quad S\{F(x)\} = \int_0^l F(x) \sin \frac{n\pi x}{l} \, dx = f_S(n), \quad (n = 1, 2, 3, \cdots).$$

If $F'(x)$ is a sectionally continuous function over the interval $(0,l)$ and if at each point $\bar{x}$ of discontinuity $F(x)$ is defined so that

$$F(x) = \tfrac{1}{2}[F(\bar{x} + 0) + F(\bar{x} - 0)] \qquad (0 < x > l),$$

then it is well known from the theory of Fourier series that

$$(10.1.2) \qquad\qquad F(x) = \frac{2}{l} \sum_{n=1}^{\infty} a_n \sin \frac{n\pi x}{l},$$

where

$$a_n = \int_0^l F(x) \sin \frac{n\pi x}{l} \, dx.$$

However, from (10.1.1), we see that $a_n = f_S(n)$, so that

$$(10.1.3) \qquad\qquad F(x) = \frac{2}{l} \sum_{n=1}^{\infty} f_S(n) \sin \frac{n\pi x}{l}.$$

This expression is the inversion formula for the finite sine transform (10.1.1).

The *finite cosine transform* of $F(x)$ is defined by

$$(10.1.4) \quad C\{F(x)\} = \int_0^l F(x) \cos \frac{n\pi x}{l} \, dx = f_C(n), \quad (n = 0, 1, 2, \cdots).$$

If $F(x)$ satisfies the same conditions as in the case of the finite sine transform, then the inversion formula for (10.1.4) is

$$(10.1.5) \qquad\qquad F(x) = \frac{f_C(0)}{l} + \frac{2}{l} \sum_{n=1}^{\infty} f_C(n) \cos \frac{n\pi x}{l}.$$

* G. Doetsch, *Math. Ann.*, **62**, 52 (1935).
† I. N. Sneddon, *Phil. Mag.*, 7, 37 (1946).

Exercise. Show that (a) $C\{e^{kx}\} = \dfrac{kl^2}{k^2l^2 + n^2\pi^2}[(-1)^n e^{kl} - 1]$;

(b) $S\{1\} = \dfrac{l}{\pi n}[1 - (-1)^n]$; (c) $S\{x\} = (-1)^{n+1} \dfrac{l^2}{n\pi}$.

10.2 The Finite Sine and Cosine Transforms of the Derivatives of a Function

We shall now derive formulas that will be useful in the solution of certain boundary value problems by means of the finite sine and cosine transforms. These formulas will be useful in dealing with partial differential equations having terms such as $\partial^2 U(x,y)/\partial x^2$ and $\partial^4 U(x,y)/\partial x^4$.

Let $F'(x)$ be continuous and $F''(x)$ sectionally continuous on the interval $0 < x < l$. Integrating by parts twice, we find that

$$\int_0^l F''(x) \sin \frac{n\pi x}{l}\, dx = F'(x) \sin \frac{n\pi x}{l}\Big]_0^l - \frac{n\pi}{l}\int_0^l F'(x) \cos \frac{n\pi x}{l}\, dx$$

$$= -\frac{n\pi}{l}\cos \frac{n\pi x}{l} F(x)\Big]_0^l - \frac{n^2\pi^2}{l^2}\int_0^l F(x) \sin \frac{n\pi x}{l}\, dx,$$

whence

(10.2.1) $\displaystyle\int_0^l F''(x) \sin \frac{n\pi x}{l}\, dx = \frac{n\pi}{l}[F(0) + (-1)^{n+1} F(l)] - \frac{n^2\pi^2}{l^2} f_S(n).$

If, as often occurs in physical problems, both $F(0)$ and $F(l)$ vanish, then (10.2.1) reduces to the simple formula

(10.2.2) $\displaystyle\int_0^l F''(x) \sin \frac{n\pi x}{l}\, dx = -\frac{n^2\pi^2}{l^2} f_S(n).$

Now, suppose that $F'(x)$, $F''(x)$, $F'''(x)$ are continuous and $F^{(4)}(x)$ is sectionally continuous on the interval $0 < x < l$. Then replacing $F(x)$ in (10.2.1) by $F''(x)$, we have

$$\int_0^l F^{(4)}(x) \sin \frac{n\pi x}{l}\, dx = \frac{n\pi}{l}[F''(0) + (-1)^{n+1} F''(l)]$$

$$- \frac{n^2\pi^2}{l^2}\int_0^l F''(x) \sin \frac{n\pi x}{l}\, dx.$$

Hence, by a repeated use of (10.2.1) we find that

(10.2.3) $S\{F^{(4)}(x)\} = \displaystyle\int_0^l F^{(4)}(x) \sin \frac{n\pi x}{l}\, dx = \frac{n\pi}{l}[F''(0) + (-1)^{n+1} F''(l)]$

$$- \frac{n^3\pi^3}{l^3}[F(0) + (-1)^{n+1} F(l)] + \frac{n^4\pi^4}{l^4} f_S(n).$$

When $F(0) = F''(0) = F(l) = F''(l) = 0$, then (10.2.3) becomes

$$(10.2.4) \qquad \int_0^l F^{(4)}(x) \sin \frac{n\pi x}{l}\, dx = \frac{n^4 \pi^4}{l^4} f_S(n).$$

In the same manner and under the same assumptions as in the case of the finite sine transform, it can be easily shown that the following formulas for the *finite cosine transform* obtain:

$$(10.2.5) \qquad \int_0^l F''(x) \cos \frac{n\pi x}{l}\, dx = -F'(0) + (-1)^n F'(l) - \frac{n^2 \pi^2}{l^2} f_C(n).$$

$$(10.2.6) \qquad \int_0^l F^{(4)}(x) \cos \frac{n\pi x}{l}\, dx = -F'''(0) + (-1)^n F'''(l)$$

$$+ \frac{n^2 \pi^2}{l^2}[F'(0) + (-1)^{n+1} F'(l)] + \frac{n^4 \pi^4}{l^4} f_C(n).$$

Again, if $F'(0) = F'(l) = 0$, then (10.2.5) reduces to

$$(10.2.7) \qquad \int_0^l F''(x) \cos \frac{n\pi x}{l}\, dx = -\frac{n^2 \pi^2}{l^2} f_C(n),$$

while if $F'(0) = F'''(0) = F'(l) = F'''(l) = 0$, then (10.2.6) becomes

$$(10.2.8) \qquad \int_0^l F^{(4)}(x) \cos \frac{n\pi x}{l}\, dx = \frac{n^4 \pi^4}{l^4} f_C(n).$$

By a similar procedure formulas involving higher even ordered derivatives could be obtained. The formulas just derived, however, are sufficient for our purposes.

We now make the following observations. The use of a finite sine transform with respect to x, say, on a partial differential equation having the partial derivatives $\partial^2 U(x,y)/\partial x^2$ requires that $U(x,y)$ be specified at the end points $x = 0$ and $x = l$. If the term $\partial^4 U(x,y)/\partial x^4$ is present, then both $\partial^2 U(x,y)/\partial x^2$ and $U(x,y)$ must be known at $x = 0$ and $x = l$. On the other hand, the successful use of the finite cosine transform, when terms such as $\partial^2 U(x,y)/\partial x^2$ and $\partial^4 U(x,y)/\partial x^4$ are present in a differential equation, requires that $\partial U(x,y)/\partial x$ be prescribed at $x = 0$ and $x = l$ in the former case and $\partial U(x,y)/\partial x$ as well as $\partial^3 U(x,y)/\partial x^3$ at $x = 0$ and $x = l$ in the latter case. Similar considerations apply to even ordered partial derivatives higher than four. Furthermore, neither the finite sine or cosine transform is effective when applied to a partial differential equation having odd ordered derivatives. This follows from the fact that the finite sine transform (finite cosine transform) of an odd ordered derivative of U cannot be expressed in terms of a finite sine transform (finite cosine transform) of U. For instance,

$$S\{U_x(x,y)\} = \int_0^l U_x(x,y) \sin \frac{n\pi x}{l}\, dx$$

$$= -\frac{n\pi}{l}\int_0^l U(x,y) \cos \frac{n\pi x}{l}\, dx = -\frac{n\pi}{l} f_C(n)$$

and we see that the right-hand side is a finite *cosine* transform. Thus, as a simple example, if the differential equation is

$$\frac{\partial^2 U(x,y)}{\partial x^2} + \frac{\partial U(x,y)}{\partial x} = x,$$

the finite sine transform of both sides with respect to x is

$$\frac{n\pi}{l}[U(0,y) +(-1)^{n+1}U(l,y)] - \frac{n^2\pi^2}{l^2}f_S(n,y) - \frac{n\pi}{l}f_C(n,y) = (-1)^{n+1}\frac{l^2}{n\pi}$$

and we have one equation with two unknowns $f_S(n,y)$ and $f_C(n,y)$.

As in the case of Laplace transforms the finite sine and cosine transform of a number of functions can be found in tables listed in Appendices D and E.

We shall now consider a number of problems that can be solved suitably by means of the finite Fourier sine or cosine transform.

10.3 A Radiating Rectangular Plate

If a thin rectangular plate (Fig. 10.3.1) radiates heat into a surrounding medium kept at the constant temperature U_0, then the steady temperature $U(x,y)$ of the plate satisfies the differential equation

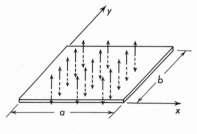

FIG. 10.3.1

(10.3.1) $\quad U_{xx}(x,y) + U_{yy}(x,y)$
$$= \alpha^2[U(x,y) - U_0]$$
$$(0 < x < a, 0 < y < b),$$

where α^2 is a constant depending on the physical properties of the plate We shall obtain an expression for the steady temperature if the edge $y = b$ is maintained at the constant temperature U_1 and the other edges are kept at zero. The boundary conditions are therefore

(10.3.2) $\qquad U(0,y) = U(a,y) = 0 \qquad (0 < y < b),$

(10.3.3) $\qquad U(x,0) = 0, \qquad U(x,b) = U_1 \qquad (0 < x < a).$

Clearly, a finite sine transform with $l = a$ is indicated. In view of this, therefore, let $S_x\{U(x,y)\} = u_S(n,y)$, where the subscript x means that the finite transform is taken with respect to x. Then the sine transform of equation (10.3.1) becomes

(10.3.4) $\dfrac{d^2}{dy^2}u_S(n,y) - \left(\alpha^2 + \dfrac{n^2\pi^2}{a^2}\right)u_S(n,y) = -\dfrac{\alpha^2 U_0 a}{n\pi}[1 - (-1)^n],$

where use of conditions (10.3.2) was made. Transforming the conditions (10.3.3), we have

(10.3.5) $u_S(n,0) = 0, \qquad u_S(n,b) = \dfrac{U_1 a}{n\pi}[1 - (-1)^n].$

The solution of (10.3.4) is easily seen to be

(10.3.6) $u_S(n,y) = c_1 \cosh \sqrt{\alpha^2 + n^2\pi^2/a^2}\, y + c_2 \sinh \sqrt{\alpha^2 + n^2\pi^2/a^2}\, y$
$$+ \frac{\alpha^2 U_0 a[1 - (-1)^n]}{n\pi(\alpha^2 + n^2\pi^2/a^2)}.$$

Making use of conditions (10.3.5), we find that

$c_1 = -\dfrac{\alpha^2 U_0 a[1 - (-1)^n]}{n\pi(\alpha^2 + n^2\pi^2/a^2)}, \quad c_2 = \dfrac{a}{n\pi}[1 - (-1)^n]$
$$\left\{\frac{U_1(\alpha^2 + n^2\pi^2/a^2) + \alpha^2 U_0 (\cosh b\sqrt{\alpha^2 + n^2\pi^2/a^2} - 1)}{(\alpha^2 + n^2\pi^2/a^2) \sinh b\sqrt{\alpha^2 + n^2\pi^2/a^2}}\right\}.$$

Substituting these values in (10.3.6) and taking the inverse transform, we obtain after some simplification

$$U(x,y) = \frac{4}{\pi} \sum_{n=1,3,5,\dots}^{\infty} \frac{1}{n(\alpha^2 + n^2\pi^2/a^2)}$$
$$\left\{\frac{U_1(\alpha^2 + n^2\pi^2/a^2) + \alpha^2 U_0 (\cosh b\sqrt{\alpha^2 + n^2\pi^2/a^2} - 1)}{\sinh b\sqrt{\alpha^2 + n^2\pi^2/a^2}}\sinh y\sqrt{\alpha^2 + n^2\pi^2/a^2}\right.$$
$$\left. + \alpha^2 U_0(1 - \cosh y\sqrt{\alpha^2 + n^2\pi^2/a^2})\right\} \sin \frac{n\pi x}{a}.$$

Exercise. Solve the following boundary value problem:
$$U_{xx}(x,y) + U_{yy}(x,y) = \alpha^2 U(x,y) - \alpha^2 U_0$$
$$(0 < x < a,\ 0 < y < b),$$
$$U(x,0) = 0, \quad U_y(x,b) = U_1, \quad (0 < x < a); \qquad U(0,y) = U(a,y) = 0,$$
$$(0 < y < b).$$

Ans. $U(x,y) = \dfrac{4}{\pi} \displaystyle\sum_{n=1,3,5,\dots}^{\infty} \dfrac{1}{n\beta_n}\left\{\alpha^2 U_0(1 - \cosh y\sqrt{\beta_n})\right.$
$$\left. + (U_1\sqrt{\beta_n} + \alpha^2 U_0 \sinh b\sqrt{\beta_n}) \frac{\sinh y\sqrt{\beta_n}}{\cosh b\sqrt{\beta_n}}\right\} \sin \frac{n\pi x}{a}.$$

where $\beta_n = \alpha^2 + n^2\pi^2/a^2$.

10.4 Tranverse Vibrations of a Hinged Beam

Let a uniform beam of length l, hinged at both ends, carry a load given by the function $F(x,t) = F_0 x$ (Fig. 10.4.1). Then, by equation (7.8.3), the transverse displacements are given by

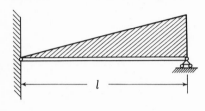

FIG. 10.4.1

(10.4.1)
$$Y_{xxxx}(x,t) + a^2 Y_{tt}(x,t) = F_0 x/(EI)$$
$$(0 < x < l, t > 0).$$

If the beam is initially at rest, then

(10.4.2)
$$Y(x,0) = Y_t(x,0) = 0 \quad (0 < x < l)$$

and the fact that the beam is hinged implies that

(10.4.3) $$Y(0,t) = Y_{xx}(0,t) = Y(l,t) = Y_{xx}(l,t) = 0 \qquad (t > 0).$$

We shall again use the finite Fourier sine transform to solve this boundary value problem.

Let $S_x\{Y(x,t)\} = y_S(n,t)$. Then the transform of (10.4.1) is readily seen to be

$$\frac{d^2}{dt^2} y_S(n,t) + \frac{n^4 \pi^4}{a^2 l^4} y_S(n,t) = (-1)^{n+1} \frac{F_0 l^2}{n\pi a^2},$$

whose solution is

(10.4.4) $$y_S(n,t) = c_1 \cos \frac{n^2 \pi^2}{al^2} t + c_2 \sin \frac{n^2 \pi^2}{al^2} t + (-1)^{n+1} \frac{F_0 l^6}{n^5 \pi^5}.$$

The transform of (10.4.2) is $y_S(n,0) = \dfrac{d}{dy} y_S(n,0) = 0$, which when

applied to (10.4.4) give the values $c_1 = (-1)^{n+2} \dfrac{F_0 l^6}{n^5 \pi^5}$, $c_2 = 0$. Thus

$$y_S(n,t) = (-1)^{n+1} \frac{F_0 l^6}{n^5 \pi^5} [1 - \cos \frac{n^2 \pi^2}{al^2} t]$$

and by the inversion formula

(10.4.5) $$Y(x,t) = \frac{2 F_0 l^5}{\pi^5} \sum_{n=1}^{\infty} (-1)^{n+1} \left[1 - \cos \frac{n^2 \pi^2}{al^2} t \right] \sin \frac{n\pi x}{l}.$$

Exercise. Making use of problem 4, p. 110, solve the preceding boundary value problem for the more general case when $F(x,t) = G(x)$ and verify the result (10.4.5).

Ans. $Y(x,t)$
$$= \frac{2l}{a\pi^2} \sum_{n=1}^{\infty} \frac{1}{n^2} \left\{ \int_0^t \left(\int_0^l G(x) \sin \frac{n\pi x}{l} \, dx \right) \sin \frac{n^2 \pi^2}{al^2}(t - \tau) \, d\tau \right\} \sin \frac{n\pi x}{l}.$$

10.5 An Iterated Use of Finite Transforms

Consider a thin membrane stretched across the fixed rectangle of Fig. 10.5.1. If an external force $F(x,y,t)$ per unit area acts perpendicular to the membrane, then the transverse displacements $Z(x,y,t)$ satisfy the non-homogeneous partial differential equation

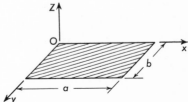

FIG. 10.5.1

(10.5.1)
$$Z_{tt}(x,y,t) = c^2[Z_{xx}(x,y,t) \\ + Z_{yy}(x,y,t)] + dF(x,y,t) \\ (0 < x < a, \, 0 < y < b, \, t > 0).$$

Because the edges of the rectangle are fixed, the boundary conditions are

(10.5.1) $$Z(0,y,t) = Z(a,y,t) = 0 \qquad (0 < x < a, \, t > 0),$$

(10.5.3) $$Z(x,0,t) = Z(x,b,t) = 0 \qquad (0 < y < b, \, t > 0).$$

Now, if the initial displacement and velocity of each point of the membrane are specified, i.e., if

(10.5.3) $$Z(x,y,0) = G(x,y), \qquad Z_t(x,y,0) = H(x,y) \\ (0 < x < a, \, 0 < y < b)$$

are given, then we have sufficient data to find a solution of (10.5.1) satisfying these conditions.

Since the differential equation for the vibrating membrane has *three* independent variables, a single use of finite transforms will only reduce this equation to a partial differential equation having *two* independent variables. However, a double use of a finite transform will reduce the original partial differential equation to an ordinary one, thus reducing the complexity of the problem.

In order to illustrate the use of repeated finite transforms, we shall solve the following boundary value problem

(10.5.4) $$Z_{tt}(x,y,t) = c^2[Z_{xx}(x,y,t) + Z_{yy}(x,y,t)] \\ (0 < x < a, \, 0 < y < b, \, t > 0),$$

(10.5.5) $$Z(0,y,t) = Z(a,y,t) = 0 \qquad (0 < x < a, \, t > 0),$$

(10.5.6) $$Z(x,0,t) = Z(x,b,t) = 0 \qquad (0 < y < b, \, t > 0),$$

(10.5.7) $$Z(x,y,0) = xy(a - x)(b - y), \, Z_t(x,y,0) = 0 \\ (0 < x < a, \, 0 < y < b).$$

In view of the boundary conditions, the use of a finite sine transform is indicated. Therefore, let $S_y\{Z(x,y,t)\} = \int_0^b Z(x,y,t) \sin \frac{n\pi y}{b} \, dy$ $= z(x,n,t)$. Then the preceding problem transforms into

(10.5.8) $$z_{tt}(x,n,t) = c^2\left[z_{xx}(x,n,t) - \frac{n^2\pi^2}{b^2}\,z(x,n,t)\right],$$

(10.5.9) $$z(0,n,t) = z(a,n,t) = 0,$$

(10.5.10) $$z(x,n,0) = \frac{2a^3}{\pi^3 n^3}\,[1 - (-1)^n]y(b-y), \qquad z_t(x,n,0) = 0.$$

Now, let $S_x\{z(x,n,t)\} = \displaystyle\int_0^a z(x,n,t)\,\sin\frac{m\pi x}{a}\,dx = \bar{z}(m,n,t)$. Then, transforming the above conditions, we obtain

(10.5.11) $$\frac{d^2}{dt^2}\,\bar{z}(m,n,t) + \frac{c^2\pi^2}{a^2 b^2}\,(a^2 n^2 + b^2 m^2)\bar{z}(m,n,t) = 0,$$

(10.5.12) $$\bar{z}(m,n,t) = \frac{4a^3 b^3}{\pi^3 m^3 n^3}[1 - (-1)^n][1 - (-1)^m],$$

$$\frac{d}{dt}\,\bar{z}(m,n,t) = 0.$$

The solution of (10.5.11) satisfying conditions (10.5.12) is

(10.5.13) $$z(m,n,t) = \frac{4a^3 b^3}{\pi^3 m^3 n^3}[1 - (-1)^n][1 - (-1)^m]$$

$$\cos\left(\frac{c\pi}{ab}\sqrt{m^2 b^2 + a^2 n^2}t\right).$$

Inverting with respect to y, we get

$$z(m,y,t) = \frac{8a^3 b^2}{\pi^3 n^3}[1 - (-1)^n]\sum_{m=1}^{\infty}\frac{[1 - (-1)^m]}{m^3}$$

$$\cos\left(\frac{c\pi}{ab}\sqrt{m^2 b^2 + a^2 n^2}\,t\right)\sin\frac{m\pi}{b}y,$$

or

$$z(m,y,t) = \frac{16a^3 b^2}{\pi^3 n^3}[1 - (-1)^n]\sum_{m=1,3,5,\cdots}^{\infty}\frac{1}{m^3}$$

$$\cos\left(\frac{c\pi}{ab}\sqrt{m^2 b^2 + a^2 n^2}\,t\right)\sin\frac{m\pi}{b}y.$$

Finally, another inversion with respect to x yields the result

$$Z(x,y,t) = \frac{64a^2 b^2}{\pi^3}\sum_{n=1,3,5,\cdots}^{\infty}\sum_{m=1,3,5,\cdots}^{\infty}\frac{1}{n^3 m^3}\cos\left(\frac{c\pi}{ab}\sqrt{m^2 b^2 + a^2 n^2}\,t\right)$$

$$\sin\frac{m\pi}{b}y\,\sin\frac{n\pi}{a}x.$$

Exercise.   Solve the preceding problem of the vibrating membrane if the initial displacement and velocity are $Z(x,y,0) = 0$ and $Z_t(x,y,0) = V_0$ (const.), respectively.

$$Ans. \quad Z(x,y,t) = \frac{16 V_0\, ab}{c\pi^2} \sum_{n=1,3,5,\cdots}^{\infty} \sum_{m=1,3,5,\cdots}^{\infty} \frac{1}{mn\sqrt{a^2 n^2 + m^2 b^2}}$$

$$\sin\left(\frac{c\pi}{ab}\sqrt{a^2 n^2 + b^2 m^2}\, t\right) \sin\frac{m\pi}{b} y \sin\frac{n\pi}{a} x.$$

10.6 Deflection of a Simply Supported Rectangular Plate Under Uniform Load

It is well known* that for small deflections of a plate subjected to a load acting normal to its surface the following fourth order partial differential equation obtains

$$(10.6.1) \qquad W_{xxxx}(x,y) + 2W_{xxyy}(x,y) + W_{yyyy}(x,y) = q(x,y)/D,$$

where $W(x,y)$ is the vertical deflection, $q(x,y)$ is the load intensity (lb/unit area) and D is the flexural rigidity of the plate.   For the case of a simply supported rectangular plate (Fig. 10.6.1) the boundary conditions are

$$(10.6.2)$$
$$W(0,y) = W(a,y) = W_{xx}(0,y)$$
$$= W_{xx}(a,y) = 0,$$

and

$$(10.6.3)$$
$$W(x,0) = W(x,b) = W_{yy}(x,0)$$
$$= W_{yy}(x,b) = 0.$$

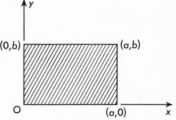

Fɪɢ. 10.6.1

These conditions, together with the fact that the above differential equation has even ordered derivatives, point to the use of the Fourier sine transform with $l = a$.

We shall find an expression for the deflection of a rectangular plate if the load is uniformly distributed over its surface, i.e., if $q(x,y) = q_0$ (const.), so that equation (10.6.1) is now

$$(10.6.4) \qquad W_{xxxx}(x,y) + 2W_{xxyy}(x,y) + W_{yyyy}(x,y) = q_0/D.$$

Let $S_x\{ W(x,y)\} = w(n,y)$.   Then, upon taking the sine transform of both sides of equation (10.6.4) and making use of formulas (10.2.4) and (10.2.2) as well as the table of sine transforms, we find that

$$(10.6.5) \qquad \frac{d^4}{dy^4} w(n,y) - 2\frac{n^2\pi^2}{a^2} w(n,y) + \frac{n^4\pi^4}{a^4} w(n,y) = \frac{q_0 a}{n\pi D}[1 - (-1)^n].$$

---

* See e.g., S. Timoshenko, *Theory of Plates and Shell*, McGraw-Hill Book Co., New York, 1940.

Furthermore, the sine transform of conditions (10.6.3) yields

$$(10.6.6) \qquad w(n,0) = \frac{d^2}{dy^2}w(n,0) = w(n,b) = \frac{d^2}{dy^2}w(n,b) = 0.$$

Thus, we have reduced the original problem to that of solving a fourth order ordinary differential equation subject to the boundary conditions (10.6.6). The solution of (10.6.5), which can be written down at once, is

$$(10.6.7) \qquad w(n,y) = \left(c_1 + \frac{n\pi y}{a}c_2\right)\sinh\frac{n\pi y}{a} + \left(c_3 + \frac{n\pi y}{a}c_4\right)\cosh\frac{n\pi y}{a}$$

$$+ \frac{q_0 a^5}{n^5\pi^5 D}[1 - (-1)^n].$$

The use of boundary conditions (10.6.6) now gives the following system of equations

$$0 = c_3 + \frac{q_0 a^5}{n^5\pi^5 D}[1 - (-1)^n],$$

$$0 = c_3 + 2c_2,$$

$$0 = (c_1 + 2\beta_n c_2)\sinh 2\beta_n + (c_3 + 2\beta_n c_4)\cosh 2\beta_n + \frac{q_0 a^5}{n^5\pi^5 D}[1 - (-1)^n],$$

$$0 = (c_1 + 2\beta_n c_2)\sinh 2\beta_n + (c_3 + 2\beta_n c_4)\cosh 2\beta_n + 2c\cosh 2\beta_n$$
$$+ 2c_4\sinh 2\beta_n,$$

where $n\pi b/a = 2\beta_n$. Solving this system, we readily obtain

$$c_3 = -\frac{q_0 a^5}{n^5\pi^5 D}[1 - (-1)^n], \qquad c_2 = \frac{q_0 a^5}{2n^5\pi^5 D}[1 - (-1)^n],$$

$$c_4 = \frac{q_0 a^5}{2n^5\pi^5 D}[1 - (-1)^n](\operatorname{csch} 2\beta_n - \coth 2\beta_n),$$

$$c_1 = -\frac{q_0 a^5}{n^5\pi^5 D}[\beta_n + (1 + \beta_n \coth 2\beta_n)(\operatorname{csch} 2\beta_n - \coth 2\beta_n)].$$

These values when substituted in (10.6.7) give the result

$$w(n,y) = \frac{q_0 a^5}{n^5\pi^5 D}[1 - (-1)^n]\Big\{1 + [\beta_n(y - b)/b$$

$$- (1 + \beta_n \coth 2\beta_n)(\operatorname{csch} 2\beta_n - \coth 2\beta_n)]\sinh\frac{2\beta_n}{b}y$$

$$+ [\beta_n y(\operatorname{csch} 2\beta_n - \coth 2\beta_n)/b - 1]\cosh\frac{2\beta_n}{b}y\Big\}.$$

Whence, by the inversion formula (10.1.3), we finally obtain

$$W(x,y) = \frac{4q_0 a^4}{\pi^5 D} \sum_{n=1,3,5,\ldots}^{\infty} \frac{1}{n^5}\left\{1 + [\beta_n(y-b)/b\right.$$

$$- (1 + \beta_n \coth 2\beta_n)(\operatorname{csch} 2\beta_n - \coth 2\beta_n)] \sinh \frac{2\beta_n}{b} y$$

$$\left.+ [\beta_n y (\operatorname{csch} 2\beta_n - \coth 2\beta_n)/b - 1] \cosh \frac{2\beta_n}{b} y\right\} \sin \frac{2\beta_n}{b} x.$$

10.7 A Diffusion Problem Solved by the Use of a Finite Cosine Transform

In many problems of diffusion the dissolved substances react chemically. If $f(C)$ is the law of reaction rate, the diffusion equation is

$$(10.7.1) \qquad C_t(x,t) = DC_{xx}(x,t) + f(C).$$

In practice $f(C)$ is often equal to $-kC$, where k is a constant. Equation (10.7.1) then becomes

$$(10.7.2) \qquad C_t(x,t) = DC_{xx}(x,t) - kC(x,t).$$

If the initial concentration of a substance lying between $x = 0$ and $x = a$ (Fig. 10.7.1) is $F(x)$, the flux of transport across both boundaries $x = 0$ and $x = a$ is 0, it is required to find the concentration $C(x,t)$ for $t > 0$. Stated symbolically, we are to solve (10.7.2) subject to the following conditions

$$(10.7.3) \qquad C(x,0) = F(x),$$

$$(10.7.4) \qquad C_x(0,t) = 0, \quad C_x(a,t) = 0.$$

The preceding boundary conditions suggest the use of a finite cosine transform with respect to x. In view of this, let $c(n,t)$

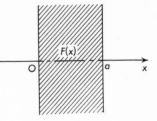

FIG. 10.7.1

$$= \int_0^a C(x,t) \cos \frac{n\pi x}{a}\, dx.$$ Transforming equation (10.7.2) and the initial condition (10.7.3), we find that

$$(10.7.5) \qquad \frac{d}{dt}c(n,t) + (k + Dn^2\pi^2/a^2)c(n,t) = 0$$

and

$$(10.7.6) \qquad c(n,0) = \int_0^a F(\xi) \cos \frac{n\pi\xi}{a}\, d\xi.$$

The solution of (10.7.5) satisfying condition (10.7.6) is

$$(10.7.7) \qquad c(n,t) = e^{-(k+Dn^2\pi^2/a^2)t} \int_0^a F(\xi) \cos \frac{n\pi\xi}{a}\, d\xi.$$

Using the inversion formula (10.1.5), we obtain

$$C(x,t) = \frac{1}{a}\int_0^a F(\xi)\,d\xi + \frac{2}{a}\sum_{n=1}^{\infty} e^{-(k+Dn^2\pi^2/a^2)t}\cos\frac{n\pi x}{a}\int_0^a F(\xi)\cos\frac{n\pi\xi}{a}\,d\xi.$$

It is readily verified that this formula satisfies equation (10.7.2) and the initial and boundary conditions.

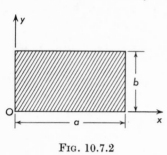

FIG. 10.7.2

Exercise. Using the finite cosine transform with respect to x, find the steady-state temperature distribution in the rectangle of Fig. 10.7.2 if the temperature $U(x,y)$ satisfies the equation $U_{xx}(x,y) + U_{yy}(x,y) = 0$ and the boundary conditions

$$U_x(0,y) = U_x(a,y) = 0,$$
$$U(x,0) = 0,$$
$$U(x,b) = F(x).$$

Ans. $U(x,y)$

$$= \frac{y}{ab}\int_0^a F(\xi)\,d\xi + \frac{2}{a}\sum_{n=1}^{\infty}\left(\sinh\frac{n\pi}{a}y\cos\frac{n\pi}{a}x/\sinh\frac{n\pi}{a}b\right)\int_0^a F(\xi)\cos\frac{n\pi\xi}{a}\,d\xi.$$

10.8 The Finite Hankel Transform

A transform which is very useful in the solution of boundary value problems dealing with physical systems having axial symmetry is the so-called finite Hankel transform introduced by Sneddon.* Of the several types that have been introduced, we shall only consider the one defined by

$$(10.8.1)\qquad \mathbf{J}_\nu\{F(x)\} = \int_0^l xF(x)J_\nu(xp_n)\,dx = f_{J_\nu}(p_n),\qquad (n = 1, 2, 3, \cdots),$$

where $F(x)$ and $F'(x)$ are sectionally continuous functions over the finite interval $0 < x < l$ and $F(x)$ is defined to be equal to $\frac{1}{2}[F(\bar{x} + 0) + F(\bar{x} - 0)]$ at each point of discontinuity $\bar{x}$. Moreover, p_n is a *positive* root of the equation

$$(10.8.2)\qquad\qquad J_\nu(lp_n) = 0 \qquad\qquad (\nu \geqslant 0).$$

Now, from the theory of Fourier–Bessel series it is well known that for a function $F(x)$ satisfying the conditions mentioned above,

$$F(x) = \frac{2}{l^2}\sum_{n=1}^{\infty} a_n\frac{J_\nu(xp_n)}{[J_\nu'(lp_n)]^2},$$

* I. N. Sneddon, "Finite Hankel Transforms," *Phil. Mag.*, 37, 1946.

where

$$a_n = \int_0^l xF(x)J_\nu(xp_n)\,dx.$$

But by (10.8.1), $a_n = f_{J_\nu}(p_n)$ and therefore

(10.8.3) $$F(x) = \frac{2}{l^2}\sum_{n=1}^{\infty} f_{J_\nu}(p_n)J_\nu(xp_n)/[J_\nu'(lp_n)]^2.$$

This expression constitutes the inversion formula for the finite Hankel transform (10.8.1).

In order to solve certain partial differential equations we shall need a fundamental formula to be developed in what follows. Integrating by parts, we have

$$\int_0^l [xF'(x)]'J_\nu(xp_n)\,dx = \left[xF'(x)J_\nu(xp_n)\right]_0^l - p_n\int_0^l xF'(x)J_\nu'(xp_n)\,dx,$$

$$= \left[xF'(x)J_\nu(xp_n)\right]_0^l - p_n[xF(x)J_\nu'(xp_n)]_0^l$$

$$+ p_n\int_0^l F(x)[xp_nJ_\nu''(xp_n) + J_\nu'(xp_n)]\,dx,$$

where the primes indicate differentiation with respect to x. The first and second expressions on the right clearly vanish at the lower limit $x = 0$ and if we assume that p_n is a root of equation (10.8.2) the first expression also vanishes at the upper limit $x = l$. Therefore,

(10.8.4) $$\int_0^l \left\{[xF'(x)]' - \frac{\nu^2}{x}F(x)\right\}J_\nu(xp_n)\,dx = -lp_nF(l)J_\nu'(lp_n)$$

$$+ p_n\int_0^l F(x)\left[xp_nJ_\nu''(xp_n) + J_\nu'(xp_n) - \frac{\nu^2}{xp_n}J_\nu(xp_n)\right]dx.$$

But $J_\nu(xp_n)$ satisfies the differential equation

$$xp_nJ_\nu''(xp_n) + J_\nu'(xp_n) + \left(xp_n - \frac{\nu^2}{xp_n}\right)J_\nu(xp_n) = 0,$$

and hence (10.8.4) becomes

$$\int_0^l \left\{[xF'(x)]' - \frac{\nu^2}{x}F(x)\right\}J_\nu(xp_n)\,dx$$

$$= -lp_nF(l)J_\nu'(lp_n) - p_n^2\int_0^l xF(x)J_\nu(xp_n)\,dx.$$

Performing the indicated differentiation under the integral sign, we finally obtain the desired formula

(10.8.5) $$\int_0^l \left\{F''(x) + \frac{1}{x}F'(x) - \frac{\nu^2}{x^2}F(x)\right\}xJ_\nu(xp_n)\,dx$$

$$= -lp_nF(l)J_\nu'(lp_n) - p_n^2\int_0^l xF(x)J_\nu(xp_n)\,dx,$$

or, equivalently,

$$(10.8.6) \quad \mathbf{J}_\nu\left\{F''(x) + \frac{1}{x}F'(x) - \frac{\nu^2}{x^2}F(x)\right\} = -lp_nF(l)J_\nu'(lp_n) - p_n^2 f_{J_\nu}(p_n).$$

In the special, but important case, when $\nu = 0$ formula (10.8.6) becomes

$$(10.8.7) \quad \mathbf{J}_0\left\{F''(x) + \frac{1}{x}F'(x)\right\} = lp_nF(l)J_1(lp_n) - p_n^2 f_{J_0}(p_n),$$

where we have made use of the fact that $J_0'(\zeta) = -J_1(\zeta)$.

For purposes of comparison with the method of Laplace transforms, we shall solve the problem of diffusion in a circular cylinder considered in section 9.3 by employing the finite Hankel transform. We found there that the concentration $C(r,t)$ must satisfy the following conditions

$$(10.8.8) \quad C_{rr}(r,t) + \frac{1}{r}C_r(r,t) = \frac{1}{D}C_t(r,t) \quad (0 \leqslant r < R, t > 0),$$

$$(10.8.9) \quad C(r,0) = C_0, \quad (0 \leqslant r < R); \quad C(R,t) = C_1, \quad (t > 0).$$

The form of the left-hand side of equation (10.8.8) together with the fact that $C(r,t)$ is specified at the upper limit $r = R$ reveals that formula (10.8.7) is appropriate. Hence, if we let

$$\mathbf{J}_0\{C(r,t)\} = \int_0^R C(r,t)rJ_0(rp_n)\,dr = c_{J_0}(p_n,t),$$

we see that

$$\mathbf{J}_0\left\{C_{rr}(r,t) + \frac{1}{r}C_r(r,t)\right\} = Rp_nC(R,t)J_1(Rp_n) - p_n^2 c_{J_0}(p_n,t)$$

and the Hankel transform of equation (10.8.8) is

$$(10.8.10) \quad \frac{d}{dt}c_{J_0}(p_n,t) + p_n^2 Dc_{J_0}(p_n,t) = C_1DRp_nJ_1(Rp_n).$$

Now, it can be easily verified directly that

$$(10.8.11) \quad \mathbf{J}_0\{1\} = \int_0^R rJ_0(rp_n)\,dr = \frac{R}{p_n}J_1(Rp_n),$$

so that the Hankel transform of the first condition in (10.8.9) is

$$(10.8.12) \quad \mathbf{J}_0\{C(r,0)\} = c_{J_0}(p_n,0) = \frac{C_0R}{p_n}J_1(Rp_n).$$

The solution of (10.8.10) subject to (10.8.12) is readily found to be

$$c_{J_0}(p_n,t) = \frac{C_1R}{p_n}J_1(Rp_n) + \frac{R(C_0 - C_1)}{p_n}e^{-Dp_n^2t}J_1(Rp_n)$$

whence, upon inverting,

$$(10.8.13) \quad C(r,t) = C_1 + \frac{2}{R}(C_0 - C_1)\sum_{n=1}^\infty \frac{e^{-Dp_n^2t}}{p_n}\frac{J_1(Rp_n)J_0(rp_n)}{[J_0'(Rp_n)]^2}.$$

Making use of the substitution $Rp_n = \alpha_n$ and the fact that $J_0'(Rp_n) = -J_1(Rp_n)$, we find that (10.8.13) becomes

$$(10.8.14) \qquad C(r,t) = C_1 + 2(C_0 - C_1) \sum_{n=1}^{\infty} \frac{e^{-D(\alpha_n^2/R^2)t}J_0(r\alpha_n/R)}{\alpha_n J_1(\alpha_n)},$$

where α_n is a positive root of $J_0(\zeta) = 0$. This result is in agreement with that obtained in section 9.3 by Laplace transforms. As we see, the employment of the Hankel transform here obviated the necessity of the use of the calculus of residues.

Exercise 1. Replacing ν by $\nu + 1$ in formula 5(c), p. 272, show that

$$\mathbf{J}_\nu\{x^\nu\} = \frac{l^{\nu+1}}{p_n}J_{\nu+1}(lp_n) \qquad\qquad (\nu \geqslant -1).$$

In particular, show that

$$\mathbf{J}_0(k) = \frac{lk}{p_n}J_1(lp_n),$$

where k is a constant.

Exercise 2. Solve the following problem of diffusion in a circular cylinder by the use of the finite Hankel transform

$$C_{rr}(r,t) + \frac{1}{r}C_r(r,t) - \frac{k}{D}C(r,t) = \frac{1}{D}C_t(r,t) \qquad (0 \leqslant r < R, t > 0),$$

$$C(r,0) = C_0, \quad (0 \leqslant r < R); \qquad C(R,t) = C_1, \quad (t > 0).$$

Ans. $C(r,t)$
$$= \frac{2}{R}\sum_{n=1}^{\infty}\left\{\frac{DC_1p_n}{k + Dp_n^2} + \frac{C_0k + Dp_n^2(C_0 - C_1)}{p_n(k + Dp_n^2)}e^{-(k+Dp_n^2)t}\right\}\frac{J_0(rp_n)}{J_1(Rp_n)}.$$

PROBLEMS

Solve the following boundary value problems:
1. $\qquad U_{xx}(x,y) + U_{yy}(x,y) = \alpha^2 U(x,y)$
$$\qquad\qquad (0 < x < a, 0 < y < b),$$
$$U(0,y) = U(a,y) = 0 \qquad\qquad (0 < y < b),$$
$$U_y(x,0) = U_y(x,b) = U_1 \qquad\qquad (0 < x < a).$$

Ans. $U(x,y) = \frac{4U_1}{\pi}\sum_{n=1}^{\infty}\frac{1}{n\beta_n}\{(\operatorname{csch} b\beta_n - \coth b\beta_n)\cosh y\beta_n$

$$+ \sinh y\beta_n\}\sin\frac{n\pi x}{a}, \text{ where } \beta_n = \alpha^2 + n^2\pi^2/a^2.$$

2. $\qquad U_{xx}(x,y) + U_{yy}(x,y) = 0$
$$\qquad\qquad (0 < x < a, 0 < y < b),$$
$$U(0,y) = U(a,y) = 0 \qquad\qquad (0 < y < b),$$
$$U(x,0) = U_0, \qquad U(x,b) = U_1 \qquad (0 < x < a).$$

3.
$$C_t(x,t) = DC_{xx}(x,t) \qquad (0 < x < l, \, t > 0),$$
$$C(x,0) = F(x) \qquad (0 < x < l),$$
$$C(0,t) = C(l,t) = 0 \qquad (t > 0).$$

4.
$$U_{tt}(x,t) - U_{xx}(x,t) = 0 \qquad (0 < x < l, \, t > 0),$$
$$U(x,0) = f(x), \qquad U_t(x,0) = g(x) \qquad (0 < x < l),$$
$$U(0,t) = U(l,t) = 0 \qquad (t > 0).$$

Ans. $U(x,t) = \dfrac{2}{l} \displaystyle\sum_{n=1}^{\infty} \cos\left(\dfrac{n\pi}{l}t\right) \sin\left(\dfrac{n\pi}{l}x\right) \int_0^l f(x) \sin\left(\dfrac{n\pi}{l}x\right) dx$

$$+ \dfrac{2}{\pi} \sum_{n=1}^{\infty} \dfrac{1}{n} \sin\left(\dfrac{n\pi}{l}t\right) \sin\left(\dfrac{n\pi}{l}x\right) \int_0^l g(x) \sin\left(\dfrac{n\pi}{l}x\right) dx.$$

5.
$$Y_{xxxx}(x,t) + a^2 Y_{tt}(x,t) = 0 \qquad (0 < x < l, \, t > 0),$$
$$Y(x,0) = x(l - x), \qquad Y_t(x,0) = 0 \qquad (0 < x < l),$$
$$Y(0,t) = Y_{xx}(0,t) = Y(l,t) = Y_{xx}(l,t) = 0 \qquad (t > 0).$$

Ans. $Y(x,t) = \dfrac{8l^2}{\pi^3} \displaystyle\sum_{n=1,3,5,\dots}^{\infty} \dfrac{1}{n^3} \cos\left(\dfrac{n^2\pi^2}{al^2}t\right) \sin\left(\dfrac{n\pi}{l}x\right).$

6.
$$Y_{xxxx}(x,t) + a^2 Y_{tt}(x,t) = 0 \qquad (0 < x < l, \, t > 0),$$
$$Y(x,0) = 0, \qquad Y_t(x,0) = \sin\frac{\pi}{l}x \qquad (0 < x < l),$$
$$Y(0,t) = Y_{xx}(0,t) = Y(l,t) = Y_{xx}(l,t) = 0 \qquad (t > 0).$$

Ans. $Y(x,t) = \dfrac{al^2}{\pi^2} \sin\left(\dfrac{\pi^2}{al^2}t\right) \sin\left(\dfrac{\pi}{l}x\right).$

7.
$$Y_{xxxx}(x,t) + Y_{tttt}(x,t) = 0 \qquad (0 < x < a, \, 0 < t < b),$$
$$Y_x(0,t) = Y_x(a,t) = Y_{xxx}(0,t) = Y_{xxx}(a,t) = 0 \quad (0 < t < b),$$
$$Y(x,0) = Y(x,b) = Y_t(x,0) = 0, \; Y_t(x,b) = Y_0 \quad (0 < x < a).$$

Ans. $Y(x,t) = \dfrac{Y_0}{b^2}t^2(t - b).$

8.
$$U_{xx}(x,y,t) + U_{yy}(x,y,t) = (1/\alpha^2)U_t(x,y,t)$$
$$(0 < x < a, \, 0 < y < b, \, t > 0),$$
$$U(0,y,t) = U(a,y,t) = 0 \qquad (0 < x < a),$$
$$U(x,0,t) = U(x,b,t) = 0 \qquad (0 < y < b),$$
$$U(x,y,0) = F(x,y) \qquad (0 < x < a, \, 0 < y < b).$$

Ans. $U(x,y,t)$

$$= \dfrac{4}{ab} \sum_{m=1}^{\infty} \sum_{n=1}^{\infty} e^{-\alpha^2\pi^2(m^2/a^2 + n^2/b^2)t} \sin\left(\dfrac{m\pi}{a}x\right) \sin\left(\dfrac{n\pi}{b}x\right) \int_0^a \int_0^b F(x,y)$$

$$\sin\left(\dfrac{m\pi}{a}x\right) \sin\left(\dfrac{n\pi}{b}y\right) dx \, dy.$$

9. The free symmetrical vibrations of circular membrane of radius R are governed by the equation

$$U_{rr}(r,t) + \frac{1}{r}U_r(r,t) = \frac{1}{c^2}U_{tt}(r,t).$$

Assuming that the periphery of the membrane is fixed, so that $U(R,t) = 0$, find the displacement of the membrane if it is set in motion from the position $U(r,0) = F(r)$ with velocity $U_t(r,0) = G(r)$. Use the finite Hankel transform.

Ans. $U(r,t) = \dfrac{2}{R^2} \displaystyle\sum_{n=1}^{\infty} \Bigg\{ \cos cp_n t \int_0^R rF(r)J_0(rp_n)\, dr$

$$+ \sin \frac{cp_n t}{cp_n} \int_0^a rG(r)J_0(rp_n)\, dr \Bigg\} \frac{J_0(rp_n)}{[J_1(Rp_n)]^2}.$$

APPENDIX A

REFERENCES

1. G. A. Campbell and R. M. Foster, *Fourier Integrals for Practical Applications*, Bell Telephone System, Technical Publication, 1931.

2. H. S. Carslaw and J. C. Jaeger, *Operational Methods in Applied Mathematics*, Oxford University Press, New York, 1948.

3. J. R. Carson, *Electric Circuit Theory and the Operational Calculus*, McGraw-Hill Book Co., New York, 1926.

4. R. V. Churchill, *Modern Operational Mathematics in Engineering*, McGraw-Hill Book Co., New York, 1944.

5. G. Doetsch, *Theorie und Anwendung der Laplace-Transformation*, Springer, Berlin, 1937.

6. G. Doetsch, *Tabellen zur Laplace-Transformation und Anleitung zum Gebrauch*, Springer, Berlin, 1947.

7. P. Franklin, *Fourier Methods*, McGraw-Hill Book Co., New York, 1949.

8. M. Gardner and I. Barnes, *Transients in Linear Systems*, Vol. 1, John Wiley & Sons, New York, 1942.

9. F. B. Hildebrand, *Advanced Calculus*, Prentice-Hall, New York, 1949.

10. H. Jeffreys and B. Jeffreys, *Methods of Mathematical Physics*, Cambridge University Press, London, 1950.

11. W. Jost, *Diffusion in Solids, Liquids, Gases*, Academic Press, New York, 1952.

12. N. W. McLachlan, *Complex Variable and Operational Calculus with Technical Applications*, Cambridge University Press, London, 1942.

13. N. W. McLachlan and P. Humbert, *Formulaire pour le Calcul Symbolique*, Gauthier Villars, Paris, 1950.

14. N. W. McLachlan, *Modern Operational Calculus*, Macmillan, London, 1948.

15. L. A. Pipes, *Applied Mathematics for Engineers and Physicists*, McGraw-Hill Book Co., New York, 1946.

16. L. N. Sneddon, *Fourier Transforms*, McGraw-Hill Book Co., New York, 1951.

17. J. D. Tamarkin and W. Feller, *Partial Differential Equations*. Mimeographed notes of lectures at Brown University, 1941.
315

18. E. C. Titchmarsh, *Theory of Fourier Integrals*, Oxford University Press, New York, 1937.

19. E. C. Titchmarsh, *The Theory of Functions*, Oxford University Press, 1939.

20. C. J. Tranter, *Integral Transforms in Mathematical Physics*, John Wiley & Sons, 1951.

21. B. Van der Pol and H. Bremmer, *Operational Calculus*, Cambridge University Press, London, 1950.

22. D. V. Widder, *The Laplace Transform*, Princeton University Press, Princeton, N.J., 1941.

TABLE OF OPERATIONS

No.	$f(p)$	$F(t)$
1	$\displaystyle\int_0^\infty e^{-pt}\,F(t)\,dt$	$F(t)$
2	$A_1 f_1(p) + A_2 f_2(p) + \cdots + A_n f_n(p)$	$A_1 F_1(t) + A_2 F_2(t) + \cdots + A_n F_n(t)$
3	$p^n f(p) - p^{n-1} F(0+) - \cdots$ $- F^{(n-1)}(0+)$	$F^{(n)}(t)$
4	$\dfrac{f(p)}{p}$	$\displaystyle\int_0^t F(\tau)\,d\tau$
5	$e^{-ap} f(p)$	$F(t-a)\,1\,(t-a), \quad a > 0$
6	$f(p+a)$	$e^{-at}\,F(t)$
7	$(-1)^n f^{(n)}(p)$	$t^n\,F(t)$
8	$f_1(p) f_2(p)$	$\displaystyle\int_0^t F_1(\tau)\,F_2(t-\tau)\,d\tau$
9	$\displaystyle\int_p^\infty f(\zeta)\,d\zeta$	$F(t)/t$

APPENDIX C

TABLE OF LAPLACE TRANSFORMS

The letters a, b, and c in this table represent distinct constants.

No.	$f(p)$	$F(t)$
1	$\dfrac{1}{p}$	1
2	$\dfrac{1}{p^2}$	t
3	$\dfrac{1}{p^n}, \quad n = 1, 2, \cdots$	$\dfrac{t^{n-1}}{(n-1)!}$
4	$\dfrac{1}{p^\nu}, \ \mathrm{Re}(\nu) > 0$	$\dfrac{t^{\nu-1}}{\Gamma(\nu)}$
5	$\dfrac{1}{p-a}$	e^{at}
6	$\dfrac{1}{(p-a)^2}$	te^{at}
7	$\dfrac{1}{(p-a)^n}, \ n = 1, 2, \cdots$	$\dfrac{t^{n-1}e^{at}}{(n-1)!}$
8	$\dfrac{1}{(p-a)^\nu}, \ \mathrm{Re}(\nu) > 0$	$\dfrac{t^{\nu-1}e^{at}}{\Gamma(\nu)}$
9	$\dfrac{1}{p(p-a)}$	$\dfrac{e^{at}-1}{a}$
10	$\dfrac{1}{(p-a)(p-b)}$	$\dfrac{e^{bt}-e^{at}}{b-a}$
11	$\dfrac{p}{(p-a)(p-b)}$	$\dfrac{be^{bt}-ae^{at}}{b-a}$
12	$\dfrac{1}{(p-a)(p-b)(p-c)}$	$\dfrac{(c-b)e^{at}+(a-c)e^{bt}+(b-a)e^{ct}}{(a-b)(b-c)(c-a)}$
13	$\dfrac{a}{p^2+a^2}$	$\sin at$

TABLE OF LAPLACE TRANSFORMS—*continued*

No.	$f(p)$	$F(t)$
14	$\dfrac{p}{p^2 + a^2}$	$\cos at$
15	$\dfrac{a}{p^2 - a^2}$	$\sinh at$
16	$\dfrac{p}{p^2 - a^2}$	$\cosh at$
17	$\dfrac{b}{(p + a)^2 + b^2}$	$e^{-at}\sin bt$
18	$\dfrac{p + a}{(p + a)^2 + b^2}$	$e^{-at}\cos bt$
19	$\dfrac{b}{(p + a)^2 - b^2}$	$e^{-at}\sinh bt$
20	$\dfrac{p + a}{(p + a)^2 - b^2}$	$e^{-at}\sinh bt$
21	$\dfrac{p^2}{p^3 + a^3}$	$\dfrac{1}{3}(e^{-at} + e^{-jat} + e^{-j^2at}),\quad j^3 = 1$
22	$\dfrac{p}{p^3 + a^3}$	$-\dfrac{1}{3a}(e^{-at} + j^2e^{-jat} + je^{-j^2at}),\quad j^3 = 1$
23	$\dfrac{1}{p^3 + a^3}$	$\dfrac{1}{3a^2}(e^{-at} + je^{-jat} + j^2e^{-j^2at}),\quad j^3 = 1$
24	$\dfrac{1}{p(p^2 - a^2)}$	$\dfrac{\cosh at - 1}{a^2}$
25	$\dfrac{1}{p(p^2 + a^2)}$	$\dfrac{1 - \cos at}{a^2}$
26	$\dfrac{p^3}{p^4 - a^4}$	$\dfrac{1}{2}(\cosh at + \cos at)$
27	$\dfrac{p^2}{p^4 - a^4}$	$\dfrac{1}{2a}(\sinh at + \sin at)$
28	$\dfrac{p}{p^4 - a^4}$	$\dfrac{1}{2a^2}(\cosh at - \cos at)$
29	$\dfrac{1}{p^4 - a^4}$	$\dfrac{1}{2a^3}(\sinh at - \sin at)$

TABLE OF LAPLACE TRANSFORMS—*continued*

No.	$f(p)$	$F(t)$
30	$\dfrac{p^3}{p^4 + 4a^4}$	$\cos at \cosh at$
31	$\dfrac{p^2}{p^4 + 4a^4}$	$\dfrac{1}{2a}(\cos at \sinh at + \sin at \cosh at)$
32	$\dfrac{p}{p^4 + 4a^4}$	$\dfrac{1}{2a^2} \sin at \sinh at$
33	$\dfrac{1}{p^4 + 4a^4}$	$\dfrac{1}{4a^3}(\sin at \cosh at - \cos at \sinh at)$
34	$\dfrac{1}{(p^2 - a^2)(p^2 - b^2)}$	$\dfrac{b \sin at - a \sinh bt}{ab(a^2 - b^2)}$
35	$\dfrac{1}{(p^2 + a^2)(p^2 + b^2)}$	$\dfrac{a \sin bt - b \sin at}{ab(a^2 - b^2)}$
36	$\dfrac{p}{(p^2 - a^2)(p^2 - b^2)}$	$\dfrac{\cosh bt - \cosh at}{b^2 - a^2}$
37	$\dfrac{p}{(p^2 + a^2)(p^2 + b^2)}$	$\dfrac{\cos bt - \cos at}{a^2 - b^2}$
38	$\dfrac{1}{p}\left(\dfrac{p-1}{p}\right)^n$	$L_n(t) = \dfrac{e^t}{n!}\dfrac{d^n}{dt^n}(t^n e{-}t)$ *
39	$\dfrac{(1 - p)^n}{p^{n+\frac{3}{2}}}$	$-\dfrac{n!}{\sqrt{\pi}(2n + 1)!}H_{2n+1}(\sqrt{t})$ †
40	$\dfrac{a}{\sqrt{p}(1 + a\sqrt{p})}$	$e^{t/a^2} \operatorname{erfc} \dfrac{\sqrt{t}}{a}$
41	$\dfrac{1}{p(a + \sqrt{p})}$	$\dfrac{1}{a}(1 - e^{a^2t} \operatorname{erfc} a\sqrt{t})$
42	$\dfrac{\sqrt{p + a}}{p + b}$	$\dfrac{e^{-at}}{\sqrt{\pi t}} + \sqrt{a - b}\, e^{-bt} \operatorname{erf}\sqrt{(a - b)t}$
43	$\dfrac{1}{(p + a)\sqrt{p + b}}$	$\dfrac{e^{-at}}{\sqrt{b - a}} \operatorname{erf} \sqrt{(b - a)t}$
44	$\dfrac{1}{\sqrt{p} + a}$	$\dfrac{1}{\sqrt{\pi t}} - ae^{a^2t} \operatorname{erfc} a\sqrt{t}$

* $L_n(t)$ is the Laguerre polynomial of degree n.

† $H_n(t) = e^{t^2}\dfrac{d^n}{dt^n}(e^{-t^2})$ is the Hermite polynomial.

TABLE OF LAPLACE TRANSFORMS—*continued*

No.	$f(p)$	$F(t)$
45	$\sqrt{p-a} - \sqrt{p-b}$	$\dfrac{1}{2\sqrt{\pi t^3}}(e^{bt} - e^{at})$
46	$\dfrac{1}{\sqrt{p^2+a^2}}$	$J_0(at)$
47	$\dfrac{(\sqrt{p^2+a^2}-p)^{\nu}}{\sqrt{p^2+a^2}}, \quad \mathrm{Re}(\nu) > -1$	$a^{\nu}J_{\nu}(at)$
48	$(\sqrt{p^2+a^2}-p)^{\nu}, \quad \mathrm{Re}(\nu) > 0$	$\dfrac{\nu a^{\nu}}{t} J_{\nu}(at)$
49	$\dfrac{1}{(p^2+a^2)^{\nu}}, \quad \mathrm{Re}(\nu) > 0$	$\dfrac{\sqrt{\pi}}{\Gamma(\nu)}\left(\dfrac{t}{2a}\right)^{\nu-\frac12} J_{\nu-\frac12}(at)$
50	$\dfrac{b^2-a^2}{(p-a^2)(b+\sqrt{p})}$	$e^{a^2t}[b - a\,\mathrm{erf}\,(a\sqrt{t})]$ $- be^{b^2t}\,\mathrm{erfc}\,(b\sqrt{t})$
51	$\dfrac{b^2-a^2}{\sqrt{p}(p-a^2)(b+\sqrt{p})}$	$e^{a^2t}\left[\dfrac{b}{a}\,\mathrm{erf}\,(a\sqrt{t}) - 1\right]$ $+ e^{b^2t}\,\mathrm{erfc}\,(b\sqrt{t})$
52	$\dfrac{1}{\sqrt{p^2-a^2}}$	$I_0(at)$
53	$\dfrac{(p-\sqrt{p^2-a^2})^{\nu}}{\sqrt{p^2-a^2}}, \quad \mathrm{Re}(\nu) > -1$	$a^{\nu}I_{\nu}(at)$
54	$\dfrac{1}{(p^2-a^2)^{\nu}}, \quad \mathrm{Re}(\nu) > 0$	$\dfrac{\sqrt{\pi}}{\Gamma(\nu)}\left(\dfrac{t}{2a}\right)^{\nu-\frac12} I_{\nu-\frac12}(at)$
55	$\dfrac{1}{\sqrt{p+a}\sqrt{p+b}}$	$e^{-[(a+b)/2]t}I_0\left(\dfrac{a-b}{2}\,t\right)$
56	$\dfrac{1}{(p+a)^{\nu}(p+b)^{\nu}}, \quad \mathrm{Re}(\nu) > 0$	$\dfrac{\sqrt{\pi}}{\Gamma(\nu)}\left(\dfrac{t}{a-b}\right)^{\nu-\frac12} e^{-\frac12(a+b)t}I_{\nu-\frac12}\left(\dfrac{a-b}{2}\,t\right)$
57	$\dfrac{1}{p}\sqrt{\dfrac{p+b}{p+a}}$	$e^{-[(a+b)/2]t}\,I_0\left(\dfrac{a-b}{2}t\right)$ $+ b\displaystyle\int_0^t e^{-[(a+b)/2]\tau}\,I_0\left(\dfrac{a-b}{2}\,\tau\right)d\tau$
58	$(p-\sqrt{p^2-a^2})^{\nu}, \quad \mathrm{Re}(\nu) > 0$	$\dfrac{\nu a^{\nu}}{t}\,I_{\nu}(at)$

TABLE OF LAPLACE TRANSFORMS—*continued*

No.	$f(p)$	$F(t)$
59	$\dfrac{(\sqrt{p+a}-\sqrt{p})^{\nu}}{\sqrt{p+a}+\sqrt{p}}, \quad \mathrm{Re}(\nu) > 0$	$\dfrac{e^{-at/2}\,I_{\nu}\left(\dfrac{at}{2}\right)}{\nu t}$
60	$\dfrac{\sqrt{p}}{\sqrt{p+a}(\sqrt{p}+\sqrt{p+a})^{2\nu}},$ $\mathrm{Re}(\nu) > -1$	$\dfrac{e^{-at/2}}{4a^{\nu-1}}\left[I_{\nu-1}\left(\dfrac{at}{2}\right) - 2I_{\nu}\left(\dfrac{at}{2}\right)\right.$ $\left. + I_{\nu+1}\left(\dfrac{at}{2}\right)\right]$
61	$\dfrac{1}{(p+a)^{\frac{1}{2}}(p+b)^{\frac{3}{2}}}$	$te^{-[(a+b)/2]t}\left[I_0\left(\dfrac{a-b}{2}t\right)\right.$ $\left. + I_1\left(\dfrac{a-b}{2}t\right)\right]$
62	$\dfrac{\sqrt{p+2a}-\sqrt{p}}{\sqrt{p+2a}+\sqrt{p}}$	$\dfrac{1}{t}e^{-at}\,I_1(at)$
63	$\dfrac{(a-b)^{k}}{(\sqrt{p+a}+\sqrt{p+b})^{2k}}, \quad k > 0$	$\dfrac{k}{t}e^{-[(a+b)/2]t}\,I_k\left(\dfrac{a-b}{2}t\right)$
64	$\dfrac{e^{-a\sqrt{p}}}{\sqrt{p}}, \quad \mathrm{Re}(a) \geqslant 0$	$\dfrac{1}{\sqrt{\pi t}}\,\exp\left(-\dfrac{a^2}{4t}\right)$
65	$\dfrac{e^{-a\sqrt{p}}}{p^{\frac{3}{2}}}, \quad \mathrm{Re}(a) \geqslant 0$	$2\sqrt{\dfrac{t}{\pi}}\,\exp\left(-\dfrac{a^2}{4t}\right)$ $- a\,\mathrm{erfc}\left(\dfrac{a}{2\sqrt{t}}\right)$
66	$e^{-a\sqrt{p}}, \quad \mathrm{Re}(a) > 0$	$\dfrac{a}{2\sqrt{\pi t^3}}\,\exp\left(-\dfrac{a^2}{4t}\right)$
67	$\dfrac{e^{-a\sqrt{p}}}{p}, \quad \mathrm{Re}(a) \geqslant 0$	$\mathrm{erfc}\left(\dfrac{a}{2\sqrt{t}}\right)$
68	$\dfrac{e^{-a/p}}{p}$	$J_0(2\sqrt{at})$
69	$\dfrac{e^{-a/p}}{p^{\nu+1}}, \quad \mathrm{Re}(\nu) > -1$	$\left(\dfrac{t}{a}\right)^{\nu/2}J_{\nu}(2\sqrt{at})$
70	$\dfrac{e^{-a/p}}{\sqrt{p}}$	$\dfrac{1}{\sqrt{\pi t}}\,\cos 2\sqrt{at}$
71	$\dfrac{e^{-a/p}}{p^{\frac{3}{2}}}$	$\dfrac{1}{\sqrt{\pi a}}\,\sin 2\sqrt{at}$

TABLE OF LAPLACE TRANSFORMS—*continued*

No.	$f(p)$	$F(t)$
72	$\dfrac{e^{a/p}}{\sqrt{p}}$	$\dfrac{1}{\sqrt{\pi t}}\cosh 2\sqrt{at}$
73	$\dfrac{e^{a/p}}{p^{\frac{3}{2}}}$	$\dfrac{1}{\sqrt{\pi a}}\sinh 2\sqrt{at}$
74	$\dfrac{e^{a/p}}{p^{\nu+1}},\quad \mathrm{Re}(\nu)>1$	$\left(\dfrac{t}{a}\right)^{\nu/2}I_\nu(2\sqrt{at})$
75	$\dfrac{e^{a/\sqrt{p}}}{p}$	$\dfrac{1}{2\sqrt{\pi a}\,t^{\frac{3}{2}}}\displaystyle\int_0^\infty \tau^{\frac{3}{2}}e^{-\tau^2/4t}\,I_1(2\sqrt{a\tau})\,d\tau$
76	$\dfrac{(\sqrt{p+a}-\sqrt{p})^{2\nu}}{\sqrt{p(p+a)}},\quad \mathrm{Re}(\nu)>-1$	$a^\nu e^{-(a/2)t}I_\nu\left(\dfrac{a}{2}t\right)$
77	$\dfrac{(\sqrt{p}-\sqrt{p-a})^{2\nu}}{\sqrt{p(p-a)}},\quad \mathrm{Re}(\nu)>-1$	$a^\nu e^{(a/2)t}I_\nu\left(\dfrac{a}{2}t\right)$
78	$e^{-bp}-e^{-b\sqrt{p^2+a^2}}$	$\dfrac{ab}{\sqrt{t^2-b^2}}J_1(a\sqrt{t^2-b^2})\,1(t-b)\;*$
79	$e^{-b\sqrt{p^2-a^2}}-e^{-bp}$	$\dfrac{ab}{\sqrt{t^2-b^2}}I_1(a\sqrt{t^2-b^2})\,1(t-b)$
80	$\dfrac{e^{-b\sqrt{p^2+a^2}}}{\sqrt{p^2+a^2}}\left(\dfrac{a}{p+\sqrt{p^2+a^2}}\right)^\nu,$ $\mathrm{Re}(\nu)>-1$	$\left(\dfrac{t-b}{t+b}\right)^{\nu/2}J_\nu(a\sqrt{t^2-b^2})\,1(t-b)$
81	$\dfrac{e^{-b\sqrt{p^2-a^2}}}{\sqrt{p^2-a^2}}\left(\dfrac{a}{p+\sqrt{p^2+a^2}}\right)^\nu,$ $\mathrm{Re}(\nu)>-1$	$\left(\dfrac{t-b}{t+b}\right)^{\nu/2}I_\nu(a\sqrt{t^2-b^2})\,1(t-b)$
82	$\dfrac{e^{-b(\sqrt{p^2+a^2}-p)}}{\sqrt{p^2+a^2}}\left(\dfrac{a}{p+\sqrt{p^2+a^2}}\right)^\nu,$ $\mathrm{Re}(\nu)>-1$	$\dfrac{t^{\nu/2}}{(t+2b)^{\nu/2}}J_\nu(a\sqrt{t^2+2bt})$
83	$\dfrac{\ln p}{p}$	$\Gamma'(1)-\ln t,\quad[\Gamma'(1)=-0{\cdot}5772$ $\cdots]$
84	$\dfrac{\ln p}{p^n},\quad n>0$	$t^{n-1}\left\{\dfrac{\Gamma'(n)}{[\Gamma(n)]^2}-\dfrac{\ln t}{\Gamma(n)}\right\}$
85	$\dfrac{\ln(p+a)}{p},\quad \mathrm{Re}(a)>0$	$\ln a + EI(at)\;\dagger$

* See section 3.3 for the definition of $1(t-t_0)$.

$\dagger$ The exponential-integral $EI(t)=\displaystyle\int_t^\infty \dfrac{e^{-\tau}}{\tau}d\tau\quad(t>0)$ is tabulated in Jahnke and Emde, *Table of Functions*.

TABLE OF LAPLACE TRANSFORMS—*continued*

No.	$f(p)$	$F(t)$
86	$\dfrac{\ln{(p-a)}}{p}, \quad \mathrm{Re}(a) > 0$	$\ln a + EI(-at)$
87	$\dfrac{\ln{(1+ap)}}{p}, \quad a > 0$	$EI\left(\dfrac{t}{a}\right)$
88	$\ln\dfrac{p-a}{p-b}$	$\dfrac{e^{bt} - e^{at}}{t}$
89	$\ln\dfrac{p^2 + a^2}{p^2}$	$\dfrac{2\,(1 - \cos at)}{t}$
90	$\ln\dfrac{p^2 - a^2}{p^2}$	$\dfrac{2(1 - \cosh at)}{t}$
91	$\dfrac{\ln p}{p^2 + 1}$	$\cos t\left(\dfrac{\pi}{2} - SI(t)\right) + \sin t\, CI(t)$ *
92	$\dfrac{p \ln p}{p^2 + 1}$	$-\left[\sin t\left(\dfrac{\pi}{2} - SI(t)\right) - \cos t\, CI(t)\right]$
93	$\dfrac{\ln{(\sqrt{p} + \sqrt{p+a})}}{\sqrt{p}}$	$\dfrac{1}{2\sqrt{\pi t}}[\ln a + EI(at)]$
94	$\dfrac{1}{p}\cos\dfrac{1}{p}$	$\mathrm{ber}\,(2\sqrt{t})$
95	$\dfrac{1}{p}\sin\dfrac{1}{p}$	$\mathrm{bei}\,(2\sqrt{t})$
96	$\dfrac{1}{\sqrt{p}}\cos\dfrac{1}{p}$	$\dfrac{\cosh\sqrt{2t}\,\cos\sqrt{2t}}{\sqrt{\pi t}}$
97	$\dfrac{1}{\sqrt{p}}\sin\dfrac{1}{p}$	$\dfrac{\sinh\sqrt{2t}\,\sin\sqrt{2t}}{\sqrt{\pi t}}$
98	$\arctan\dfrac{a}{p}$	$\dfrac{\sin at}{t}$
99	$e^{a^2 p^2}\,\mathrm{erfc}\,(ap), \quad a > 0$	$\dfrac{1}{a\sqrt{\pi}}\exp\left(-\dfrac{t^2}{4a^2}\right)$
100	$\dfrac{1}{p}e^{a^2 p^2}\,\mathrm{erfc}\,(ap), \quad a > 0$	$\mathrm{erf}\left(\dfrac{t}{2a}\right)$
101	$e^{ap}\,\mathrm{erfc}\,\sqrt{ap}, \quad a > 0$	$\dfrac{\sqrt{a}}{\pi(t+a)\sqrt{t}}$

* $SI(t)$ and $CI(t)$ are defined in section 8.7.

TABLE OF LAPLACE TRANSFORMS—*continued*

No.	$f(p)$	$F(t)$
102	$\dfrac{1}{\sqrt{p}}\,\mathrm{erfc}\,(\sqrt{ap}),\quad a>0$	$\dfrac{1}{\sqrt{\pi(t+a)}}$
103	$\mathrm{erf}\left(\dfrac{a}{\sqrt{p}}\right)$	$\dfrac{1}{\pi t}\sin\,(2a\sqrt{t})$
104	$\dfrac{1}{\sqrt{p}}e^{a^2/p}\,\mathrm{erfc}\left(\dfrac{a}{\sqrt{p}}\right)$	$\dfrac{1}{\sqrt{\pi t}}e^{-2a\sqrt{t}}$
105	$K_0(ap)$	$(t^2-a^2)^{-\frac{1}{2}}1(t-a)$
106	$K_0(a\sqrt{p})$	$\dfrac{1}{2t}\exp\left(-\dfrac{a^2}{4t}\right)$
107	$K_\nu(p)$	$\dfrac{\cosh\,(\nu\,\mathrm{arc\,cosh}\,t)}{\sqrt{t^2-1}}1(t-1)$
108	$\dfrac{K_\nu(p)}{p}$	$\left\{\displaystyle\int_1^t\dfrac{\cosh\,(\nu\,\mathrm{arc\,cosh}\,\xi)}{\sqrt{\xi^2-1}}\,d\xi\right\}1(t-1)$
109	$e^{-ap}I_0(ap)$	$\dfrac{1}{\pi\sqrt{t(2a-t)}}$ when $0<t<2a$, $0\qquad$ when $t<2a$
110	$e^{-ap}I_1(ap)$	$\dfrac{a-t}{\pi a\sqrt{t(2a-t)}}$ when $0<t<2a$, $0\qquad$ when $t>2a$
111	$\dfrac{1}{\sqrt{p}}I_0\left(\dfrac{a^2}{p}\right)e^{-a^2/p}$	$\dfrac{J_0(a\sqrt{8t})}{\sqrt{\pi t}}$

TABLE OF FINITE SINE TRANSFORMS

No.	$f_S(n)$	$F(x)$
1	$f_S(n) = \displaystyle\int_0^l F(x) \sin \frac{n\pi x}{l} dx, \quad n = 1, 2, \cdots$	$F(x)$
2	$\dfrac{l}{n\pi}[1 - (-1)^n]$	1
3	$(-1)^{n+1}\dfrac{l^2}{n\pi}$	x
4	$\dfrac{l^2}{n\pi}$	$l - x$
5	$(-1)^{n-1}\dfrac{l^3}{n\pi} - \dfrac{2l^3}{n^3\pi^3}[1 - (-1)^n]$	x^2
6	$\dfrac{2l^3}{n^3\pi^3}[1 - (-1)^n]$	$x(l - x)$
7	$(-1)^n\dfrac{l^4}{\pi^5}\left(\dfrac{6}{n^3} - \dfrac{\pi^2}{n}\right)$	x^3
8	$(-1)^{n+1}\dfrac{6l^4}{n^3\pi^3}$	$x(l^2 - x^2)$
9	$(-1)^{n+1}\dfrac{l^5}{n\pi} + (-1)^n\dfrac{l^5}{n^3\pi^3} + \dfrac{24l^5}{n^5\pi^5}[1 - (-1)^n]$	x^4
10	$(-1)^{n+1}\dfrac{l^5}{n^3\pi^3} - \dfrac{24l^5}{n^5\pi^5}[1 - (-1)^n]$	$x(l^3 - x^3)$
11	$\dfrac{n\pi l}{n^2\pi^2 + a^2l^2}[1 - (-1)^n e^{al}]$	e^{ax}
12	$\dfrac{l}{2}$ when n $= m$ 0 when $n \neq m$	$\sin \dfrac{m\pi x}{l}, \quad m = 1, 2, \cdots$
13	$\dfrac{nl}{\pi(n^2 - m^2)}[1 - (-1)^{n+m}]$ when $n \neq m$ 0 when $n = m$	$\cos \dfrac{m\pi x}{l}, \quad m = 1, 2, \cdots$
14	$\dfrac{n\pi l}{n^2\pi^2 - k^2l^2}[1 - (-1)^n \cos kl], \quad n \neq \dfrac{kl}{\pi}$	$\cos kx$

TABLE OF FINITE COSINE TRANSFORMS

No.	$f_C(n)$	$F(x)$
1	$f_C(n) = \displaystyle\int_0^l F(x) \cos \frac{n\pi x}{l}\, dx, \quad n = 0, 1, 2, \cdots$	$F(x)$
2	l when $n = 0$ 0 when $n = 1, 2, 3, \cdots$	1
3	$\dfrac{l^2}{2}$ when $n = 0$ $\left(\dfrac{l}{n\pi}\right)^2 [(-1)^n - 1]$ when $n = 1, 2, 3, \cdots$	x
4	$\dfrac{l^2}{2}$ when $n = 0$ $\left(\dfrac{l}{n\pi}\right)^2 [1 - (-1)^n]$ when $n = 1, 2, 3, \cdots$	$l - x$
5	$\dfrac{l^3}{3}$ when $n = 0$ $(-1)^n \dfrac{2l^3}{n^2\pi^2}$ when $n = 1, 2, 3, \cdots$	x^2
6	$\dfrac{l^3}{3}$ when $n = 0$ $\dfrac{2l^3}{n^2\pi^2}$ when $n = 1, 2, 3, \cdots$	$(l - x)^2$
7	$\dfrac{l^4}{4}$ when $n = 0$ $(-1)^n \dfrac{3l^4}{n^2\pi^2} + \dfrac{6}{n^4\pi^4}[(-1)^n - 1]$ when $n = 1, 2, 3, \cdots$	x^3

TABLE OF FINITE COSINE TRANSFORMS—*continued*

No.	$f_C(n)$	$F(x)$
8	$\dfrac{3}{2} \, l^3$ when $n = 0$ $(-1)^{n+1} \dfrac{2l^3}{n^2\pi^2}$ when $n = 1, 2, 3, \cdots$	$l^2 - x^2$
9	0 when $n = m$ $\dfrac{ml}{\pi(n^2 - m^2)}[(-1)^{n+m} - 1]$ when $n \neq m$	$\sin \dfrac{m\pi x}{l}, \quad m = 1, 2, \cdots$
10	$\dfrac{kl^2}{n^2\pi^2 - l^2k^2}[(-1)^n \cos kl - 1], \, n \neq \dfrac{kl}{\pi}$	$\sin kx$
11	$\dfrac{al^2}{a^2l^2 + n^2\pi^2}[(-1)^n e^{al} - 1]$	e^{ax}

INDEX